Penguin Modern Psychology U P S 8

Decision Making

DECISION MAKING

Selected Readings

Edited by Ward Edwards and Amos Tversky

Penguin Books

Penguin Books Ltd, Harmondsworth,
Middlesex, England
Penguin Books Inc., 3300 Clipper Mill Road,
Baltimore 11, Md 21211, U.S.A.
Penguin Books Australia Ltd, Ringwood,
Victoria, Australia

First published by Penguin Books 1967

Printed in the United States of America

Contents

Introduction

Men make choices. They choose what to have for dinner, whom to marry, whether or not to make war. Decision theory is an attempt to describe in an orderly way what variables influence choices.

You and your friend plan a weekend trip in March. Will it be to Gstaad for the skiing, or to Saint Tropez for the sun? You may prefer the hiss of a parallel Christie to the splash of waves, the sweat of exercise to the sting of sunburn, *glogg* to *vin rouge*. But if the weatherman forecasts a blizzard in Gstaad throughout the weekend, while Saint Tropez will be sunny and hot, you may decide to pack your bathing suit and go to Saint Tropez – perhaps to curse your bad luck when it turns out to rain there.

Two classes of variables are visible in the example. One is your evaluation of the relative attractivenesses of skiing on a good day, baking in the sun, skiing in a blizzard, or watching rain through a hotel room window. The other is your evaluation of the chances, or probability, that it will snow in Gstaad and that it will rain in Saint Tropez. The first class of variable is called utility. The second is called probability. These two intervening variables structure the key questions of decision theory:

1. How do men make judgements of the utility or attractiveness of various things that might happen to them, and how can these utilities be measured?

2. How do men judge the probabilities of events that control what happens to them, and how can these judgements of probability be measured?

3. How are judged probabilities changed by the arrival of new information?

4. How are probabilities and utilities combined to control decisions?

5. How should psychologists account for, or think about, the fact that the same man, put in the same situation twice, will often not make the same decision?

This book attempts to bring together a number of papers and excerpts from books that are addressed to these questions.

Decision theory differs in strategy from many more familiar approaches to psychological theorizing. Perhaps the most important difference is that decision theorists look to the current situation, rather than to the past experiences of the decider, for the variables that control the decision. Kurt Lewin (influenced by an early series of lectures given by John von Neumann) sharply distinguished between historical and ahistorical explanations of behaviour. Historical explanations, like learning theories, usually invoke the law of effect or some similar principle to link the occurrence of a response with the results of past occurrences of that same response. Often such theories are interested not in what response was made, but only in whether or not a particular response (e.g., a bar press) was made. Ahistorical explanations, such as those found in what has been called static decision theory, attempt to specify what response will be chosen from a set of possibilities on the basis of the anticipatable outcomes of each of the possible responses. Past experiences are taken into account in ahistorical explanations as determiners of these anticipations. Both historical and ahistorical explanations are sensible; a complete theory should interweave both. Dynamic decision theory, also represented in this book, attempts to deal with both kinds of explanation simultaneously; inevitably, it focuses on the impact of information processing on decision making.

Mathematical ideas have appeared in psychology since the days of Fechner, mostly in order to describe behaviour. Decision theorists tend to use mathematical ideas for a different purpose: to specify what an organism should do, rather than describing what it does do. But the distinction between what an organism should do and what it does do is slippery. For one thing, when the stakes are high we try very hard to do what we should; in this sense, models of what we should do have descriptive as well as prescriptive usefulness. For another thing, every psychological model describes not only the behaving organism but also the environment in which it is behaving. Decision theory may be viewed as primarily an analysis of the environment; that is, an orderly summary of those features of the environment that control behaviour. Such a description of the environment, combined with simple assumptions about behaviour tendencies that the organism brings to that environment, may yield an effective description of behaviour. From this viewpoint, the role of prescriptive decision theory in the study of choices is like the role of physical optics in the study of vision, or of grammar in the study of language.

The earliest decision theorists were mathematicians advising gamblers in the French court about how to tell fair from unfair bets. Decision theory has remained in intimate contact with real problems of application ever since. The decision-theoretical literature in economics, business, applied statistics, and even law, medicine, and politics is much more abundant than in psychology. The major ideas of decision theory discussed in this book are in daily use, helping men to make real, substantial decisions.

Since it seems impossible to give an adequate representation to the extensive literature on game theory and sequential decision problems within the limitations of this book we have made no attempt to do so. Several volumes of readings in game theory are available, notably Shubik (1964). Similarly, no attempt has been made to cover learning and personality variables in decision making.

We have tried to avoid duplications with other available secondary sources, such as the second volume of the *Readings in mathematical psychology*, Luce *et al.* (1965).

The present volume is intended to serve as supplementary reading for an advanced undergraduate or an elementary graduate course in behavioural decision theory. Consequently, mathematics is kept to a minimum, and the emphasis is on the conceptual rather than on the mathematical aspects of the subject. For an extensive survey of the field from a somewhat more mathematical viewpoint read Luce and Suppes' chapter entitled 'Preferences, utility and subjective probability' in the third volume of the *Handbook of mathematical psychology*, Luce *et al.* (1965).

Decision theory is diverse; there is challenge and excitement in it for tastes ranging from the most applied to the most basic, from the most verbal to the most mathematical. Decision theorists are correspondingly diverse. Among the authors included in this book are mathematical statisticians (Mosteller, Raiffa, Savage), philosophers (Adams, Davidson, DeGroot, Suppes), a mathematical economist (Marschak), and psychologists (everyone else); and at least five aeroplane pilots (Becker, Davidson, Edwards, Luce, Yntema) – along with one paratrooper (Tversky), just in case. Active though not represented here are clinicians interested in diagnostic decisions, test designers interested in personnel selection, mathematicians interested in beating the dealer at blackjack, military officers interested in designing command systems, businessmen interested in deciding whether to introduce

9

new products – just about anyone who combines the need to make decisions with interest in how they are made. Decision theory has a problem for every taste, and there is far too much for any one man to do.

References
LUCE, R. D., BUSH, R. R., and GALANTER, E. (eds.), *Readings in mathematical psychology*, Wiley, 1965.
LUCE, R. D., and SUPPES, P., 'Preference, utility and subjective probability', in Luce, R. D., Bush, R. R., and Galanter, E. (eds.), *Handbook of mathematical psychology*, Wiley, 1965, vol. 3.
SHUBIK, M., *Game theory and related approaches to social behavior*, Wiley, 1964.

Part One THEORY OF DECISION MAKING: A GENERAL REVIEW

The first set of papers is a historical and conceptual introduction to the world of behavioural decision theory. Edwards's (1954) paper is the first extensive review of the theory of decision making in the psychological literature. It ranges from the earliest utility notions of Bernoulli and the nineteenth-century economists to the modern utility theories of the mid-fifties. Edwards's second paper (1961), starts where the first one leaves off and describes the development of the field up to the sixties, with an emphasis on empirical applications in psychology. For other reviews of more formal viewpoints, see Adams (1960), Arrow (1963), and Luce and Suppes (1965).

Three summary statements emerge from these reviews: (*a*) decision theory is a complex body of knowledge developed mostly outside psychology by economists and mathematicians in an attempt to prescribe how decisions should be made, (*b*) there are intimate, though subtle, interrelations between the ways in which decisions are and ought to be made, (*c*) there is an increasing body of psychological and other research leading to more elaborate descriptive models and more sophisticated prescriptive applications.

The third paper in this section is an excerpt from Savage's (1954) *The foundations of statistics*. It contains several historical and critical comments on utility, together with a discussion of a hypothetical choice situation (due to Allais) where Savage's intuition runs counter to utility theory. Savage's analysis demonstrates the use of axioms as guidelines in making decisions. In this sense the axioms are viewed as prescriptive principles for an actual individual rather than as descriptive principles for an ideal individual.

When obstinate intuitive preferences contradict the sacred precepts of decision theory, some theorists use the theory to revise their preferences, as Savage does. Others follow Samuelson's advice: satisfy your preferences, and let the axioms satisfy themselves.

Luce and Raiffa's discussion of utility theory is taken from their *Games and decisions* in which utility theory plays a fundamental role. The excerpt contains a simplified axiomatization of utility coupled with a simple constructive proof of the existence of an interval utility scale. It is interesting to note that their proof parallels the construction of a utility scale from actual data, which increases the transparency of the method.

References

ADAMS, A. J., 'Bernoullian utility theory', in Solomon, H. (ed.), *Mathematical thinking in the measurement of behavior*, Free Press, 1960.

ARROW, K. J., 'Utility and expectations in economic behavior', in Koch, S. (ed.), *Psychology: a study of a science*, McGraw-Hill, 1963.

LUCE, R. D., and SUPPES, P., 'Preference, utility and subjective probability', in *Handbook of mathematical psychology*, Wiley, 1965, vol. 3.

1 W. Edwards

The Theory of Decision Making

W. Edwards, 'The theory of decision making', *Psychol. Bull.*, vol. 51 (1954), no. 4, pp. 380–417.

Many social scientists other than psychologists try to account for the behavior of individuals. Economists and a few psychologists have produced a large body of theory and a few experiments that deal with individual decision making. The kind of decision making with which this body of theory deals is as follows: given two states, *A* and *B*, into either one of which an individual may put himself, the individual chooses *A* in preference to *B* (or vice versa). For instance, a child standing in front of a candy counter may be considering two states. In state *A* the child has $0.25 and no candy. In state *B* the child has $0.15 and a ten-cent candy bar. The economic theory of decision making is a theory about how to predict such decisions.

Economic theorists have been concerned with this problem since the days of Jeremy Bentham (1738–1832). In recent years the development of the economic theory of consumer's decision making (or, as the economists call it, the theory of consumer's choice) has become exceedingly elaborate, mathematical, and voluminous. This literature is almost unknown to psychologists, in spite of sporadic pleas in both psychological (40, 84, 103, 104) and economic (101, 102, 123, 128, 199, 202) literature for greater communication between the disciplines.

The purpose of this paper is to review this theoretical literature, and also the rapidly increasing number of psychological experiments (performed by both psychologists and economists) that are relevant to it. The review will be divided into five sections: the theory of riskless choices, the application of the theory of riskless choices to welfare economics, the theory of risky choices, transitivity in decision making, and the theory of games and of statistical decision functions. Since this literature is unfamiliar and relatively inaccessible to most psychologists, and since I could not find any thorough bibliography on the theory of choice in the economic literature, this paper includes a rather extensive bibliography of the literature since 1930.

The Theory of Riskless Choices[1]

Economic man. – The method of those theorists who have been concerned with the theory of decision making is essentially an armchair method. They make assumptions, and from these assumptions they deduce theorems which presumably can be tested, though it sometimes seems unlikely that the testing will ever occur. The most important set of assumptions made in the theory of riskless choices may be summarized by saying that it is assumed that the person who makes any decision to which the theory is applied is an economic man.

What is an economic man like? He has three properties. (*a*) He is completely informed. (*b*) He is infinitely sensitive. (*c*) He is rational.

Complete information. – Economic man is assumed to know not only what all the courses of action open to him are, but also what the outcome of any action will be. Later on, in the sections on the theory of risky choices and on the theory of games, this assumption will be relaxed somewhat. (For the results of attempts to introduce the possibility of learning into this picture, see 51, 77.)

Infinite sensitivity. – In most of the older work on choice, it is assumed that the alternatives available to an individual are continuous, infinitely divisible functions, that prices are infinitely divisible, and that economic man is infinitely sensitive. The only purpose of these assumptions is to make the functions that they lead to continuous and differentiable. Stone (182), has recently shown that they can be abandoned with no serious changes in the theory of choice.

Rationality. – The crucial fact about economic man is that he is rational. This means two things: He can weakly order the states

1. No complete review of this literature is available. Kauder (105, 106) has reviewed the very early history of utility theory. Stigler (180) and Viner (194) have reviewed the literature up to approximately 1930. Samuelson's book (164) contains an illuminating mathematical exposition of some of the content of this theory. Allen (6) explains the concept of indifference curves. Schultz (172) reviews the developments up to but not including the Hicks–Allen revolution from the point of view of demand theory. Hicks's book (87) is a complete and detailed exposition of most of the mathematical and economic content of the theory up to 1939. Samuelson (167) has reviewed the integrability problem and the revealed preference approach. And Wold (204, 205, 206) has summed up the mathematical content of the whole field for anyone who is comfortably at home with axiom systems and differential equations.

into which he can get, and he makes his choices so as to maximize something.

Two things are required in order for economic man to be able to put all available states into a weak ordering. First, given any two states into which he can get, A and B, he must always be able to tell either that he prefers A to B, or that he prefers B to A, or that he is indifferent between them. If preference is operationally defined as choice, then it seems unthinkable that this requirement can ever be empirically violated. The second requirement for weak ordering, a more severe one, is that all preferences must be transitive. If economic man prefers A to B and B to C, then he prefers A to C. Similarly, if he is indifferent between A and B and between B and C, then he is indifferent between A and C. It is not obvious that transitivity will always hold for human choices, and experiments designed to find out whether or not it does will be described in the section on testing transitivity.

The second requirement of rationality, and in some ways the more important one, is that economic man must make his choices in such a way as to maximize something. This is the central principle of the theory of choice. In the theory of riskless choices, economic man has usually been assumed to maximize utility. In the theory of risky choices, he is assumed to maximize expected utility. In the literature on statistical decision making and the theory of games, various other fundamental principles of decision making are considered, but they are all maximization principles of one sort or another.

The fundamental content of the notion of maximization is that economic man always chooses the best alternative from among those open to him, as he sees it. In more technical language, the fact that economic man prefers A to B implies and is implied by the fact that A is higher than B in the weakly ordered set mentioned above. (Some theories introduce probabilities into the above statement, so that if A is higher than B in the weak ordering, then economic man is more likely to choose A than B, but not certain to choose A.)

This notion of maximization is mathematically useful, since it makes it possible for a theory to specify a unique point or a unique subset of points among those available to the decider. It seems to me psychologically unobjectionable. So many different kinds of functions can be maximized that almost any point actually available in an experimental situation can be regarded as a maximum of some sort. Assumptions about maximization only become specific, and therefore possibly wrong, when they specify what is being maximized.

There has, incidentally, been almost no discussion of the possibility that the two parts of the concept of rationality might conflict. It is conceivable, for example, that it might be costly in effort (and therefore in negative utility) to maintain a weakly ordered preference field. Under such circumstances, would it be 'rational' to have such a field?

It is easy for a psychologist to point out that an economic man who has the properties discussed above is very unlike a real man. In fact, it is so easy to point this out that psychologists have tended to reject out of hand the theories that result from these assumptions. This isn't fair. Surely the assumptions contained in Hullian behavior theory (91) or in the Estes (60) or Bush-Mosteller (36, 37) learning theories are no more realistic than these. The most useful thing to do with a theory is not to criticize its assumptions but rather to test its theorems. If the theorems fit the data, then the theory has at least heuristic merit. Of course, one trivial theorem deducible from the assumptions embodied in the concept of economic man is that in any specific case of choice these assumptions will be satisfied. For instance, if economic man is a model for real men, then real men should always exhibit transitivity of real choices. Transitivity is an assumption, but it is directly testable. So are the other properties of economic man as a model for real men.

Economists themselves are somewhat distrustful of economic man (119, 156), and we will see in subsequent sections the results of a number of attempts to relax these assumptions.

Early utility maximization theory. – The school of philosopher-economists started by Jeremy Bentham and popularized by James Mill and others held that the goal of human action is to seek pleasure and avoid pain. Every object or action may be considered from the point of view of pleasure- or pain-giving properties. These properties are called the *utility* of the object, and pleasure is given by positive utility and pain by negative utility. The goal of action, then, is to seek the maximum utility. This simple hedonism of the future is easily translated into a theory of choice. People choose the alternative, from among those open to them, that leads to the greatest excess of positive over negative utility. This notion of utility maximization is the essence of the utility theory of choice. It will reappear in various forms throughout this paper. (Bohnert [30] discusses the logical structure of the utility concept.)

This theory of choice was embodied in the formal economic analyses of all the early great names in economics. In the hands of Jevons, Walras, and Menger it reached increasingly sophisticated mathematical expression and it was embodied in the thinking of Marshall, who published the first edition of his great *Principles of economics* in 1890, and revised it at intervals for more than 30 years thereafter (137).

The use to which utility theory was put by these theorists was to establish the nature of the demand for various goods. On the assumption that the utility of any good is a monotonically increasing negatively accelerated function of the amount of that good, it is easy to show that the amounts of most goods which a consumer will buy are decreasing functions of price, functions which are precisely specified once the shapes of the utility curves are known. This is the result the economists needed and is, of course, a testable theorem. (For more on this, see 87, 159.)

Complexities arise in this theory when the relations between the utilities of different goods are considered. Jevons, Walras, Menger, and even Marshall had assumed that the utilities of different commodities can be combined into a total utility by simple addition; this amounts to assuming that the utilities of different goods are independent (in spite of the fact that Marshall elsewhere discussed the notions of competing goods, like soap and detergents, and completing goods, like right and left shoes, which obviously do not have independent utilities). Edgeworth (53), who was concerned with such nonindependent utilities, pointed out that total utility was not necessarily an additive function of the utilities attributable to separate commodities. In the process he introduced the notion of indifference curves, and thus began the gradual destruction of the classical utility theory. We shall return to this point shortly.

Although the forces of parsimony have gradually resulted in the elimination of the classical concept of utility from the economic theory of riskless choices, there have been a few attempts to use essentially the classical theory in an empirical way. Fisher (63) and Frisch (75) have developed methods of measuring marginal utility (the change in utility [u] with an infinitesimal change in amount possessed [Q], i.e., du/dQ) from market data, by making assumptions about the interpersonal similarity of consumer tastes. Recently Morgan (141) has used several variants of these techniques, has discussed mathematical and logical flaws

17

in them, and has concluded on the basis of his empirical results that the techniques require too unrealistic assumptions to be workable. The crux of the problem is that, for these techniques to be useful, the commodities used must be independent (rather than competing or completing), and the broad commodity classifications necessary for adequate market data are not independent. Samuelson (164) has shown that the assumption of independent utilities, while it does guarantee interval scale utility measures, puts unwarrantably severe restrictions on the nature of the resulting demand function. Elsewhere Samuelson (158) presented, primarily as a logical and mathematical exercise, a method of measuring marginal utility by assuming some time-discount function. Since no reasonable grounds can be found for assuming one such function rather than another, this procedure holds no promise of empirical success. Marshall suggested (in his notion of 'consumer's surplus') a method of utility measurement that turns out to be dependent on the assumption of constant marginal utility of money, and which is therefore quite unworkable. Marshall's prestige led to extensive discussion and debunking of this notion (e.g., 28), but little positive comes out of this literature. Thurstone (186) is currently attempting to determine utility functions for commodities experimentally, but has reported no results as yet.

Indifference curves. – Edgeworth's introduction of the notion of indifference curves to deal with the utilities of nonindependent goods was mentioned above. An indifference curve is, in Edgeworth's formulation, a constant-utility curve. Suppose that we consider apples and bananas, and suppose that you get the same amount of utility from 10-apples-and-1-banana as you do from 6-apples-and-4-bananas. Then these are two points on an indifference curve, and of course there are an infinite number of other points on the same curve. Naturally, this is not the only indifference curve you may have between apples and bananas. It may also be true that you are indifferent between 13-apples-and-5-bananas and 5-apples-and-15-bananas. These are two points on another, higher indifference curve. A whole family of such curves is called an indifference map. Figure 1 presents such a map. One particularly useful kind of indifference map has amounts of a commodity on one axis and amounts of money on the other. Money is a commodity, too.

The notion of an indifference map can be derived, as Edgeworth derived it, from the notion of measurable utility. But it does not have to be. Pareto (146, see also 151) was seriously concerned about the assumption that utility was measurable up to a linear transformation. He felt that people could tell whether they preferred to be in state *A* or state *B*, but could not tell how much they preferred one state over the other. In other words, he hypothesized a utility function measurable only on an ordinal scale. Let us follow the usual economic language, and call utility measured on an ordinal scale *ordinal* utility, and utility measured

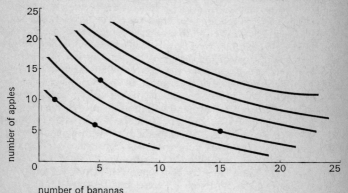

number of bananas

Figure 1   A hypothetical indifference map

on an interval scale, *cardinal* utility. It is meaningless to speak of the slope, or marginal utility, of an ordinal utility function; such a function cannot be differentiated. However, Pareto saw that the same conclusions which had been drawn from marginal utilities could be drawn from indifference curves. An indifference map can be drawn simply by finding all the combinations of the goods involved among which the person is indifferent. Pareto's formulation assumes that higher indifference curves have greater utility, but does not need to specify how much greater that utility is.

It turns out to be possible to deduce from indifference curves all of the theorems that were originally deduced from cardinal utility measures. This banishing of cardinal utility was furthered considerably by splendid mathematical papers by Johnson (97) and Slutsky (177). (In modern economic theory, it is customary to think of an *n*-dimensional commodity space, and of indifference hyperplanes in that space, each such hyperplane having, of course, *n* – 1 dimensions. In order to avoid unsatisfactory preference structures, it is necessary to assume that consumers always have a complete weak ordering for all commodity bundles, or points in commodity space. Georgescu-Roegen [76], Wold [204, 205, 206, 208], Houthakker [90], and Samuelson [167] have discussed this problem.)

Pareto was not entirely consistent in his discussion of ordinal utility. Although he abandoned the assumption that its exact value could be known, he continued to talk about the sign of the marginal utility coefficient, which assumed that some knowledge about the utility function other than purely ordinal knowledge was available. He also committed other inconsistencies. So Hicks and Allen (88), in 1934, were led to their classic paper in which they attempted to purge the theory of choice of its last introspective elements. They adopted the conventional economic view about indifference curves as determined from a sort of imaginary questionnaire, and proceeded to derive all of the usual conclusions about consumer demand with no reference to the notion of even ordinal utility (though of course the notion of an ordinal scale of preferences was still embodied in their derivation of indifference curves). This paper was for economics something like the behaviorist revolution in psychology.

Lange (116), stimulated by Hicks and Allen, pointed out another inconsistency in Pareto. Pareto had assumed that if a person considered four states, A, B, C, and D, he could judge whether the difference between the utilities of A and B was greater than, equal to, or less than the difference between the utilities of C and D. Lange pointed out that if such a comparison was possible for any A, B, C, and D, then utility was cardinally measurable. Since it seems introspectively obvious that such comparisons can be made, this paper provoked a flood of protest and comment (7, 22, 117, 147, 209). Nevertheless, in spite of all the comment, and even in spite of skepticism by a distinguished economist as late as 1953 (153), Lange is surely right. Psychologists should know this at once; such comparisons are the basis of the psychophysical Method of Equal Sense Distances, from which an interval scale is derived. (Samuelson [162] has pointed out a very interesting qualification. Not only must such judgments of difference be possible, but they must also be transitive in order to define an interval scale.) But since such judgments of differences did not seem to be necessary for the development of consumer demand theory, Lange's paper did not force the reinstatement of cardinal utility.

Indeed, the pendulum swung further in the behavioristic direction. Samuelson developed a new analytic foundation for the theory of consumer behavior, the essence of which is that indifference curves and hence the entire structure of the theory of consumer choice can be derived simply from observation of choices among alternative groups of purchases available to a consumer (160, 161). This approach has been extensively developed by Samuelson (164, 165, 167, 169) and others (50, 90, 125, 126). The essence of the idea is that each choice defines a point and a slope in commodity space. Mathematical approximation methods make it possible to combine a whole family of such slopes into an indifference hyperplane. A family of such hyperplanes forms an indifference 'map'.

In a distinguished but inaccessible series of articles, Wold (204, 205, 206; see also 208 for a summary presentation) has presented the mathematical content of the Pareto, Hicks and Allen, and revealed preference (Samuelson) approaches, as well as Cassel's demand function approach, and has shown that if the assumption about complete weak ordering of bundles of commodities which was discussed above is made, then all these approaches are mathematically equivalent.

Nostalgia for cardinal utility. – The crucial reason for abandoning cardinal utility was the argument of the ordinalists that indifference curve analysis in its various forms could do everything that cardinal utility could do, with fewer assumptions. So far as the theory of riskless choice is concerned, this is so. But this is only an argument for parsimony, and parsimony is not always welcome. There was a series of people who, for one reason or another, wanted to reinstate cardinal utility, or at least marginal utility. There were several mathematically invalid attempts to show that marginal utility could be defined even in an ordinal-utility universe (23, 24, 163; 25, 114). Knight (110), in 1944, argued extensively for cardinal utility; he based his arguments in part on introspective considerations and in part on an examination of psychophysical scaling procedures. He stimulated a number of replies (29, 42, 111). Recently Robertson (154) pleaded for the reinstatement of cardinal utility in the interests of welfare economics (this point will be discussed again below). But in general the indifference curve approach, in its various forms, has firmly established itself as the structure of the theory of riskless choice.

Experiments on indifference curves. – Attempts to measure marginal utility from market data were discussed above. There have been three experimental attempts to measure indifference curves. Schultz, who pioneered in deriving statistical demand curves, interested his colleague at the University of Chicago, the psychologist Thurstone, in the problem of indifference curves. Thurstone (185) performed a very simple experiment. He gave one subject a series of combinations of hats and overcoats, and required the subject to judge whether she preferred each combination to a standard. For instance, the subject judged whether she preferred eight hats and eight overcoats to fifteen hats and three overcoats. The same procedure was repeated for hats and shoes, and for shoes and overcoats. The data were fitted with indifference curves derived from the assumptions that utility curves fitted Fechner's Law and that the utilities of the various objects were independent. Thurstone says that Fechner's Law fitted the data better than the other possible functions he considered, but presents no evidence for this assertion. The crux of the experiment was the attempt to predict the indifference curves between shoes and overcoats from the other indifference curves. This was done by using the other two indifference curves to infer utility functions for shoes and for overcoats separately, and then using these two utility functions to predict the total utility of various amounts of shoes and overcoats jointly. The prediction worked rather well. The judgments of the one subject used are extraordinarily orderly; there is very little of the inconsistency and variability that others working in this area have found. Thurstone says, 'The subject . . . was entirely naive as regards the psychophysical problem involved and had no knowledge whatever of the nature of the curves that we expected to find' (185, p. 154). He adds, 'I selected as subject a research assistant in my laboratory who knew nothing about psychophysics. Her work was largely clerical in nature. She had a very even disposition, and I instructed her to take an even motivational attitude on the successive occasions . . . I was surprised at the consistency of the judgments that I obtained, but I am pretty sure that they were the result of careful instruction to assume a uniform motivational attitude.[2] From the economist's point of view, the main criticism of this experiment is that it involved imaginary rather than real transactions (200).

The second experimental measurement of indifference curves is reported by the economists Rousseas and Hart (157). They required large numbers of students to rank sets of three combinations of different amounts of bacon and eggs. By assuming

2. Thurstone, L. L. Personal communication, December 7, 1953.

that all students had the same indifference curves, they were able to derive a composite indifference map for bacon and eggs. No mathematical assumptions were necessary, and the indifference map is not given mathematical form. Some judgments were partly or completely inconsistent with the final map, but not too many. The only conclusion which this experiment justifies is that it is possible to derive such a composite indifference map.

The final attempt to measure an indifference curve is a very recent one by the psychologists Coombs and Milholland (49). The indifference curve involved is one between risk and value of an object, and so will be discussed below in the section on the theory of risky decisions. It is mentioned here because the same methods (which show only that the indifference curve is convex to the origin, and so perhaps should not be called measurement) could equally well be applied to the determination of indifference curves in riskless situations.

Mention should be made of the extensive economic work on statistical demand curves. For some reason the most distinguished statistical demand curve derivers feel it necessary to give an account of consumer's choice theory as a preliminary to the derivation of their empirical demand curves. The result is that the two best books in the area (172, 182) are each divided into two parts; the first is a general discussion of the theory of consumer's choice and the second a quite unrelated report of statistical economic work. Stigler (179) has given good reasons why the statistical demand curves are so little related to the demand curves of economic theory, and Wallis and Friedman (200) argue plausibly that this state of affairs is inevitable. At any rate, there seems to be little prospect of using large-scale economic data to fill in the empirical content of the theory of individual decision making.

Psychological comments. – There are several commonplace observations that are likely to occur to psychologists as soon as they try to apply the theory of riskless choices to actual experimental work. The first is that human beings are neither perfectly consistent nor perfectly sensitive. This means that indifference curves are likely to be observable as indifference regions, or as probability distributions of choice around a central locus. It would be easy to assume that each indifference curve represents the modal value of a normal sensitivity curve, and that choices should have statistical properties predictable from that hypothesis as the amounts of the commodities (locations in product space) are changed. This implies that the definition of indifference between two collections of commodities should be that each collection is preferred over the other 50 per cent of the time. Such a definition has been proposed by an economist (108), and used in experimental work by psychologists (142). Of course, 50 per cent choice has been a standard psychological definition of indifference since the days of Fechner.

Incidentally, failure on the part of an economist to understand that a just noticeable difference (j.n.d.) is a statistical concept has led him to argue that the indifference relation is intransitive, that is, that if A is indifferent to B and B is indifferent to C, then A need not be indifferent to C (8, 9, 10). He argues that if A and B are less than one j.n.d. apart, then A will be indifferent to B; the same of course is true of B and C; but A and C may be more than one j.n.d. apart, and so one may be preferred to the other. This argument is, of course, wrong. If A has slightly more utility than B, then the individual will choose A in preference to B slightly more than 50 per cent of the time, even though A and B are less than one j.n.d. apart in utility. The 50 per cent point is in theory a precisely defined point, not a region. It may in fact be difficult to determine because of inconsistencies in judgments and because of changes in taste with time.

The second psychological observation is that it seems impossible even to dream of getting experimentally an indifference map in n-dimensional space where n is greater than 3. Even the case of $n = 3$ presents formidable experimental problems. This is less important to the psychologist who wants to use the theory of choice to rationalize experimental data than to the economist who wants to derive a theory of general static equilibrium.

Experiments like Thurstone's (185) involve so many assumptions that it is difficult to know what their empirical meaning might be if these assumptions were not made. Presumably, the best thing to do with such experiments is to consider them as tests of the assumption with the least face validity. Thurstone was willing to assume utility maximization and independence of the commodities involved (incidentally, his choice of commodities seems singularly unfortunate for justifying an assumption of independent utilities), and so used his data to construct a utility function. Of course, if only ordinal utility is assumed, then experimental indifference curves cannot be used this way. In fact, in an ordinal utility universe neither of the principal assumptions made by Thurstone can be tested by means of experimental indifference curves. So the assumption of cardinal utility, though not necessary, seems to lead to considerably more specific uses for experimental data.

At any rate, from the experimental point of view the most interesting question is: What is the observed shape of indifference curves between independent commodities? This question awaits an experimental answer.

The notion of utility is very similar to the Lewinian notion of valence (120, 121). Lewin conceives of valence as the attractiveness of an object or activity to a person (121). Thus, psychologists might consider the experimental study of utilities to be the experimental study of valences, and therefore an attempt at quantifying parts of the Lewinian theoretical schema.

Application of the Theory of Riskless Choices to Welfare Economics[3]

The classical utility theorists assumed the existence of interpersonally comparable cardinal utility. They were thus able to find a simple answer to the question of how to determine the best economic policy: That economic policy is best which results in the maximum total utility, summed over all members of the economy.

The abandonment of interpersonal comparability makes this answer useless. A sum is meaningless if the units being summed are of varying sizes and there is no way of reducing them to some common size. This point has not been universally recognized, and certain economists (e.g., 82, 154) still defend cardinal (but not interpersonally comparable) utility on grounds of its necessity for welfare economics.

Pareto's principle. – The abandonment of interpersonal comparability and then of cardinal utility produced a search for some other principle to justify economic policy. Pareto (146), who first abandoned cardinal utility, provided a partial solution. He suggested that a change should be considered desirable if it left everyone at least as well off as he was before, and made at least one person better off.

Compensation principle. – Pareto's principle is fine as far as it goes, but it obviously does not go very far. The economic

3. The discussion of welfare economics given in this paper is exceedingly sketchy. For a picture of what the complexities of modern welfare economics are really like see 11, 13, 14, 86, 118, 124, 127, 139, 140, 148, 154, 155, 166, 174.

decisions which can be made on so simple a principle are few and insignificant. So welfare economics languished until Kaldor (98) proposed the compensation principle. This principle is that if it is possible for those who gain from an economic change to compensate the losers for their losses and still have something left over from their gains, then the change is desirable. Of course, if the compensation is actually paid, then this is simply a case of Pareto's principle.

But Kaldor asserted that the compensation need not actually be made; all that was necessary was that it could be made. The fact that it could be made, according to Kaldor, is evidence that the change produces an excess of good over harm, and so is desirable. Scitovsky (173) observed an inconsistency in Kaldor's position: Some cases could arise in which, when a change from A to B has been made because of Kaldor's criterion, then a change back from B to A would also satisfy Kaldor's criterion. It is customary, therefore, to assume that changes which meet the original Kaldor criterion are only desirable if the reverse change does not also meet the Kaldor criterion.

It has gradually become obvious that the Kaldor–Scitovsky criterion does not solve the problem of welfare economics (see e.g., 18, 99). It assumes that the unpaid compensation does as much good to the person who gains it as it would if it were paid to the people who lost by the change. For instance, suppose that an industrialist can earn $10,000 a year more from his plant by using a new machine, but that the introduction of the machine throws two people irretrievably out of work. If the salary of each worker prior to the change was $4,000 a year, then the industrialist could compensate the workers and still make a profit. But if he does not compensate the workers, then the added satisfaction he gets from his extra $10,000 may be much less than the misery he produces in his two workers. This example only illustrates the principle; it does not make much sense in these days of progressive income taxes, unemployment compensation, high employment, and strong unions.

Social welfare functions. – From here on the subject of welfare economics gets too complicated and too remote from psychology to merit extensive exploration in this paper. The line that it has taken is the assumption of a social welfare function (21), a function which combines individual utilities in a way which satisfies Pareto's principle but is otherwise undefined. In spite of its lack of definition, it is possible to draw certain conclusions from such a function (see e.g., 164). However, Arrow (14) has recently shown that a social welfare function that meets certain very reasonable requirements about being sensitive in some way to the wishes of all the people affected, etc., cannot in general be found in the absence of interpersonally comparable utilities (see also 89).

Psychological comment. – Some economists are willing to accept the fact that they are inexorably committed to making moral judgments when they recommend economic policies (e.g., 152, 153). Others still long for the impersonal amorality of a utility measure (e.g., 154). However desirable interpersonally comparable cardinal utility may be, it seems utopian to hope that any experimental procedure will ever give information about individual utilities that could be of any practical use in guiding large-scale economic policy.

The Theory of Risky Choices[4]

Risk and uncertainty. – Economists and statisticians distinguish between risk and uncertainty. There does not seem to be any general agreement about which concept should be associated with which word, but the following definitions make the most important distinctions.

Almost everyone would agree that when I toss a coin the probability that I will get a head is 0·5. A proposition about the future to which a number can be attached, a number that represents the likelihood that the proposition is true, may be called a *first-order risk*. What the rules are for attaching such numbers is a much-debated question, which will be avoided in this paper.

4. Strotz (183) and Alchian (1) present non-technical and sparkling expositions of the von Neumann and Morgenstern utility measurement proposals. Georgescu-Roegen (78) critically discusses various axiom systems so as to bring some of the assumptions underlying this kind of cardinal utility into clear focus. Allais (3) reviews some of these ideas in the course of criticizing them. Arrow (12, 14) reviews parts of the field.

There is a large psychological literature on one kind of risky decision making, the kind which results when psychologists use partial reinforcement. This literature has been reviewed by Jenkins and Stanley (96). Recently a number of experimenters, including Jarrett (95), Flood (69, 70), Bilodeau (27), and myself (56) have been performing experiments on human subjects who are required to choose repetitively between two or more alternatives, each of which has a probability of reward greater than zero and less than one. The problems raised by these experiments are too complicated and too far removed from conventional utility theory to be dealt with in this paper. This line of experimentation may eventually provide the link which ties together utility theory and reinforcement theory.

Some propositions may depend on more than one probability distribution. For instance, I may decide that if I get a tail, I will put the coin back in my pocket, whereas if I get a head, I will toss it again. Now, the probability of the proposition 'I will get a head on my second toss' is a function of two probability distributions, the distribution corresponding to the first toss and that corresponding to the second toss. This might be called a *second-order risk*. Similarly, risks of any order may be constructed. It is a mathematical characteristic of all higher-order risks that they may be compounded into first-order risks by means of the usual theorems for compounding probabilities. (Some economists have argued against this procedure [83], essentially on the grounds that you may have more information by the time the second risk comes around. Such problems can best be dealt with by means of von Neumann and Morgenstern's [197] concept of strategy, which is discussed below. They become in general problems of uncertainty, rather than risk.)

Some propositions about the future exist to which no generally accepted probabilities can be attached. What is the probability that the following proposition is true: Immediately after finishing this paper, you will drink a glass of beer? Surely it is neither impossible nor certain, so it ought to have a probability between zero and one, but it is impossible for you or me to find out what that probability might be, or even to set up generally acceptable rules about how to find out. Such propositions are considered cases of *uncertainty*, rather than of risk. This section deals only with the subject of first-order risks. The subject of uncertainty will arise again in connection with the theory of games.

Expected utility maximization. – The traditional mathematical notion for dealing with games of chance (and so with risky decisions) is the notion that choices should be made so as to maximize *expected value*. The expected value of a bet is found by multiplying the value of each possible outcome by its probability of occurrence and summing these products across all possible outcomes. In symbols:

$$EV = p_1\$_1 + p_2\$_2 + \ldots + p_n\$_n$$

where p stands for probability, $\$$ stands for the value of an outcome, and $p_1 + p_2 + \ldots + p_n = 1$.

The assumption that people actually behave the way this mathematical notion says they should is contradicted by observable behavior in many risky situations. People are willing to buy insurance, even though the person who sells the insurance makes a profit. People are willing to buy lottery tickets, even though the lottery makes a profit. Consideration of the problem of insurance and of the St Petersburg paradox led Daniel Bernoulli, an eighteenth century mathematician, to propose that they could be resolved by assuming that people act so as to maximize *expected utility*, rather than expected value (26). (He also assumed that utility followed a function that more than a century later was proposed by Fechner for subjective magnitudes in general and is now called Fechner's Law.) This was the first use of the notion of expected utility.

The literature on risky decision making prior to 1944 consists primarily of the St Petersburg paradox and other gambling and probability literature in mathematics, some literary discussion in economics (e.g., 109, 187), one economic paper on lotteries (189), and the early literature of the theory of games (31, 32, 33, 34, 195), which did not use the notion of utility. The modern period in the study of risky decision making began with the publication in 1944 of von Neumann and Morgenstern's monumental book *Theory of games and economic behavior* (196, see also 197), which we will discuss more fully later. Von Neumann and Morgenstern pointed out that the usual assumption that economic man can always say whether he prefers one state to another or is indifferent between them needs only to be slightly modified in order to imply cardinal utility. The modification consists of adding that economic man can also completely order probability combinations of states. Thus, suppose that an economic man is indifferent between the certainty of $7.00 and a 50–50 chance of gaining $10.00 or nothing. We can assume that his indifference between these two prospects means that they have the same utility for him. We may define the utility of $0.00 as zero utiles (the usual name for the unit of utility, just as sone is the name for the unit of auditory loudness), and the utility of $10.00 as 10 utiles. These two arbitrary definitions correspond to defining the two undefined constants which are permissible since cardinal utility is measured only up to a linear transformation. Then we may calculate the utility of $7.00 by using the concept of expected utility as follows:

$$U(\$7.00) = 0.5U(\$10.00) + 0.5U(\$0.00)$$
$$= 0.5(10) + 0.5(0) = 5.$$

Thus we have determined the cardinal utility of $7.00 and found that it is 5 utiles. By varying the probabilities and by using the already found utilities it is possible to discover the utility of any other amount of money, using only the two permissible arbitrary definitions. It is even more convenient if instead of +$10.00, −$10.00 or some other loss is used as one of the arbitrary utilities.

A variety of implications is embodied in this apparently simple notion. In the attempt to examine and exhibit clearly what these implications are, a number of axiom systems, differing from von Neumann and Morgenstern's but leading to the same result, have been developed (73, 74, 85, 135, 136, 171). This paper will not attempt to go into the complex discussions (e.g., 130, 131, 168, 207) of these various alternative axiom systems. One recent discussion of them (78) has concluded, on reasonable grounds, that the original von Neumann and Morgenstern set of axioms is still the best.

It is profitable, however, to examine what the meaning of this notion is from the empirical point of view if it is right. First, it means that risky propositions can be ordered in desirability, just as riskless ones can. Second, it means that the concept of expected utility is behaviorally meaningful. Finally, it means that choices among risky alternatives are made in such a way that they maximize expected utility.

If this model is to be used to predict actual choices, what could go wrong with it? It might be that the probabilities by which the utilities are multiplied should not be the objective probabilities; in other words, a decider's estimate of the subjective importance of a probability may not be the same as the numerical value of that probability. It might be that the method of combination of probabilities and values should not be simple multiplication. It might be that the method of combination of the probability-value products should not be simple addition. It might be that the process of gambling has some positive or negative utility of its own. It might be that the whole approach is wrong, that people just do not behave as if they were trying to maximize expected utility. We shall examine some of these possibilities in greater detail below.

Economic implications of maximizing expected utility. – The utility-measurement notions of von Neumann and Morgenstern were enthusiastically welcomed by many economists (e.g., 73, 193), though a few (e.g., 19) were at least temporarily (20) unconvinced. The most interesting economic use of them was proposed by Friedman and Savage (73), who were concerned with the question of why the same person who buys insurance (with a negative expected money value), and therefore is willing to pay in order not to take risks, will also buy lottery tickets (also with a negative expected money value) in which he pays in order to take risks. They suggested that these facts could be reconciled by a doubly inflected utility curve for money, like that in Figure 2. If I represents the person's current income, then he is clearly willing to accept 'fair' insurance (i.e., insurance with zero expected money value) because the serious loss against which he is

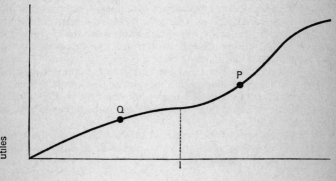

Figure 2   Hypothetical utility curve for money, proposed by Friedman and Savage

insuring would have a lower expected utility than the certain loss of the insurance premium. (Negatively accelerated total utility curves, like that from the origin to I, are what you get when marginal utility decreases; thus, decreasing marginal utility is consistent with the avoidance of risks.) The person would also be willing to buy lottery tickets, since the expected utility of the lottery ticket is greater than the certain loss of the cost of the ticket, because of the rapid increase in the height of the utility function. Other considerations make it necessary that the utility curve turn down again. Note that this discussion assumes that gambling has no inherent utility.

Markowitz (132) suggested an important modification in this hypothesis. He suggested that the origin of a person's utility curve for money be taken as his customary financial status, and that on both sides of the origin the curve be assumed first concave and then convex. If the person's customary state of wealth changes, then the shape of his utility curve will thus remain generally the same with respect to where he now is, and so his risk-taking behavior will remain pretty much the same instead of changing with every change of wealth as in the Friedman–Savage formulation.

Criticism of the expected-utility maximization theory. – It is fairly easy to construct examples of behavior that violate the von Neumann–Morgenstern axioms (for a particularly ingenious example, see 183). It is especially easy to do so when the amounts of money involved are very large, or when the probabilities or probability differences involved are extremely small. Allais (5) has constructed a questionnaire full of items of this type. For an economist interested in using these axioms as a basis for a completely general theory of risky choice, these examples may be significant. But psychological interest in this model is more modest. The psychologically important question is: Can such a model be used to account for simple experimental examples of risky decisions?

Of course a utility function derived by von Neumann–Morgenstern means is not necessarily the same as a classical utility function (74, 203; see also 82).

Experiment on the von Neumann–Morgenstern model. – A number of experiments on risky decision making have been performed. Only the first of them, by Mosteller and Nogee (142), has been in the simple framework of the model described above. All the rest have in some way or another centered on the concept of probabilities effective for behavior which differ in some way from the objective probabilities, as well as on utilities different from the objective values of the objects involved.

Mosteller and Nogee (142) carried out the first experiment to apply the von Neumann–Morgenstern model. They presented Harvard undergraduates and National Guardsmen with bets stated in terms of rolls at poker dice, which each subject could accept or refuse. Each bet gave a 'hand' at poker dice. If the subject could beat the hand, he won an amount stated in the bet. If not, he lost a nickel. Subjects played with $1.00, which they were given at the beginning of each experimental session. They were run together in groups of five; but each decided and rolled the poker dice for himself. Subjects were provided with a table in which the mathematically fair bets were shown, so that a subject could immediately tell by referring to the table whether a given bet was fair, or better or worse than fair.

In the data analysis, the first step was the determination of 'indifference offers'. For each probability used and for each player, the amount of money was found for which that player would accept the bet 50 per cent of the time. Thus equality was defined as 50 per cent choice, as it is likely to be in all psychological experiments of this sort. Then the utility of $0.00 was defined as 0 utiles, and the utility of losing a nickel was defined as −1 utile. With these definitions and the probabilities involved, it was easy to calculate the utility corresponding to the amount of money involved in the indifference offer. It turned out that, in general, the Harvard undergraduates had diminishing marginal utilities, while the National Guardsmen had increasing marginal utilities.

The utilities thus calculated were used in predicting the results of more complex bets. It is hard to evaluate the success of these predictions. At any rate, an auxiliary paired-comparisons experiment showed that the hypothesis that subjects maximized expected utility predicted choices better than the hypothesis that subjects maximized expected money value.

The utility curve that Mosteller and Nogee derive is different from the one Friedman and Savage (73) were talking about. Suppose that a subject's utility curve were of the Friedman–Savage type, as in Figure 2, and that he had enough money to put him at point P. If he now wins or loses a bet, then he is moved to a different location on the indifference curve, say Q. (Note that the amounts of money involved are much smaller than in the original Friedman–Savage use of this curve.) However, the construction of a Mosteller–Nogee utility curve assumes that the individual is always at the same point on his utility curve, namely the origin. This means that the curve is really of the Markowitz (132) type discussed above, instead of the Friedman–Savage type. The curve is not really a curve of utility of money in general, but rather it is a curve of the utility-for-n-more dollars. Even so, it must be assumed further that as the total amount of money possessed by the subject changes during the experiment, the utility-for-n-more dollars curve does not change. Mosteller and Nogee argue, on the basis of detailed examination of some of their data, that the amount of money possessed by the subjects did not seriously influence their choices. The utility curves they reported showed changing marginal utility within the amounts of money used in their experiment. Consequently, their conclusion that the amount of money possessed by the subjects was not seriously important can only be true if their utility curves are utility-for-n-more dollars curves and if the shapes of such curves are not affected by changes in the number of dollars on hand. This discussion exhibits a type of problem which must always arise in utility measurement and which is new in psychological scaling. The effects of previous judgments on present judgments are a familiar story in psychophysics, but they are usually assumed to be contaminating influences that can be minimized or eliminated by proper experimental design. In utility scaling, the fundamental idea of a utility scale is such that the whole structure of a subject's choices should be altered as a result of each previous choice (if the choices are real ones involving money gains or losses). The Markowitz solution to this problem is the most practical one available at present, and that solution is not entirely satisfactory since all it does is to assume that people's utilities for money operate in such a way that the problem does not really exist. This assumption is plausible for money, but it gets rapidly less plausible when other commodities with a less continuous character are considered instead.

Probability preferences. – In a series of recent experiments (55, 57, 58, 59), the writer has shown that subjects, when they bet, prefer some probabilities to others (57), and that these preferences cannot be accounted for by utility considerations (59). All the experiments were basically of the same design. Subjects were required to choose between pairs of bets according to the method of paired comparisons. The bets were of three kinds: positive expected value, negative expected value, and zero expected value. The two members of each pair of bets had the same expected value, so that there was never (in the main experiment [57, 59]) any objective reason to expect that choosing one bet would be more desirable than choosing the other.

Subjects made their choices under three conditions: just imagining they were betting; betting for worthless chips; and betting for real money. They paid any losses from their own funds, but they were run in extra sessions after the main experiment to bring their winnings up to $1.00 per hour.

The results showed that two factors were most important in determining choices: general preferences or dislikes for risk-taking, and specific preferences among probabilities. An example of the first kind of factor is that subjects strongly preferred low probabilities of losing large amounts of money to high probabilities of losing small amounts of money – they just didn't like to lose. It also turned out that on positive expected value bets, they were more willing to accept long shots when playing for real money than when just imagining or playing for worthless chips. An example of the second kind of factor is that they consistently preferred bets involving a 4/8 probability of winning to all others, and consistently avoided bets involving a 6/8 probability of winning. These preferences were reversed for negative expected value bets.

These results were independent of the amounts of money involved in the bets, so long as the condition of constant expected value was maintained (59). When pairs of bets which differed from one another in expected value were used, the choices were a compromise between maximizing expected amount of money and betting at the preferred probabilities (58). An attempt was made to construct individual utility curves adequate to account for the results of several subjects. For this purpose, the utility of $0.30 was defined as 30 utiles, and it was assumed that subjects cannot discriminate utility differences smaller than half a utile. Under these assumptions, no individual utility curves consistent with the data could be drawn. Various minor experiments showed that these results were reliable and not due to various possible artifacts (59). No attempt was made to generate a mathematical model of probability preferences.

The existence of probability preferences means that the simple von Neumann–Morgenstern method of utility measurement cannot succeed. Choices between bets will be determined not only by the amounts of money involved, but also by the preferences the subjects have among the probabilities involved. Only an experimental procedure which holds one of these variables constant, or otherwise allows for it, can hope to measure the other. Thus my experiments cannot be regarded as a way of measuring probability preferences; they show only that such preferences exist.

It may nevertheless be possible to get an interval scale of the utility of money from gambling experiments by designing an experiment which measures utility and probability preferences simultaneously. Such experiments are likely to be complicated and difficult to run, but they can be designed.

Subjective probability. – First, a clarification of terms is necessary. The phrase *subjective probability* has been used in two ways: as a name for a school of thought about the logical basis of mathematical probability (51, 52, 80) and as a name for a transformation on the scale of mathematical probabilities which is somehow related to behavior. Only the latter usage is intended here. The clearest distinction between these two notions arises from consideration of what happens when an objective probability can be defined (e.g., in a game of craps). If the subjective probability is assumed to be different from the objective probability, then the concept is being used in its second, or psychological, sense. Other terms with the same meaning have also been used: personal probability, psychological probability, expectation (a poor term because of the danger of confusion with expected value). (For a more elaborate treatment of concepts in this area, see 192.)

In 1948, prior to the Mosteller and Nogee experiment, Preston and Baratta (149) used essentially similar logic and a somewhat similar experiment to measure subjective probabilities instead of subjective values. They required subjects to bid competitively for the privilege of taking a bet. All bids were in play money, and the data consisted of the winning bids. If each winning bid can be considered to represent a value of play money such that the winning bidder is indifferent between it and the bet he is bidding for, and if it is further assumed that utilities are identical with the money value of the play money and that all players have the same subjective probabilities, then these data can be used to construct a subjective probability scale. Preston and Baratta constructed such a scale. The subjects, according to the scale, overestimate low probabilities and underestimate high ones, with an indifference point (where subjective equals objective probability) at about 0·2. Griffith (81) found somewhat similar results in an analysis of parimutuel betting at race tracks, as did Attneave (17) in a guessing game, and Sprowls (178) in an analysis of various lotteries. The Mosteller and Nogee data (142) can, of course, be analyzed for subjective probabilities instead of subjective values. Mosteller and Nogee performed such an analysis and said that their results were in general agreement with Preston and Baratta's. However, Mosteller and Nogee found no indifference point for their Harvard students, whereas the National Guardsmen had an indifference point at about 0·5. They are not able to reconcile these differences in results.

The notion of subjective probability has some serious logical difficulties. The scale of objective probability is bounded by 0 and 1. Should a subjective probability scale be similarly bounded, or not? If not, then many different subjective probabilities will correspond to the objective probabilities 0 and 1 (unless some transformation is used so that 0 and 1 objective probabilities correspond to infinite subjective probabilities, which seems unlikely). Considerations of the addition theorem to be discussed in a moment have occasionally led people to think of a subjective probability scale bounded at 0 but not at 1. This is surely arbitrary. The concept of absolute certainty is neither more nor less indeterminate than is the concept of absolute impossibility.

Even more drastic logical problems arise in connection with the addition theorem. If the objective probability of event A is P, and that of A not occurring is Q, then $P + Q = 1$. Should this

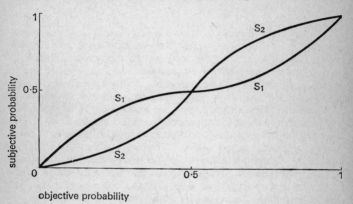

Figure 3   Hypothetical subjective probability curves

rule hold for subjective probabilities? Intuitively it seems necessary that if we know the subjective probability of A, we ought to be able to figure out the subjective probability of not-A, and the only reasonable rule for figuring it out is subtraction of the subjective probability of A from that of complete certainty. But the acceptance of this addition theorem for subjective probabilities plus the idea of bounded subjective probabilities means that the subjective probability scale must be identical with the objective probability scale. Only for a subjective probability scale identical with the objective probability scale will the subjective probabilities of a collection of events, one of which must happen, add up to 1. In the special case where only two events, A and not-A, are considered, a subjective probability scale like S_1 or S_2 in Figure 3 would meet the requirements of additivity, and this fact has led to some speculation about such scales, particularly about

S_1. But such scales do not meet the additivity requirements when more than two events are considered.

One way of avoiding these difficulties is to stop thinking about a scale of subjective probabilities and, instead, to think of a weighting function applied to the scale of objective probabilities which weights these objective probabilities according to their ability to control behavior. Presumably, I was studying this ability in my experiments on probability preferences (55, 57, 58, 59). There is no reason why such weighted probabilities should add up to 1 or should obey any other simple combinatory principle.

Views and experiments which combine utility and subjective probability. – The philosopher Ramsey published in 1926 (reprinted in 1931, see 150) an essay on the subjective foundations of the theory of probability; this contained an axiom system in which both utility and subjective probability appeared. He used 0·5 subjective probability as a reference point from which to determine utilities, and then used these utilities to determine other subjective probabilities. Apparently, economists did not discover Ramsey's essay until after von Neumann and Morgenstern's book aroused interest in the subject. The only other formal axiom system in which both utility and subjective probability play a part is one proposed by Savage (171), which is concerned with uncertainty, rather than risk, and uses the concept of subjective probability in its theory-of-probability sense.

The most extensive and important experimental work in the whole field of decision making under risk and uncertainty is now being carried out by Coombs and his associates at the University of Michigan. Coombs's thinking about utility and subjective probability is an outgrowth of his thinking about psychological scaling in general. (For a discussion of his views, see 43, 44, 45, 46, 47.) The essence of his work is the attempt to measure both utility and subjective probability on an ordered metric scale. An ordered metric scale has all the properties of an ordinal scale, and, in addition, the distances between some or all of the stimuli can be rank ordered. Coombs has developed various experimental procedures for obtaining such information about the spacings of stimuli.

In the most important article on utility and subjective probability to come out of the Coombs approach, Coombs and Beardslee (48) present an analysis of gambling decisions involving three independent variables: utility for prize, utility for stake, and subjective probability. All three are assumed measurable only up to an ordered metric, although it is assumed that the psychological probability of losing the stake is one minus the psychological probability of winning the prize, an assumption that limits the permissible underlying psychological probability functions to shapes like those in Figure 3. An elaborate graphic analysis of the indifference surfaces in this three-dimensional space is given, containing far too many interesting relationships to summarize here. An experiment based on this model was designed. Coombs is reluctant to use sums of money as the valuable objects in his experiments because of the danger that subjects will respond to the numerical value of the amount of dollars rather than to the psychological value. Therefore he used various desirable objects (e.g., a radio) as stimuli, and measured their utility by the techniques he has developed to obtain ordered metric scales. He used simple numerical statements of probability as the probability stimuli, and assumed that subjective probability was equal to objective probability. The subject from whose judgments the ordered metric utility measurements was constructed was then presented with imaginary bets involving these objects and probabilities, and it turned out that she almost always chose the one with the higher expected utility. This experiment is significant only as an illustration of the application of the method; the conclusion that subjects attempt to maximize expected utility cannot very comfortably be generalized to other subjects and to real choices without better evidence.

Coombs and Milholland (49) did a much more elaborate experiment in which they established ordered metric scales, both for the utilities of a collection of objects and for the subjective probabilities of a collection of statements (e.g., Robin Roberts will win 20 games next year). Statements and objects were combined into 'bets', and the two subjects for whom the ordered metric scales had been established were asked to make judgments about which bet they would most, and which they would least, prefer from among various triads of bets. These judgments were examined to discover whether or not they demonstrated the existence of at least one convex indifference curve between utility and subjective probability (the requirements for demonstrating the convexity of an indifference curve by means of ordered metric judgments are fairly easy to state). A number of cases consistent with a convex indifference curve were found, but a retest of the ordered metric data revealed changes which eliminated all of the cases consistent with a convex indifference curve for one subject, and all but one case for the other. It is not possible to make a statistical test of whether or not that one case might have come about by chance. No evidence was found for the existence of concave indifference curves, which are certainly inconsistent with the theory of risky decisions. This experiment is a fine example of the strength and weakness of the Coombs approach. It makes almost no assumptions, takes very little for granted, and avoids the concept of error of judgment; as a result, much of the potential information in the data is unused and rarely can any strong conclusions be drawn.

A most disturbing possibility is raised by experiments by Marks (133) and Irwin (94) which suggest that the shape of the subjective probability function is influenced by the utilities involved in the bets. If utilities and subjective probabilities are not independent, then there is no hope of predicting risky decisions unless their law of combination is known, and it seems very difficult to design an experiment to discover that law of combination. However, the main differences that Marks and Irwin found were between probabilities attached to desirable and undesirable alternatives. It is perfectly possible that there is one subjective probability function for bets with positive expected values and a different one for bets with negative expected values, just as the negative branch of the Markowitz utility function is likely to be different from the positive branch. The results of my probability preference experiments showed very great differences between the probability preference patterns for positive and for negative expected-value bets (57), but little difference between probability preferences at different expected-value levels so long as zero expected value was not crossed (59). This evidence supports the idea that perhaps only two subjective probability functions are necessary.

Santa Monica Seminar. – In the summer of 1952 at Santa Monica, California, a group of scientists conferred on problems of decision making. They met in a two-month seminar sponsored by the University of Michigan and the Office of Naval Research. The dittoed reports of these meetings are a gold mine of ideas for the student of this problem. Some of the work done at this seminar is now being prepared for a book on *Decision processes* edited by R. M. Thrall, C. H. Coombs, and R. L. Davis, of the University of Michigan.

Several minor exploratory experiments were done at this seminar. Vail (190) did an experiment in which he gave four children the choice of which side of various bets they wanted to be on. On the assumption of linear utilities, he was able to compute subjective probabilities for these children. The same children, however, were used as subjects for a number of other experiments; so, when Vail later tried them out on some other bets, he found that they consistently chose the bet with the highest probability of winning, regardless of the amounts of money involved. When 50–50 bets were involved, one subject consistently chose the bet with the *lowest* expected value. No generalizable conclusions can be drawn from these experiments.

Kaplan and Radner (100) tried out a questionnaire somewhat like Coombs's method of measuring subjective probability. Subjects were asked to assign numbers to various statements. The numbers could be anything from 0 to 100 and were to represent the likelihood that the statement was true. The hypotheses to be tested were: (*a*) for sets of exhaustive and mutually exclusive statements in which the numbers assigned (estimates of degree of belief) were nearly equal, the sums of these numbers over a set would increase with the number of alternatives (because low probabilities would be overestimated); (*b*) for sets with the same numbers of alternatives, those with one high number assigned would have a lower set sum than those with no high numbers. The first prediction was verified; the second was not. Any judgments of this sort are so much more likely to be made on the basis of number preferences and similar variables than on subjective probabilities that they offer very little hope as a method of measuring subjective probabilities.

Variance preferences. – Allais (2, 3, 4) and Georgescu-Roegen (78) have argued that it is not enough to apply a transform on objective value and on objective probability in order to predict risky decisions from expected utility (see also 188); it is also necessary to take into account at least the variance, and possibly the higher moments, of the utility distribution. There are instances in which this argument seems convincing. You would probably prefer the certainty of a million dollars to a 50–50 chance of getting either four million or nothing. I do not think that this preference is due to the fact that the expected utility of the 50–50 bet is less than the utility of one million dollars to you, although this is possible. A more likely explanation is simply that the variances of the two propositions are different. Evidence in favor of this is the fact that if you knew you would be offered this choice 20 times in succession, you would probably take the 50–50 bet each time. Allais (5) has constructed a number of more sophisticated examples of this type. However, from a simple-minded psychological point of view, these examples are irrelevant. It is enough if the theory of choice can predict choices involving familiar amounts of money and familiar probability differences – choices such as those which people are accustomed to making. It may be necessary for economic theory that the theory of choice be universal and exceptionless, but experimental psychologists need not be so ambitious. This is fortunate, because the introduction of the variance and higher moments of the utility distribution makes the problem of applying the theory experimentally seem totally insoluble. It is difficult enough to derive reasonable methods of measuring utility alone from risky choices; when it also becomes necessary to measure subjective probability and to take the higher moments of the utility distribution into account, the problem seems hopeless. Allais apparently hopes to defeat this problem by using psychophysical methods to measure utility (and presumably subjective probability also). This is essentially what Coombs has done, but Coombs has recognized that such procedures are unlikely to yield satisfactory interval scales. The dollar scale of the value of money is so thoroughly taught to us that it seems almost impossible to devise a psychophysical situation in which subjects would judge the utility, rather than the dollar value, of dollars. They might judge the utility of other valuable objects, but since dollars are the usual measure of value, such judgments would be less useful, and even these judgments would be likely to be contaminated by the dollar values of the objects. I would get more utility from a new electric shaver than I would from a new washing machine, but because of my knowledge of the relative money values of these objects, I would certainly choose the washing machine if given a choice between them. Somewhat similar arguments can be applied against using psychophysical methods to measure subjective probability. A final point is that, since these subjective scales are to be used to predict choices, it would be best if they could be derived from similar choices.

Other approaches. – Shackle (175) has proposed a theory of decision making under risk and uncertainty. This theory is unique in that it does not assume any kind of maximizing behavior. For every possible outcome of a decision made in a risky or uncertain situation, Shackle assumes that there is a degree of potential surprise that this, rather than some other, outcome would occur. Every outcome-potential surprise pair is ranked in accordance with its ability to stimulate the mind (stimulation increases with increasing outcome and decreases with increasing potential surprise). The highest-ranking positive outcome-potential surprise pair and the highest-ranking negative pair are found, and these two possibilities alone determine what the individual will do. Semi-mathematical methods are used to predict the outcome of consideration of possible lines of action. Although attempts have been made to relate it to Wald's minimax principle for statistical decision functions (see below), the fact remains that most critics of the Shackle point of view have judged it to be either too vague to be useful, or if specified in detail, too conducive to patently absurd predictions (e.g., 201).

Shackle's point of view was developed primarily to deal with unique choices – choices which can be made only once. Allais (3) has similarly criticized conventional utility theory's attack on this problem. Since the usual frequency theory of probability conceives of the probability as the limit of the outcomes of a large number of similar trials, it is questionable that notions which use probability in the ordinary sense (like the notion of maximizing expected utility) are applicable to unique choices. However, this seems to be an experimental problem. If notions which use ordinary probability are incapable of predicting actual unique choices, then it will be necessary to seek other theoretical tools. But so long as a generally acceptable probability can be defined (e.g., as in the unique toss of a coin), it is not necessary to assume *a priori* that theories based on conventional probabilities will be inadequate. When no generally acceptable probability can be defined, then the problem becomes very different.

Cartwright and Festinger (38, 41) have proposed a theory about the time it takes to make decisions which is in some ways similar to those discussed in this section. The main difference is that they add the concept of restraining forces, and that they conceive of all subjective magnitudes as fluctuating randomly around a mean value. From this they deduce various propositions about decision times and the degree of certainty which subjects will feel about their decisions, and apparently these propositions work out experimentally pretty well (38, 39, 61, 62). The Lewinian theoretical orientation seems to lead to this kind of model; Lewin, Dembo, Festinger, and Sears (122) present a formally similar theory about level of aspiration. Of course, the notion of utility is very similar to the Lewinian notion of valence.

Landahl (115) has presented a mathematical model for risk-taking behavior based on the conceptual neurology of the mathematical biophysics school.

Psychological comments. – The area of risky decision making is full of fascinating experimental problems. Of these, the development of a satisfactory scale of utility of money and of subjective probability must come first, since the theory of risky decision making is based on these notions. The criterion for satisfactoriness of these scales must be that they successfully predict choices other than those from which they were derived. To be really satisfactory, it is desirable that they should predict choices in a wide variety of differing situations. Unlike the subjective scales usually found in psychophysics, it is likely that these scales will differ widely from person to person, so a new determination of each scale must be made for each new subject. It can only be hoped that the scales do not change in time to any serious degree; if they do, then they are useless.

Once scales of utility and subjective probability are available, then many interesting questions arise. What about the addition theorem for subjective probabilities? Does gambling itself have utility, and how much? To what extent can these subjective scales be changed by learning? To what degree do people differ, and can these differences be correlated with environmental, historical, or personality differences? Finally, psychologists might be able to shed light on the complex economic problem of interacting utilities of different goods.

The area of risky decision making, like the area of the theory of games, tends to encourage in those interested in it the custom of carrying out small pilot experiments on their sons, laboratory assistants, or secretaries. Such experiments are too seldom adequately controlled, and are almost never used as a basis for larger-scale, well-designed experiments. Whether an ill-designed and haphazardly executed little experiment is better than no experiment at all is questionable. The results of such pilot experiments too often are picked up and written into the literature without adequate warning about the conditions under which they were performed and the consequent limitations on the significance of the results.

The Transitivity of Choices

In the section on riskless choices this paper presented a definition of economic man. The most important part of this definition can be summed up by saying that economic man is rational. The concept of rationality involves two parts: that of a weak ordering of preferences, and that of choosing so as to maximize something. Of these concepts, the one which seems most dubious is the one of a weakly ordered preference field. This is dubious because it implies that choices are transitive; that is, if A is preferred to B, and B is preferred to C, then A is preferred to C.

Two economists have designed experiments specifically intended to test the transitivity of choices. Papandreou performed an elaborate and splendidly controlled experiment (145) designed to discover whether or not intransitivities occurred in imagined-choice situations. He prepared triplets of hypothetical bundles of admissions to plays, athletic contests, concerts, etc., and required his subjects to choose between pairs of bundles. Each bundle consisted of a total of four admissions to two events, e.g., 3 plays and 1 tennis tournament. In the main experiment, each bundle is compared with two others involving the same kinds of events, but in the better-designed auxiliary experiment, a total of six different events are used, so that each bundle has no events in common with the other two bundles in its triplet. Since there are three bundles in each triplet, there are three choices between pairs for each triplet, and these choices may, or may not, be transitive. The subjects were permitted to say that they were indifferent between two bundles; consequently there were 27 possible configurations of choices, of which only 13 satisfied the transitivity axiom. In the main experiment, 5 per cent of the triplets of judgments were intransitive; in the auxiliary experiment, only 4 per cent. Papandreou develops a stochastic model for choices under such conditions; the results are certainly consistent with the amount of intransitivity permitted by his model. Papandreou concludes that at least for his specific experimental conditions, transitivity does exist.

May (138), using different kinds of stimuli in a less elaborate experiment, comes up with results less consistent with transitivity. May required a classroom group to make pairwise choices between three marriage partners who were identified only by saying how intelligent, good-looking, and rich they were. Judgments of indifference were not permitted. The results were that 27 per cent of the subjects gave intransitive triads of choices. May suggests, very plausibly, that intransitive choices may be expected to occur whenever more than one dimension exists in the stimuli along which subjects may order their preferences. However, May would probably have gotten fewer intransitivities if he had permitted the indifference judgment. If subjects are really indifferent among all three of the elements of a triad of objects, but are required to choose between them in pairs and do so by chance, then they will choose intransitively one-fourth of the time. Papandreou's stochastic model gives one theory about what happens when preferences diverge just slightly from indifference, but presumably a more detailed model can be worked out. Papandreou's model permits only three states: prefer A to B, prefer B to A, and indifferent. It ought to be possible to base a model for such situations on the cumulative normal curve, and thus to permit any degree of preference. For every combination of degrees of preference, such a model would predict the frequency of intransitive choices.

In the paired comparisons among bets (57) described in the section on risky choices, quite elaborate intransitivities could and did occur. However, it is easy to show that any intransitivity involving four or more objects in a paired comparisons judgment situation will necessarily produce at least one intransitivity involving three objects. Consequently, the intransitive triplet or circular triad is the best unit of analysis for intransitivities in these more complicated judgment situations. I counted the frequency of occurrence of circular triads and found that they regularly occurred about 20 per cent of the total number of times they could occur. (Of course, no indifference judgments could be permitted.) The experiment fulfills May's criterion for the occurrence of intransitivities, since both probability and amount of money were present in each bet, and subjects could be expected to take both into account when making choices. It might be supposed that the difference between the imaginary choices of the Papandreou and May experiments and the real choices in my experiment would lead to differences in the frequency of occurrence of intransitivities, but there were no substantial differences in my experiment between the frequencies of occurrence in the just-imagining sessions and in the real gambling sessions, and what differences there were, were in the direction of greater transitivity when really gambling. These facts should facilitate further experiments on this problem.

In one sense, transitivity can never be violated. A minimum of three choices is required to demonstrate intransitivity. Since these choices will necessarily be made in sequence, it can always be argued that the person may have changed his tastes between the first choice and the third. However, unless the assumption of constancy of tastes over the period of experimentation is made, no experiments on choice can ever be meaningful, and the whole theory of choice becomes empty (see 184 for a similar situation). So this quibble can be rejected at once.

Utility maximization will not work except with a transitive preference field. Consequently, if the models discussed in this paper are to predict experimental data, it is necessary that intransitivities in these data be infrequent enough to be considered as errors. However, from a slightly different point of view (54) the occurrence or nonoccurrence of transitive choice patterns is an experimental phenomenon, and presumably a lawful one. May has suggested what that law is: Intransitivities occur when there are conflicting stimulus dimensions along which to judge. This notion could certainly be tested and made more specific by appropriate experiments.

A final contribution in a related, but different, area is Vail's stochastic utility model (191). Vail assumes that choices are dependent on utilities that oscillate in a random manner around a mean value. From this assumption plus a few other reasonable ones, he deduces that if the over-all preference is $1 > 2 > 3$, and if 1 is preferred to 2 more than 2 is preferred to 3, then the frequencies of occurrence of the six possible transitive orderings should be ordered as follows: $123 > 132 > 213 > 312 > 231 > 321$. This result is certainly easy to test experimentally, and sounds plausible.

The Theory of Games and of Decision Functions[5]

This section will not go into the theory of games or into the intimately related subject of statistical decision functions at all thoroughly. These are mathematical subjects of a highly technical sort, with few statements which lend themselves to experimental test. Rather, the purpose of this section is to show how these subjects relate to what has gone before, to give a brief summary of the contents of *Theory of games and economic behavior* by von Neumann and Morgenstern (197), and to describe a few experiments in the area of game playing – experiments which are

5. Marschak (134), Hurwicz (92), Neisser (143), Stone (181), and Kaysen (107) published reviews of *The theory of games and economic behavior* which present the fundamental ideas in much simpler language than the original source. Marschak works out in detail the possible solutions of a complicated three-person bargaining game, and thereby illustrates the general nature of a solution. The two volumes of *Contributions to the theory of games* (112, 113), plus McKinsey's book on the subject (129), provide an excellent bibliography of the mathematical literature. McKinsey's book is an exposition of the fundamental concepts, intended as a textbook, which is simpler than von Neumann and Morgenstern and pursues certain topics further. Wald's book (198) is, of course, the classical work on statistical decision functions. Bross's book (35) presents the fundamental ideas about statistical decision functions more simply, and with a somewhat different emphasis. Girshick and Blackwell's book (79) is expected to be a very useful presentation of the field.

stimulated by the theory of games although not directly relevant to it.

The theory of games. – The theory of games probably originated in the work of Borel (31, 32, 33, 34; see also 71, 72) in the 1920s. In 1928, von Neumann (195), working independently of Borel, published the first proof of the fundamental theorem in the theory, a theorem that Borel had not believed to be generally true. However, the subject did not become important until 1944, when von Neumann and Morgenstern published their epoch-making book (196). (A second edition, with an appendix on cardinal utility measurement, came out in 1947 [197].) Their purpose was to analyze mathematically a very general class of problems, which might be called problems of strategy. Consider a game of tic-tac-toe. You know at any moment in the game what the moves available to your opponent are, but you do not know which one he will choose. The only information you have is that his choice will not, in general, be completely random; he will make a move which is designed in some way to increase his chance of winning and diminish yours. Thus the situation is one of uncertainty rather than risk. Your goals are similar to your opponent's. Your problem is: what strategy should you adopt? The theory of games offers no practical help in developing strategies, but it does offer rules about how to choose among them. In the case of tic-tac-toe, these rules are trivial, since either player can force a draw. But in more complicated games of strategy, these rules may be useful. In particular, the theory of games may be helpful in analyzing proper strategy in games having random elements, like the shuffling of cards, or the throwing of dice. It should be noted that the concept of a game is an exceedingly general concept. A scientist in his laboratory may be considered to be playing a game against Nature. (Note, however, that we cannot expect Nature to try to defeat the scientist.) Negotiators in a labor dispute are playing a game against one another. Any situation in which money (or some valuable equivalent) may be gained as the result of a proper choice of strategy can be considered as a game.

To talk about game theory, a few technical terms are necessary. A *strategy* is a set of personal rules for playing the game. For each possible first move on your part, your opponent will have a possible set of responses. For each possible response by your opponent, you will have a set of responses, and so on through the game. A strategy is a list which specifies what your move will be for every conceivable previous set of moves of the particular game you are playing. Needless to say, only for the simplest games (e.g., matching pennies) does this concept of strategy have any empirical meaning.

Associated with strategies are *imputations*. An imputation is a set of payments made as a result of a game, one to each player. In general, different imputations will be associated with different sets of strategies, but for any given set of strategies there may be more than one imputation (in games involving coalitions).

Imputation X is said to *dominate* imputation Y if one or more of the players has separately greater gains (or smaller losses) in X than in Y and can, by acting together (in the case of more than one player), enforce the occurrence of X, or of some other imputation at least as good. The relationship of domination is not transitive.

A *solution* is a set of imputations, none of which dominates another, such that every imputation outside the solution is dominated by at least one imputation within the solution. Von Neumann and Morgenstern assert that the task of the theory of games is to find solutions. For any game, there may be one or more than one. One bad feature of the theory of games is that it frequently gives a large, or even infinite, number of solutions for a game.

The above definitions make clear that the only determiner of behavior in games, according to this theory, is the amounts of money which may be won or lost, or the expected amounts in games with random elements. The fun of playing, if any, is irrelevant.

The minimax loss principle. – The notions of domination and of solution imply a new fundamental rule for decision making – a rule sharply different from the rule of maximizing utility or expected utility with which this paper has been concerned up to this section. This rule is the rule of minimizing the maximum loss, or, more briefly, *minimax loss*. In other words, the rule is to consider, for each possible strategy that you could adopt, what the worst possible outcome is, and then to select that strategy which would have the least ill-effects if the worst possible outcome happened. Another way of putting the same idea is to call it the principle of maximizing the minimum gain, or *maximin gain*. This rule makes considerable sense in two-person games when you consider that the other player is out to get you, and so will do his best to make the worst possible outcome for you occur. If this rule is expressed geometrically, it asserts that the point you should seek is a saddle-point, like the highest point in a mountain pass (the best rule for crossing mountains is to minimize the maximum height, so explorers seek out such saddle-points).

Before we go any further, we need a few more definitions. Games may be among any number of players, but the simplest game is a *two-person game*, and it is this kind of game which has been most extensively and most successfully analyzed. Fundamentally, two kinds of payoff arrangements are possible. The simplest and most common is the one in which one player wins what the other player loses, or, more generally, the one for which the sum of all the payments made as a result of the game is zero. This is called a *zero-sum game*. In *nonzero-sum games*, analytical complexities arise. These can be diminished by assuming the existence of a fictitious extra player, who wins or loses enough to bring the sum of payments back to zero. Such a fictitious player cannot be assumed to have a strategy and cannot, of course, interact with any of the other players.

In zero-sum two-person games, what will happen? Each player, according to the theory, should pick his minimax strategy. But will this result in a stable solution? Not always. Sometimes the surface representing the possible outcomes of the game does not have a saddle-point. In this case, if player A chooses his minimax strategy, then player B will have an incentive not to use his own minimax strategy, because having found out his opponent's strategy, he can gain more by some other strategy. Thus the game has no solution.

Various resolutions of this problem are possible. Von Neumann and Morgenstern chose to introduce the notion of a *mixed strategy*, which is a probability distribution of two or more pure strategies. The fundamental theorem of the theory of games is that if both players in a zero-sum two-person game adopt mixed strategies which minimize the maximum *expected loss*, then the game will always have a saddle-point. Thus each person will get, in the long run, his expected loss, and will have no incentive to change his behavior even if he should discover what his opponent's mixed strategy is. Since A is already getting the minimum possible under the strategy he chose, any change in strategy by B will only increase A's payoff, and therefore cause B to gain less or lose more than he would by his own minimax strategy. The same is true of B.

Games involving more than two people introduce a new element – the possibility that two or more players will cooperate to beat the rest. Such a cooperative agreement is called a *coalition*, and it frequently involves *side-payments* among members of the coalition. The method of analysis for three-or-more-person games is to consider all possible coalitions and to solve the game for each coalition on the principles of a two-person game. This works fairly well for three-person games, but gets more complicated and less satisfactory for still more people.

This is the end of this exposition of the content of von Neumann and Morgenstern's book. It is of course impossible to condense a tremendous and difficult book into one page. The major points to be emphasized are these: the theory of games is not a model of how people actually play games (some game theorists will disagree with this), nor is it likely to be of any practical use in telling you how to play a complicated game; the crux of the theory of games is the principle of choosing the strategy which minimizes the maximum expected financial loss; and the theory defines a solution of a game as a set of imputations which satisfies this principle for all players.

Assumptions. – In their book von Neumann and Morgenstern say 'We have . . . assumed that [utility] is numerical . . . substitutable and unrestrictedly transferable between the various players' (197, p. 604). Game theorists disagree about what this and other similar sentences mean. One likely interpretation is that they assume utility to be linear with the physical value of money involved in a game and to be interpersonally comparable. The linear utility curves seem to be necessary for solving two-person games; the interpersonal comparability is used for the extension to *n* persons. Attempts are being made to develop solutions free of these assumptions (176).

Statistical decision functions. – Von Neumann (195) first used the minimax principle in his first publication on game theory in 1928. Neyman and Pearson mentioned its applicability to statistical decision problems in 1933 (144). Wald (198), who prior to his recent death was the central figure in the statistical decision-function literature, first seriously applied the minimax principle to statistical problems in 1939. Apparently, all these uses of the principle were completely independent of one another.

After *Theory of games and economic behavior* appeared in 1944, Wald (198) reformulated the problem of statistical decision making as one of playing a game against Nature. The statistician must decide, on the basis of observations which cost something to make, between policies, each of which has a possible gain or loss. In some cases, all of these gains and losses and the cost of observing can be exactly calculated, as in industrial quality control. In other cases, as in theoretical research, it is necessary to make some assumption about the cost of being wrong and the gain of being right. At any rate, when they are put in this form, it is obvious that the ingredients of the problem of statistical decision making have a gamelike sound. Wald applied the minimax principle to them in a way essentially identical with game theory.

A very frequent criticism of the minimax approach to games against Nature is that Nature is not hostile, as is the opponent in a two-person game. Nature will not, in general, use a minimax strategy. For this reason, other principles of decision making have been suggested. The simple principle of maximizing expected utility (which is the essence of the Bayes's theorem [15, 198] solution of the problem) is not always applicable because, even though Nature is not hostile, she does not offer any way of assigning a probability to each possible outcome. In other words, statistical decision making is a problem of uncertainty, rather than of risk. Savage has suggested the principle of minimaxing *regret*, where regret is defined as the difference between the maximum which can be gained under any strategy given a certain state of the world and the amount gained under the strategy adopted. Savage believes (170, also personal communication) that neither von Neumann and Morgenstern nor Wald actually intended to propose the principle of minimaxing loss; they confined their discussions to cases in which the concepts of minimax loss and minimax regret amount to the same thing. Other suggested principles are: maximizing the maximum expected gain, and maximizing some weighted average of the maximum and minimum expected gains (93). None of these principles commands general acceptance; each can be made to show peculiar consequences under some conditions (see 170).

Experimental games. – The concepts of the theory of games suggest a new field of experimentation: How do people behave in game situations? Such experimentation would center on the development of strategies, particularly mixed strategies, and, in three-or-more-person games, on the development of coalitions and on the bargaining process. You should remember that the theory of games does not offer a mathematical model predicting the outcomes of such games (except in a few special cases); all it does is offer useful concepts and language for talking about them, and predict that certain outcomes will not occur.

A few minor experiments of this kind have been conducted by Flood, a mathematician, while he was at Rand Corporation. He usually used colleagues, many of whom were experts in game theory, and secretaries as subjects. The general design of his experiments was that a group of subjects were shown a group of desirable objects on a table, and told that they, as a group, could have the first object they removed from the table, and that they should decide among themselves which object to choose and how to allocate it. In the first experiment (64) the allocation problem did not arise because enough duplicate objects were provided so that each subject could have one of the kind of object the group selected. The subjects were Harvard undergraduates, and the final selection was made by negotiation and voting. In the second experiment (65), in which the subjects were colleagues and secretaries, a long negotiation process eliminated some of the objects, but a time limit forced a selection by lot from among the rest. Further negotiations to solve the allocation problem were terminated by a secretary, who snatched the object, announced that it was hers, and then tried to sell it. No one was willing to buy, so the experiment terminated. Other experiments (66, 67) showed that coalitions sometimes form, that a sophisticated subject could blackmail the group for an extra side-payment by threatening to change his vote, and that the larcenous secretary, having succeeded once, had to be physically restrained in subsequent sessions to prevent more larceny. The general conclusion suggested by all these experiments is that even experts on game theory are less rational and more conventional than game theory might lead experimenters to expect.

Psychological comments. – The most nutritive research problems in this area seem to be the social problems of how bargaining takes place. Flood's experiments left bargainers free and used physical objects, whose utilities probably vary widely from subject to subject, as stimuli to bargain over. This is naturalistic, but produces data too complex and too nonnumerical for easy analysis. A simpler situation in which the possible communications from one bargainer to another are limited (perhaps by means of an artificial vocabulary), in which the subjects do not see one another, and in which the object bargained over is simple, preferably being merely a sum of money, would be better. Physical isolation of one subject from another would make it possible to match each subject against a standard bargainer, the experimenter or a stooge, who bargains by a fixed set of rules that are unknown to the subject. Flood (personal communication) is conducting experiments of this sort. For three-or-more-person games, Asch's (16) technique of using a group consisting of only one real subject and all the rest stooges might well be used. It would be interesting, for instance, to see how the probability of a coalition between two players changes as the number and power of players united against them increase.

The theory of games is the area among those described in this paper in which the uncontrolled and casually planned 'pilot experiment' is most likely to occur. Such experiments are at least as dangerous here as they are in the area of risky decision making. Flood's results suggest that it is especially important to use naive subjects and to use them only once, unless the effects of expertness and experience are the major concern of the experiment.

Summary

For a long time, economists and others have been developing mathematical theories about how people make choices among desirable alternatives. These theories center on the notion of the subjective value, or utility, of the alternatives among which the decider must choose. They assume that people behave rationally; that is, that they have transitive preferences and that they choose in such a way as to maximize utility or expected utility.

The traditional theory of riskless choices, a straightforward theory of utility maximization, was challenged by the demonstration that the mathematical tool of indifference curves made it possible to account for riskless choices without assuming that utility could be measured on an interval scale. The theory of riskless choices predicted from indifference curves has been worked out in detail. Experimental determination of indifference curves is possible, and has been attempted. But utility measured on an interval scale is necessary (though not sufficient) for welfare economics.

Attention was turned to risky choices by von Neumann and Morgenstern's demonstration that complete weak ordering of risky choices implies the existence of utility measurable on an interval scale. Mosteller and Nogee experimentally determined utility curves for money from gambling decisions, and used them to predict other gambling decisions. Edwards demonstrated the existence of preferences among probabilities in gambling situations, which complicates the experimental measurement of utility. Coombs developed a model for utility and subjective probability measured on an ordered metric scale, and did some experiments to test implications of the model.

Economists have become worried about the assumption that choices are transitive. Experiments have shown that intransitive patterns of choice do occur, and so stochastic models have been developed which permit occasional intransitivities.

The theory of games presents an elaborate mathematical analysis of the problem of choosing from among alternative strategies in games of strategy. This paper summarizes the main concepts of this analysis. The theory of games has stimulated interest in experimental games, and a few bargaining experiments which can be thought of in game-theoretical terms have been performed.

All these topics represent a new and rich field for psychologists, in which a theoretical structure has already been elaborately worked out and in which many experiments need to be performed.

References

1. ALCHIAN, A. The meaning of utility measurement. *Amer. econ. Rev.*, 1953, **43**, 26–50.
2. ALLAIS, M. Fondements d'une théorie positive des choix comportant un risque et critique des postulats et axiomes de l'école américaine. *Colloque Internationale du Centre National de la Recherche scientifique*, 1952, No. 36.
3. ALLAIS, M. Le comportement de l'homme rationnel devant le risque: critique des postulats et axiomes de l'école américaine. *Econometrica*, 1953, **21**, 503–546.
4. ALLAIS, M. L'Extension des théories de l'équilibre économique général et du rendement social au cas du risque. *Econometrica*, 1953, **21**, 269–290.
5. ALLAIS, M. La psychologie de l'homme rationnel devant le risque: Le théorie et l'expérience. *J. soc. Statist.*, Paris, 1953, **94**, 47–73.
6. ALLEN, R. G. D. The nature of indifference curves. *Rev. econ. Stud.*, 1933, **1**, 110–121.
7. ALLEN, R. G. D. A note on the determinateness of the utility function. *Rev. econ. Stud.*, 1934, **2**, 155–158.
8. ARMSTRONG, W. E. The determinateness of the utility function. *Econ. J.*, 1939, **49**, 453–467.
9. ARMSTRONG, W. E. Uncertainty and the utility function. *Econ. J.*, 1948, **58**, 1–10.
10. ARMSTRONG, W. E. A note on the theory of consumer's behavior. *Oxf. econ. Pap.*, 1950, **2**, 119–122.
11. ARMSTRONG, W. E. Utility and the theory of welfare. *Oxf. econ. Pap.*, 1951, **3**, 259–271.
12. ARROW, K. J. Alternative approaches to the theory of choice in risk-taking situations. *Econometrica*, 1951, **19**, 404–437.
13. ARROW, K. J. An extension of the basic theorems of classical welfare economics. In J. Neyman (Ed.), *Proceedings of the second*

Berkeley symposium on mathematical statistics and probability. Berkeley: Univ. of Calif. Press, 1951, pp. 507–532.

14. ARROW, K. J. *Social choice and individual values.* New York: Wiley, 1951.

15. ARROW, K. J., BLACKWELL, D., and GIRSHICK, M. A. Bayes and minimax solutions of sequential decision problems. *Econometrica*, 1949, **17**, 213–244.

16. ASCH, S. E. *Social psychology.* New York: Prentice-Hall, 1952.

17. ATTNEAVE, F .Psychological probability as a function of experienced frequency. *J. exp. Psychol.*, 1953, **46**, 81–86.

18. BAUMOL, W. J. Community indifference. *Rev. econ. Stud.*, 1946, **14**, 44–48.

19. BAUMOL, W. J. The Neumann–Morgenstern utility index—an ordinalist view. *J. polit. Econ.*, 1951, **59**, 61–66.

20. BAUMOL, W. J. Discussion. *Amer. econ. Rev. Suppl.*, 1953, **43**, 415–416.

21. BERGSON (BURK), A. Reformulation of certain aspects of welfare economics. *Quart. J. Econ.*, 1938, **52**, 310–334.

22. BERNARDELLI, H. Note on the determinateness of the utility function. *Rev. econ. Stud.*, 1934, **2**, 69–75.

23. BERNARDELLI, H. The end of marginal utility theory? *Economica*, 1938, **5**, 192–212.

24. BERNARDELLI, H. A reply to Mr. Samuelson's note. *Economica*, 1939, **6**, 88–89.

25. BERNARDELLI, H. A rehabilitation of the classical theory of marginal utility. *Economica*, 1952, **19**, 254–268.

26. BERNOULLI, D. Specimen theoriae novae de mensura sortis. *Comentarii academiae scientiarum imperiales petropolitanae*, 1738, **5**, 175–192. (*Trans. by L. Sommer in Econometrica*, 1954, **22**, 23–36.)

27. BILODEAU, E. A. Statistical versus intuitive confidence. *Amer. J. Psychol.*, 1952, **65**, 271–277.

28. BISHOP, R. L. Consumer's surplus and cardinal utility. *Quart. J. Econ.*, 1943, **57**, 421–449.

29. BISHOP, R. L. Professor Knight and the theory of demand. *J. polit. Econ.*, 1946, **54**, 141–169.

30. BOHNERT, H. G. The logical structure of the utility concept. In R. M. Thrall, C. H. Coombs, and R. L. Davis (Eds.), *Decision processes.* New York: Wiley, in press.

31. BOREL, E. La théorie du jeu et les équations intégrales à noyau symétrique. *C. R. Acad. Sci., Paris*, 1921, **173**, 1304–1308. (Trans. by L. J. Savage in *Econometrica*, 1953, **21**, 97–100.)

32. BOREL, E. Sur les jeux où interviennent l'hasard et l'habilité des joueurs. In E. Borel, *Théorie des probabilités.* Paris: Librairie Scientifique, J. Hermann, 1924. Pp. 204–224. (Trans. by L. J. Savage in *Econometrica*, 1953, **21**, 101–115.)

33. BOREL, E. Algèbre et calcul des probabilités. *C. R. Acad. Sci., Paris*, 1927, **184**, 52–53. (Trans. by L. J. Savage in *Econometrica*, 1953, **21**, 116–117.)

34. BOREL, E. *Traité du calcul des probabilités et de ses applications, applications des jeux de hasard.* Vol. IV, No. 2. Paris: Gauthier-Villars, 1938.

35. BROSS, I. *Design for decision.* New York: Macmillan, 1953.

36. BUSH, R. R., and MOSTELLER, F. A mathematical model for simple learning. *Psychol. Rev.*, 1951, **58**, 313–323.

37. BUSH, R. R., and MOSTELLER, F. A model for stimulus generalization and discrimination. *Psychol. Rev.*, 1951, **58**, 413–423.

38. CARTWRIGHT, D. Decision-time in relation to differentiation of the phenomenal field. *Psychol. Rev.*, 1941, **48**, 425–442.

39. CARTWRIGHT, D. The relation of decision-time to the categories of response. *Amer. J. Psychol.*, 1941, **54**, 174–196.

40. CARTWRIGHT, D. Survey research: psychological economics. In J. G. Miller (Ed.), *Experiments in social process*. New York: McGraw-Hill, 1950. Pp. 47–64.

41. CARTWRIGHT, D., and FESTINGER, L. A quantitative theory of decision. *Psychol. Rev.*, 1943, **50**, 595–621.

42. CLARK, J. M. Realism and relevance in the theory of demand. *J. polit. Econ.*, 1946, **54**, 347–353.

43. COOMBS, C. H. Psychological scaling without a unit of measurement. *Psychol. Rev.*, 1950, **57**, 145–158.

44. COOMBS, C. H. Mathematical models in psychological scaling. *J. Amer. statist. Ass.*, 1951, **46**, 480–489.

45. COOMBS, C. H. A theory of psychological scaling. *Bull. Engng. Res. Inst. Univer. Mich.*, 1952, No. 34.

46. COOMBS, C. H. Theory and methods of social measurement. In L. Festinger and D. Katz (Eds.), *Research methods in the behavioral sciences*. New York: Dryden, 1953. Pp. 471–535.

47. COOMBS, C. H. A method for the study of interstimulus similarity. *Psychometrika*, in press.

48. COOMBS, C. H., and BEARDSLEE, D. C. Decision making under uncertainty. In R. M. Thrall, C. H. Coombs, and R. L. Davis (Eds.), *Decision processes*. New York: Wiley, in press.

49. COOMBS, C. H., and MILHOLLAND, J. E. Testing the 'rationality' of an individual's decision making under uncertainty. *Psychometrika*, in press.

50. CORLETT, W. J., and NEWMAN, P. K. A note on revealed preference and the transitivity conditions. *Rev. econ. Stud.*, 1952, **20**, 156–158.

51. DE FINETTI, B. La prévision: ses lois logiques, ses sources subjectives. *Ann. Inst. Poincaré*, 1937, **7**, 1–68.

52. DE FINETTI, B. Recent suggestions for the reconciliation of theories of probability. In J. Neyman (Ed.), *Proceedings of the second Berkeley symposium on mathematical statistics and probability*. Berkeley: Univer. of Calif. Press, 1951.

53. EDGEWORTH, F. Y. *Mathematical psychics*. London: Kegan Paul, 1881.

54. EDWARDS, W. Discussion. *Econometrica*, 1953, **21**, 477. (Abstract).

55. EDWARDS, W. Experiments on economic decision-making in gambling situations. *Econometrica*, 1953, **21**, 349–350. (Abstract).

56. EDWARDS, W. Information, repetition, and reinforcement as determiners of two-alternative decisions. *Amer. Psychologist*, 1953, **8**, 345. (Abstract).

57. EDWARDS, W. Probability-preferences in gambling. *Amer. J. Psychol.*, 1953, **66**, 349–364.

58. EDWARDS, W. Probability preferences among bets with differing expected values. *Amer. J. Psychol.*, 1954, **67**, 56–67.

59. EDWARDS, W. The reliability of probability preferences. *Amer. J. Psychol.*, 1954, **67**, 68–95.

60. Estes, W. K. Toward a statistical theory of learning. *Psychol. Rev.*, 1950, **57**, 94–107.

61. Festinger, L. Studies in decision: I. Decision-time, relative frequency of judgment and subjective confidence as related to physical stimulus differences. *J. exp. Psychol.*, 1943, **32**, 291–306.

62. Festinger, L. Studies in decision: II. An empirical test of a quantitative theory of decision. *J. exp. Psychol.*, 1943, **32**, 411–423.

63. Fisher, I. A statistical method for measuring 'marginal utility' and testing the justice of a progressive income tax. In J. Hollander (Ed.), *Economic essays contributed in honor of John Bates Clark.* New York: Macmillan, 1927. Pp. 157–193.

64. Flood, M. M. A preference experiment. *Rand Corp. Memo.*, November 1951, No. P-256.

65. Flood, M. M. A preference experiment (Series 2, Trial 1). *Rand Corp. Memo.*, December 1951, No. P-258.

66. Flood, M. M. A preference experiment (Series 2, Trials 2, 3, 4). *Rand Corp. Memo.*, January 1952, No. P-263.

67. Flood, M. M. A preference experiment (Series 3). Unpublished memorandum, Rand Corporation. February 25, 1952.

68. Flood, M. M. Some experimental games. *Rand Corp. Memo.*, March 1952, No. RM-789-1. (Revised June 1952.)

69. Flood, M. M. Testing organization theories. *Rand Corp. Memo.*, November 1952, No. P-312.

70. Flood, M. M. An experimental multiple-choice situation. *Rand Corp. Memo.*, November 1952, No. P-313.

71. Fréchet, M. Emile Borel, initiator of the theory of psychological games and its application. *Econometrica*, 1953, **21**, 95–96.

72. Fréchet, M., and von Neumann, J. Commentary on the three notes of Emile Borel. *Econometrica*, 1953, **21**, 118–126.

73. Friedman, M., and Savage, L. J. The utility analysis of choices involving risk. *J. polit. Econ.*, 1948, **56**, 279–304. (Reprinted with minor changes in G. J. Stigler and K. E. Boulding (Eds.), *Readings in price theory.* Chicago: Richard D. Irwin, 1952. Pp. 57–96.)

74. Friedman, M., and Savage, L. J. The expected-utility hypothesis and the measurability of utility. *J. polit. Econ.*, 1952, **60**, 463–475.

75. Frisch, R. New methods of measuring marginal utility. In R. Frisch, *Beiträge zur ökonomischen Theorie.* Tübingen: Mohr, 1932.

76. Georgescu-Roegen, N. The pure theory of consumer's behavior. *Quart. J. Econ.*, 1936, **50**, 545–593.

77. Georgescu-Roegen, N. The theory of choice and the constancy of economic laws. *Quart. J. Econ.*, 1950, **64**, 125–138.

78. Georgescu-Roegen, N. Utility, expectations, measurability, prediction. Paper read at Econometric Soc., Kingston, September, 1953.

79. Girshick, M. A., and Blackwell, D. *Theory of games and statistical decisions.* New York: Wiley, 1954.

80. Good, I. J. *Probability ana the weighing of evidence.* London: Griffin, 1950.

81. Griffith, R. M. Odds adjustments by American horse-race bettors. *Amer. J. Psychol.*, 1949, **62**, 290–294.

82. Harsanyi, J. C. Cardinal utility in welfare economics and in the theory of risk-taking. *J. polit. Econ.*, 1953, **61**, 434–435.

83. HART, A. G. Risk, uncertainty, and the unprofitability of compounding probabilities. In O. Lange, F. McIntyre, and T. O. Yntema (Eds.), *Studies in mathematical economics and econometrics.* Chicago: Univer. of Chicago Press, 1942. Pp. 110–118.

84. HAYES, S. P., JR. Some psychological problems of economics. *Psychol. Bull.,* 1950, **47,** 289–330.

85. HERSTEIN, I. N., and MILNOR, J. An axiomatic approach to measurable utility. *Econometrica,* 1953, **21,** 291–297.

86. HICKS, J. R. The foundations of welfare economics. *Econ. J.,* 1939, **49,** 696–712.

87. HICKS, J. R. *Value and capital,* Oxford: Clarendon Press, 1939.

88. HICKS, J. R., and ALLEN, R. G. D. A re-consideration of the theory of value. *Economica,* 1934, **14,** 52–76, 196–219.

89. HILDRETH, C. Alternative conditions for social orderings. *Econometrica,* 1953, **21,** 81–94.

90. HOUTHAKKER, H. S. Revealed preference and the utility function. *Economica,* 1950, **17,** 159–174.

91. HULL, C. L. *Principles of behavior, an introduction to behavior theory.* New York: D. Appleton-Century, 1943.

92. HURWICZ, L. The theory of economic behavior. *Amer. econ. Rev.,* 1945, **35,** 909–925. (Reprinted in G. J. Stigler and K. E. Boulding (Eds.), *Readings in price theory.* Chicago: Richard D. Irwin, 1952. Pp. 505–526.)

93. HURWICZ, L. What has happened to the theory of games? *Amer. econ. Rev. Suppl.,* 1953, **43,** 398–405.

94. IRWIN, F. W. Stated expectations as functions of probability and desirability of outcomes. *J. Pers.,* 1953, **21,** 329–335.

95. JARRETT, JACQUELINE M. Strategies in risk-taking situations. Unpublished Ph.D. thesis, Harvard Univer., 1951.

96. JENKINS, W. O., and STANLEY, J. C., JR. Partial reinforcement: a review and critique. *Psychol. Bull.,* 1950, **47,** 193–234.

97. JOHNSON, W. E. The pure theory of utility curves. *Econ. J.,* 1913, **23,** 483–513.

98. KALDOR, N. Welfare propositions and inter-personal comparisons of utility. *Econ. J.,* 1939, **49,** 549–552.

99. KALDOR, N. A comment. *Rev. econ. Stud.,* 1946, **14,** 49.

100. KAPLAN, A., and RADNER, R. A questionnaire approach to subjective probability—some experimental results. Working Memorandum 41, Santa Monica Conference on Decision Problems, August 15, 1952.

101. KATONA, G. Psychological analysis of business decisions and expectations. *Amer. econ. Rev.,* 1946, **36,** 44–62.

102. KATONA, G. Contributions of psychological data to economic analysis. *J. Amer. statist. Ass.,* 1947, **42,** 449–459.

103. KATONA, G. *Psychological analysis of economic behavior.* New York: McGraw-Hill, 1951.

104. KATONA, G. Rational behavior and economic behavior. *Psychol. Rev.,* 1953, **60,** 307–318.

105. KAUDER, E. Genesis of the marginal utility theory from Aristotle to the end of the eighteenth century. *Econ. J.,* 1953, **63,** 638–650.

106. KAUDER, E. The retarded acceptance of the marginal utility theory. *Quart. J. Econ.,* 1953, **67,** 564–575.

107. KAYSEN, C. A revolution in economic theory? *Rev. econ. Stud.,* 1946, **14,** 1–15.

108. KENNEDY, C. The common sense of indifference curves. *Oxf. econ. Pap.*, 1950, **2**, 123–131.

109. KNIGHT, F. H. *Risk, uncertainty, and profit.* Boston: Houghton Mifflin, 1921.

110. KNIGHT, F. H. Realism and relevance in the theory of demand. *J. polit. Econ.*, 1944, **52**, 289–318.

111. KNIGHT, F. H. Comment on Mr. Bishop's article. *J. polit. Econ.*, 1946, **54**, 170–176.

112. KUHN, H. W., and TUCKER, A. W. (Eds.). Contributions to the theory of games. Vol. I. *Ann. Math. Stud.*, No. 24. Princeton: Princeton Univer. Press, 1950.

113. KUHN, H. W., and TUCKER, A. W. (Eds.). Contributions to the theory of games. Vol. II. *Ann. Math. Stud.*, No. 28. Princeton: Princeton Univer. Press, 1953.

114. LANCASTER, K. A refutation of Mr. Bernardelli. *Economica*, 1953, **20**, 259–262.

115. LANDAHL, H. D. A neurobiophysical interpretation of certain aspects of the problem of risks. *Bull. Math. Biophysics*, 1951, **13**, 323–335.

116. LANGE, O. The determinateness of the utility function. *Rev. econ. Stud.*, 1933, **1**, 218–225.

117. LANGE, O. Note on the determinateness of the utility function. *Rev. econ. Stud.*, 1934, **2**, 75–77.

118. LANGE, O. The foundations of welfare economics. *Econometrica*, 1942, **10**, 215–228.

119. LANGE, O. The scope and methods of economics. *Rev. econ. Stud.*, 1945, **13**, 19–32.

120. LEWIN, K. *Principles of topological psychology.* New York: McGraw-Hill, 1936.

121. LEWIN, K. Behavior and development as a function of the total situation. In L. Carmichael (Ed.), *Manual of child psychology.* New York: Wiley, 1946. Pp. 791–844.

122. LEWIN, K., DEMBO, TAMARA, FESTINGER, L., and SEARS, PAULINE S. Level of aspiration. In J. McV. Hunt (Ed.), *Personality and the behavior disorders.* Vol. I. New York: Ronald, 1944. Pp. 333–378.

123. LEWISOHN, S. A. Psychology in economics. *Polit. Sci. Quart.*, 1938, **53**, 233–238.

124. LITTLE, I. M. D. The foundations of welfare economics. *Oxf. econ. Pap.*, 1949, **1**, 227–246.

125. LITTLE, I. M. D. A reformulation of the theory of consumer's behavior. *Oxf. econ. Pap.*, 1949, **1**, 90–99.

126. LITTLE, I. M. D. The theory of consumer's behavior – a comment. *Oxf. econ. Pap.*, 1950, **2**, 132–135.

127. LITTLE, I. M. D. Social choice and individual values. *J. polit. Econ.*, 1952, **60**, 422–432.

128. MACFIE, A. L. Choice in psychology and as economic assumption. *Econ. J.*, 1953, **63**, 352–367.

129. McKINSEY, J. C. C. *Introduction to the theory of games.* New York: McGraw-Hill, 1952.

130. MALINVAUD, E. Note on von Neumann–Morgenstern's strong independence axiom. *Econometrica*, 1952, **20**, 679.

131. MANNE, A. S. The strong independence assumption – gasolene blends and probability mixtures. *Econometrica*, 1952, **20**, 665–669.

132. MARKOWITZ, H. The utility of wealth. *J. polit. Econ.*, 1952, **60**, 151–158.

133. MARKS, ROSE W. The effect of probability, desirability, and 'privilege' on the stated expectations of children. *J. Pers.*, 1951, **19**, 332–351.

134. MARSCHAK, J. Neumann's and Morgenstern's new approach to static economics. *J. polit. Econ.*, 1946, **54**, 97–115.

135. MARSCHAK, J. Rational behavior, uncertain prospects, and measurable utility. *Econometrica*, 1950, **18**, 111–141.

136. MARSCHAK, J. Why 'should' statisticians and businessmen maximize 'moral expectation'? In J. Neyman (Ed.). *Proceedings of the second Berkeley symposium on mathematical statistics and probability*. Berkeley: Univer. of Calif. Press, 1951. Pp. 493–506.

137. MARSHALL, A. *Principles of economics*. (8th Ed.). New York: Macmillan, 1948.

138. MAY, K. O. Transitivity, utility, and aggregation in preference patterns. *Econometrica*, 1954, **22**, 1–13.

139. MELVILLE, L. G. Economic welfare. *Econ. J.*, 1939, **49**, 552–553.

140. MISHAN, E. J. The principle of compensation reconsidered. *J. polit. Econ.*, 1952, **60**, 312–322.

141. MORGAN, J. N. Can we measure the marginal utility of money? *Econometrica*, 1945, **13**, 129–152.

142. MOSTELLER, F., and NOGEE, P. An experimental measurement of utility. *J. polit. Econ.*, 1951, **59**, 371–404.

143. NEISSER, H. The strategy of expecting the worst. *Soc. Res.*, 1952, **19**, 346–363.

144. NEYMAN, J., and PEARSON, E. S. The testing of statistical hypotheses in relation to probability *a priori*. *Proc. Cambr. phil. Soc.*, 1933, **29**, 492–510.

145. PAPANDREOU, A. G. An experimental test of an axiom in the theory of choice. *Econometrica*, 1953, **21**, 477. (Abstract.)

146. PARETO, V. *Manuale di economia politica, con una introduzione ulla scienza sociale*. Milan, Italy: Societa Editrice Libraria, 1906.

147. PHELPS-BROWN, E. H. Note on the determinateness of the utility function. *Rev. econ. Stud.*, 1934, **2**, 66–69.

148. PIGOU, A. C. Some aspects of welfare economics. *Amer. econ. Rev.*, 1951, **41**, 287–302.

149. PRESTON, M. G., and BARATTA, P. An experimental study of the auction-value of an uncertain outcome. *Amer. J. Psychol.*, 1948, **61**, 183–193.

150. RAMSEY, F. P. Truth and probability. In F. P. Ramsey, *The foundations of mathematics and other logical essays*. New York: Harcourt Brace, 1931.

151. RICCI, U. Pareto and pure economics. *Rev. econ. Stud.*, 1933, **1**, 3–21.

152. ROBBINS, L. Interpersonal comparisons of utility: a comment. *Econ. J.*, 1938, **48**, 635–641.

153. ROBBINS, L. Robertson on utility and scope. *Economica*, 1953, **20**, 99–111.

154. ROBERTSON, D. H. *Utility and all that and other essays*. London: George Allen & Unwin, 1952.

155. ROTHENBERG, J. Conditions for a social welfare function. *J. polit. Econ.*, 1953, **61**, 389–405.

156. ROTHSCHILD, K. W. The meaning of rationality: a note on Professor Lange's article. *Rev. econ. Stud.*, 1946, **14**, 50–52.

157. ROUSSEAS, S. W., and HART, A. G. Experimental verification of a composite indifference map. *J. polit. Econ.*, 1951, **59**, 288–318.

158. SAMUELSON, P. A. A note on measurement of utility. *Rev. econ. Stud.*, 1937, **4**, 155–161.

159. SAMUELSON, P. A. Empirical implications of utility analysis. *Econometrica*, 1938, **6**, 344–356.

160. SAMUELSON, P. A. A note on the pure theory of consumer's behavior. *Economica*, 1938, **5**, 61–71.

161. SAMUELSON, P. A. A note on the pure theory of consumer's behavior. An addendum. *Economica*, 1938, **5**, 353–354.

162. SAMUELSON, P. A. The numerical representations of ordered classifications and the concept of utility. *Rev. econ. Stud.*, 1938, **6**, 65–70.

163. SAMUELSON, P. A. The end of marginal utility: a note on Dr. Bernardelli's article. *Economica*, 1939, **6**, 86–87.

164. SAMUELSON, P. A. *Foundations of economic analysis.* Cambridge, Mass.: Harvard Univer. Press, 1947.

165. SAMUELSON, P. A. Consumption theory in terms of revealed preference. *Economica*, 1948, **15**, 243–253.

166. SAMUELSON, P. A. Evaluation of real national income. *Oxf. econ. Pap.*, 1950, **2**, 1–29.

167. SAMUELSON, P. A. The problem of integrability in utility theory. *Economica*, 1950, **17**, 355–385.

168. SAMUELSON, P. A. Probability, utility, and the independence axiom. *Econometrica*, 1952, **20**, 670–678.

169. SAMUELSON, P. A. Consumption theorems in terms of overcompensation rather than indifference comparisons. *Economica*, 1953, **20**, 1–9.

170. SAVAGE, L. J. The theory of statistical decision. *J. Amer. statist. Ass.*, 1951, **46**, 55–67.

171. SAVAGE, L. J. An axiomatic theory of reasonable behavior in the face of uncertainty. Unpublished manuscript, Statistical Research Center, Univer. of Chicago, No. SRC-21222S14.

172. SCHULTZ, H. *The theory and measurement of demand.* Chicago: Univer. of Chicago Press, 1938.

173. SCITOVSKY, T. A note on welfare propositions in economics. *Rev. econ. Stud.*, 1941, **9**, 77–88.

174. SCITOVSKY, T. The state of welfare economics. *Amer. econ. Rev.*, 1951, **41**, 303–315.

175. SHACKLE, G. L. S. *Expectations in economics.* Cambridge, Eng.: Cambridge Univer. Press, 1949.

176. SHAPLEY, L. S., and SHUBIK, M. Solutions of n-person games with ordinal utilities. *Econometrica*, 1953, **21**, 348–349. (Abstract.)

177. SLUTSKY, E. E. Sulla teoria del bilancio del consumatore, *Giornale degli economisti*, 1915, **51**, 1–26. (Trans. by O. Ragusa and reprinted in G. J. Stigler and K. E. Boulding [Eds.], *Readings in price theory.* Chicago: Richard D. Irwin, 1952. Pp. 27–56.)

178. SPROWLS, R. C. Psychological-mathematical probability in relationships of lottery gambles. *Amer. J. Psychol.*, 1953, **66**, 126–130.

179. STIGLER, G. J. The limitations of statistical demand curves. *J. Amer. statist. Ass.*, 1939, **34**, 469–481.

180. STIGLER, G. J. The development of utility theory. *J. polit. Econ.*, 1950, **58**, 307–327, 373–396.

181. STONE, J. R. N. The theory of games. *Econ. J.*, 1948, **58**, 185–201.

182. STONE, R. (J. R. N.). *The role of measurement in economics.* Cambridge, Eng.: Cambridge Univer. Press, 1951.

183. STROTZ, R. H. Cardinal utility. *Amer. econ. Rev. Suppl.*, 1953, **43**, 384–405.

184. SWEEZY, A. R. The interpretation of subjective value theory in the writings of the Austrian economists. *Rev. econ. Stud.*, 1933, **1**, 176–185.

185. THURSTONE, L. L. The indifference function. *J. soc. Psychol.*, 1931, **2**, 139–167.

186. THURSTONE, L. L. The measurement of values. *Psychol. Rev.*, 1954, **61**, 47–58.

187. TINTNER, G. The theory of choice under subjective risk and uncertainty. *Econometrica*, 1941, **9**, 298–304.

188. TINTNER, G. A contribution to the non-static theory of choice. *Quart. J. Econ.*, 1942, **56**, 274–306.

189. TÖRNQVIST, L. On the economic theory of lottery-gambles. *Skand. Aktuar-Tidskr.*, 1945, **28**, 228–246.

190. VAIL, S. V. Expectations, degrees of belief, psychological probabilities. Unpublished manuscript Univer. of Michigan, Seminar on the Application of Mathematics to the Social Sciences, October 23, 1952.

191. VAIL, S. V. A stochastic model of utilities. Unpublished manuscript, No. 24, Univer. of Michigan, Seminar on the Applications of Mathematics to the Social Sciences, April 23, 1953.

192. VAIL, S. V. Alternative calculi of subjective probabilities. In R. M. Thrall, C. H. Coombs, and R. L. Davis (Eds.), *Decision processes.* New York: Wiley, in press.

193. VICKREY, W. S. Measuring marginal utility by reactions to risk. *Econometrica*, 1945, **13**, 319–333.

194. VINER, J. The utility concept in value theory and its critics. *J. polit. Econ.*, 1925, **33**, 369–387, 638–659.

195. VON NEUMANN, J. Zur Theorie der Gesellschaftsspiele. *Math. Ann.*, 1928, **100**, 295–320.

196. VON NEUMANN, J., and MORGENSTERN, O. *Theory of games and economic behavior.* (1st Ed.). Princeton: Princeton Univer. Press, 1944.

197. VON NEUMANN, J., and MORGENSTERN, O. *Theory of games and economic behavior.* (2nd Ed.). Princeton: Princeton Univer. Press, 1947.

198. WALD, A. *Statistical decision functions.* New York: Wiley, 1950.

199. WALKER, K. F. The psychological assumptions of economics. *Econ. Rec.*, 1946, **22**, 66–82.

200. WALLIS, W. A., and FRIEDMAN, M. The empirical derivation of indifference functions. In O. Lange, F. McIntyre, and T. O. Yntema, (Eds.), *Studies in mathematical economics and econometrics.* Chicago: Univer. of Chicago Press, 1942.

201. WECKSTEIN, R. S. On the use of the theory of probability in economics. *Rev. econ. Stud.*, 1953, **20**, 191–198.

202. WEISSKOFF, W. A. Psychological aspects of economic thought. *J. polit. Econ.*, 1949, **57**, 304–314.

203. WELDON, J. C. A note on measures of utility. *Canad. J. Econ. polit. Sci.*, 1950, **16**, 227–233.
204. WOLD, H. A synthesis of pure demand analysis. Part I. *Skand. Aktuar-Tidskr.*, 1943, **26**, 85–118.
205. WOLD, H. A synthesis of pure demand analysis. Part II. *Skand. Aktuar-Tidskr.*, 1943, **26**, 220–263.
206. WOLD, H. A synthesis of pure demand analysis. Part III. *Skand. Aktuar-Tidskr.*, 1944, **27**, 69–120.
207. WOLD, H. Ordinal preferences or cardinal utility? *Econometrica*, 1952, **20**, 661–664.
208. WOLD, H., and JURÉEN, L. *Demand analysis.* New York: Wiley, 1953.
209. ZEUTHEN, F. On the determinateness of the utility function. *Rev. econ. Stud.*, 1937, **4**, 236–239.

2   W. Edwards

Behavioral Decision Theory

W. Edwards, 'Behavioral decision theory', *Ann. Rev. Psychol.*, vol. 12 (1961), pp. 473–98.

In 1954 I published a review article (53) covering the psychological and economic theories of riskless and risky decision making, the theory of games, and the experiments which related to these theories. This review covers the same subject matter for the period 1954 through April, 1960. Like the previous review, it is confined to work on human subjects.

Other reviews. – Several books which include reviews and several review articles have appeared since 1954. Most important among them is *The foundations of statistics*, by L. J. Savage (106). This brilliant and entertaining book is mostly about subjective probability (see below), but it begins with a thorough, profound discussion of decision making. Second in importance is the multi-authored book *Decision processes* (129). Some of its chapters were reviewed in 1954 on the basis of unpublished drafts; others are reviewed later in this chapter. The third major book, *Games and decisions*, by Luce and Raiffa (88), is primarily concerned with game theory but also covers most of the rest of the field. Williams's book, *The compleat strategyst* (138) is certainly the cleverest popular exposition of game theory. Shubik (111) has defined some of the terms of risky decision theory, Bates (6) has discussed the philosophy of decision making, Arrow (2) has reviewed utility theory, as has Ellsberg (59), and Vajda (134) has summarized the mathematical content of game theory. Marschak has offered three more or less elementary expositions of riskless and risky decision theory (89, 90, 91). Wasserman and Silander (136) have prepared an annotated bibliography of the decision-making literature which is extraordinary for omitting most of the literature on risky decision making in both psychology and economics; it focuses instead on the rather extensive economic and business literature on how entrepreneurial decisions are actually made. Riley and Young (102) have prepared a bibliography of war gaming. Simon (119) has reprinted a number of his articles, some of which are reviewed below, in a book. For those who are more interested in what men should do than in what they do do, Chernoff and Moses (17) have published an elementary text on statistical decision theory, thus making accessible to the non-mathematician the ideas which Blackwell and Girshick (9) so elegantly and unintelligibly present to mathematicians only. Schlaifer (108), in a brilliant elementary textbook whose words (and equations) are for children but its meaning for men, goes much farther than any other textbook writer in demonstrating the necessity of abandoning the traditional Neyman–Pearson formulation of statistical problems, at least for business decision-making purposes, in favor of a statistical decision making approach derived primarily from Savage (106) which places very heavy emphasis on subjective probabilities. Unless someone like Schlaifer leads psychological statistics out of the wilderness of t and F tests, psychological experimenters may find themselves still seeking the magic 0·05 level when to statisticians and other applied scientists the notion of significance level is only a historical curiosity.

Static Models and Related Experiments

In the tradition which began with Daniel Bernoulli in 1738 and was firmly fixed by economic theory and by von Neumann and Morgenstern's classic book (135), theories of decision making are static theories. They are concerned with the determiners of a single choice among courses of action, rather than with a sequence of choices. Since any choice is imbedded in a sequence of other choices, any static model can be at best only a first approximation. Nevertheless, in 1960 as in 1954 most theoretical and experimental work centers on a single static model. Why? The static models work, at least to some extent, and the theoretical and experimental difficulties become unmanageably complex in most dynamic cases.

In 1955 I listed four models for static risky decision making, defined by four equations (56). The four models had in common the notion that a quantity can be obtained by taking for each possible outcome of a given course of action a number representing the value of the payoff and a number representing the probability of obtaining that payoff, multiplying the two, and then adding across all possible outcomes of the course of action. All four models assert that a decision maker behaves as though he compares these sums and chooses the course of action from among those available to him for which the sum of probability-value products is largest. The models differ in that the measure of value can be objective (in dollars, or some similar physical measure) or subjective (subjective value is usually called utility), and the measure of probability can similarly be objective or subjective; four combinations of these possibilities exist. No existing behavioral model seriously asserts that people attempt to maximize the sum of products of objective value and objective probability; too many data disprove the assertion. (But see 128.) The combination of subjective value or utility and objective probability characterizes the expected utility maximization model; von Neumann and Morgenstern (135) defended this model and thus made it important, but in 1954 it was already clear that it too does not fit the facts. Work since then has focused on the model which asserts that people maximize the product of utility and subjective probability; I have named this the subjectively expected utility maximization model (SEU model). No one since 1954 has defended the subjective probability–objective value model; this review will ignore it.

Research on Utility

In 1954 there was general agreement on what utility is and that it can be measured, but no real agreement on how to measure it. In 1960 there is at least a conceptually adequate method of measurement (assuming a SEU model) – but some doubt about whether a SEU model, and therefore any measurement methods based on it, can stand up to the facts. This section will assume the validity of a SEU model; arguments against that assumption will be considered in the section on variance preferences.

Direct estimation. – The most direct way of finding out how valuable $10 is to someone is to ask him. No one has quite done that, but Stevens (121) reports anecdotally the results of a semi-experiment in which Galanter asked Ss how much money would be twice (or half) as desirable as $10, and other amounts. He found results consistent with Stevens's general power law for psychophysics (120), with an exponent of about 0·5, which implies decreasing marginal utility. In the absence of more detailed information, it is impossible to tell how seriously to take the results. If direct psychophysical methods will in fact yield a nonlinear utility scale, and if that scale then turns out to be useful in predicting decisions, clearly they are preferable to any indirect methods. But it would require a lot of evidence to convince many researchers that subjects, asked how much money is half as desirable as $10, would systematically answer something different from $5. The numerical properties of money may be far more important in determining responses than their utility properties, no matter what instructions are given.

Measurement via the SEU model. – Several attempts at indirect measurement of the utility of money (or other valuable objects) via the SEU model have been made. All such attempts face the difficulty that choices among bets, the raw data from which utilities must be inferred, may be determined in a SEU model both by utilities and by subjective probabilities; two mechanisms, one logically sound and the other not, have been proposed to disentangle these two determiners. I presented the unsound solution in 1955 (56; see also 55); it consisted of assuming that the utility of *N* identical bets is equal to *N* times the utility of one such bet. This assumption makes possible the factoring of subjective probabilities out of the equations for the SEUs of certain bets, and so permits the direct inference of utilities. The logical difficulty is that the assumption, if taken in full generality, implies that utility is linear with money; special further assumptions are necessary to avoid this implication. The results of the experiment based on the assumption were utility curves which were generally linear in the positive quadrant, but nonlinear in the negative quadrant (losses). Internal consistency checks partially verified the *N*-bets assumption which may consequently have merit as an empirical truth, though not as a logical foundation for measurement of utility.

In 1957 Davidson, Suppes, and Siegel (42) published a monograph presenting the only satisfactory utility measurement technique which has yet been exploited. The technique, which is based on a suggestion by Ramsey (100), depends on the prior identification of an event whose subjective probability of occurrence is equal to its subjective probability of non-occurrence. After trying coin flips, penny matching, and several other possibilities, Davidson, Suppes, and Siegel ended up using a six-sided die, with the nonsense syllable ZEJ printed on three of its sides and ZOJ on the other three (other nonsense syllables were also used, with the same results). The criterion of equal subjective probability for ZEJ and ZOJ was that the subject did not care (in a precisely defined behavioral sense) which event was associated with the more favorable outcome of a two-outcome bet.

Once such a subjectively 50–50 event has been identified (and provided that it remains subjectively 50–50 regardless of what outcomes are paired with it and regardless of experience with it), equally spaced utility intervals can easily be determined, since the subjective probabilities, all being 1/2, cancel out of the equations for SEUs. However, Davidson, Suppes, and Siegel resist defining indifference as interpolated 50% preference, and so instead determined upper and lower bounds on their subjects' utility functions. These bounds were generally close together; Davidson, Suppes, and Siegel had unusual good luck in inducing their subjects to be consistent. Some of the functions look pretty linear; others don't. Davidson, Suppes, and Siegel (see also Davidson and Suppes [41]) present an elaborate axiomatization based on the notion of a finite set of objects, all of whose utilities are to be measured, but since they interpolate between adjacent utility points as soon as they apply their results to measurement of subjective probability, it is difficult to discover why they confined themselves to a finite set in the first place. Their stated reason is that they wish to construct a model and derive from it predictions which can *all* be stated and verified. Suppes and Winet (126), who present a similar axiomatization of utility, make essentially the same argument. It is obvious that such a finitistic model is nearly useless for practical purposes; the whole purpose of a model is to carry information which permits extrapolation beyond the experimental information already available.

Nothing in the fundamental Davidson, Suppes, and Siegel idea depends on the finiteness of their model or on their refusal to define indifference as 50% choice; the same technique of subjectively 50–50 events could be applied (much more simply) to determination of utility points spaced along continuous utility functions. No one has in fact yet done that, but Coombs and Komorita (35), using this method (but without experimental verification that their objectively 50–50 event was also subjectively 50–50), have tested the hypothesis that if a is greater than b and c is greater than d, where a, b, c, and d are all utilities on an underlying continuous scale, then $a + c$ should be greater than $b + d$. In 29 cases out of 30, it was. Similarly, Hurst and Siegel (74) tested predictions about choices among bets based on Siegel's (113) higher ordered metric technique, which in effect orders differences among utility intervals, and then differences among those differences, and so on up as far as the number of data points and the consistency of the data permit. Hurst and Siegel interpret their result as supporting the SEU model, and further as showing that choices opposite to those predicted by the model have longer latencies than those consistent with the model. Unfortunately, the Hurst and Siegel results are based on a data analysis method not described in their paper or published elsewhere, and so cannot be evaluated.

Davidson, Suppes, and Siegel (42), in a second experiment reported in their book, were concerned with removing the equalspacing restriction on utilities, and also with fixing up some other difficulties in their model and first experiment. They therefore attempted to measure utility by a linear programming method. They used phonograph records as their valuable objects; in general, their results were encouraging to supporters of SEU models. But Suppes and Walsh (125) have correctly pointed out that the linear programming model violates what Savage (106) has named the *sure-thing principle*. The sure-thing principle (which has also been called by other names) asserts that if course of action A is at least as good as course of action B in all possible future states of the world, and is definitely better in one or more, then B should never be preferred to A; it is about the only universally accepted and universally empirically confirmed principle in decision theory. Suppes and Walsh substituted a nonlinear programming model, in much the same spirit as the linear programming model but with a multiplicative instead of an additive constant. They performed an experiment using this model, which confirmed SEU maximization fairly well; they did not find (as Davidson, Suppes, and Siegel did) confirmation of the assumptions about probabilities of choices in cases of inconsistency which are implied by the model. (Incidentally, they used money, not phonograph records.)

Simon (116; see also 117) has argued for a utility function which has only two levels, which might as well be called good and bad. He points out that such a function can easily approximate more complicated continuous functions, and greatly reduces informational and computational requirements for correct action. Such a function has never been found experimentally, but it sounds like a handy tool for approximate solution of normative problems, e.g., in systems design.

Utility models usually start with a function relating utility to amount of some commodity, or to commodity bundles. The combination of different objects, which may interact, into bundles, has remained outside the theory. Adams and Fagot (1) have discussed the simplest case, in which the utility of a bundle is a simple additive function of the utilities of the component commodities. A treatment of the more general problem may be hard to come by.

Research on Subjective Probability

In 1954 it was already clear that expected utility maximization models were unsatisfactory and that the crucial necessary change was to replace objective with subjective probability in such models. But it was by no means clear what a subjective probability is. In 1960 it is clear what a subjective probability measure is, but it seems unlikely that subjective probabilities conceived as measures are any more adequate than objective probabilities in the face of the data. Less restrictive definitions of subjective probability, which do not require them to be measures in the sense of measure theory but which still preserve a form of the SEU model, are in much the same state of ambiguity and ill-definedness as in 1954.

Formal properties of subjective probabilities. – The crucial step toward clarity about subjective probability was the publication in 1954 (but too late for my review) of *The foundations of statistics,* by L. J. Savage (106). Savage, a mathematical statistician, based his discussion on two main assumptions. One is that all acts can be rank ordered. The second is the sure-thing principle defined above. From these two assumptions, plus a number of others which have only technical importance, he developed a measure of subjective probability (he prefers to call it personal probability) for all events. Subjective probabilities have the same mathematical properties as objective probabilities, but there the resemblance ends. A subjective probability is a number that represents the extent to which an individual thinks a given event is likely. Individuals can freely choose any subjective probabilities they like, prior to the first occurrence of an event; thereafter the change in subjective probability as a result of experience is governed by Bayes's theorem. This means that if two people observe a series of coin flips, they may start out with subjective probabilities of heads which differ widely from each other, but after a number of flips they will end up with subjective probabilities very close to each other and to the ratio of heads to total flips. This notion of subjective probability is not enough by itself to provide a complete theory of decision making in risky and uncertain situations, but the rest of Savage's theory, though elegant, is more or less a conventional SEU model.

A number of experiments which I reviewed in 1954, including in particular my probability preference experiments (50, 51, 52), seemed to indicate that on empirical grounds the Savage kind of subjective probability measure is unacceptable. (Fréchet [68] doubted its acceptability on logical and intuitive grounds, and appealed to psychologists to find out, and de Finetti [47] joined in the appeal, though insisting that a distinction be made between refusal to accept Savage's axioms and errors of judgment or calculation which might be made in applying them.) A Savage subjective probability measure requires that the sum of the probabilities of a mutually exclusive, exhaustive set of events be one. People don't behave that way; they may for example assign subjective probabilities greater than $0 \cdot 5$ to both the occurrence and the non-occurrence of an event. Probabilities which do not add up to one are not measures in the sense of measure theory. I have argued (58) that the logical difficulties which result from requiring both subjective and objective probabilities of the same events to add up to one simultaneously, combined with the experimental evidence against additivity, should lead to the abandonment of additivity in SEU models. A non-additive SEU model, in order to be internally consistent, must measure utility on a ratio scale; the true zero point for utility is where you now are. Even a SEU model with non-additive subjective probabilities implies some strong decomposability properties which can be tested experimentally.

Measurement of subjective probabilities. – Just as in the case of utility, there are two approaches to measuring subjective probability: direct psychophysical judgment methods, and inference from a SEU model. Direct psychophysical methods usually require subjects to estimate the proportion of one type of element in a display which has stimulus elements of two types. By far the most substantial study of this kind was done by Shuford (112) who used 400-element square matrices of horizontal and vertical lines as his stimuli, presented them for a brief time, and required subjects to estimate the percentage of one type of element in the matrix. The finding was that subjects performed the task extraordinarily well, producing estimates within a few percentage points of the true values. Similarly, Stevens and Galanter (122), asking subjects to make category (rating) judgments of proportion of (say) blue dots among 36 blue and green dots randomly scattered over a surface, obtained a function relating judged category to proportion which is nicely linear except for the usual distortions at the two end categories; this is consistent with a previous finding by Philip (98). I found much the same thing in an experiment like Shuford's (112). So the conclusion from direct estimation experiments is that subjective probability is linearly related to observed proportion – which should please believers in rationality.

Masanao Toda (130, 131, 132, 133) invented a complicated method of measuring subjective probability which uses a gambling game, but is more like direct estimation than like inference from a SEU model. The game requires pairs of subjects to make bids which reflect their subjective probabilities. Shuford (112) applied Toda's game to his matrices. Many of his subjects gave results which look fairly linear with proportion; others did not. Shuford also attempted to test one consequence of additivity for probabilities: the probability of obtaining two favorable outcomes in two repetitions of the same event is the square of the probability of one favorable outcome. Shuford interprets his results as indicating that his subjects reflected this square law (which none of them could state) in their behavior, but his detailed plots of data are not especially convincing.

The two utility measurement experiments reported in the previous section also measured subjective probability. Davidson, Suppes, and Siegel (42) measured only the subjective probability of an event whose objective probability was 0·25; for most subjects the subjective probability was lower than that. Davidson, Suppes, and Siegel assume that the subjective probability of any event and its complement add up to one; it is unfortunate that they did not also measure the subjective probability of the complementary event and thus test this assumption experimentally.

I also measured subjective probability in my utility measurement experiment (56), and in doing so raised a question which is likely to haunt subjective probability theory for some time to come. Subjective probability functions obtained from bets on which subjects could only win or break even indicated that subjective probability exceeded objective probability at all points between 0 and 1. But functions obtained from bets on which subjects could only lose or break even indicated that subjective probability equalled objective probability. In other words, there was a vigorous interaction between the sign of the payoff and the shape of the subjective probability function. Of course no such interaction is permitted by the SEU model. Is it possible, as Irwin (75) has suggested, that subjective probability and utility (not merely sign of payoff) interact? If so, little is left of any SEU model. At any rate, the interaction with sign makes it difficult to evaluate the many experiments (e.g., 37, 38) which conclude that low probabilities are overestimated and high ones underestimated; such experiments almost always include both signs in the same bet.

The subjective probabilities and utilities obtained in my experiment were combined to predict choices between members of pairs of equal expected value bets. The predictions were 90% correct for positive expected value, 73% correct for negative expected value (chance is 50%).

Cohen, Hansel, and their associates (18, 19, 20, 21, 22, 23, 4, 25, 26, 27, 28, 29, 30, 31, 32) have conducted a very active program of research on the nature of subjective probability, the addition and multiplication theorems, the difference between skill and chance situations, and a number of related issues. Cohen and Hansel (31) have recently summed up their findings on the relation between subjective and objective probability in a paragraph which nicely gives the flavor of the entire program. '. . . the relationship is complex and cannot be reduced to a simple formula. In certain circumstances the two types of probability tend to coincide; in other circumstances they diverge and this divergence seems to be of a systematic nature. Secondly, subjective probabilities are, in general, very much influenced by age and experience. Thirdly, the subjective probability relating to any particular preference expressed is affected by the number and value of alternatives offered.' Brim and Koenig (14), like Cohen, have concluded on the basis of a small-scale experiment that the addition theorem for subjective probabilities is not correct. Finally, McGlothlin (94) has extended Griffith's (72) earlier work on horse racing, with essentially the same results, but more detail (including a rule for betting which should enable you to beat the track).

Stochastic Theories of Choice

In 1954 the theories of choice were mostly deterministic. (But see [69].) That is, they asserted that whenever A was higher in SEU than B, A would be preferred to B. The major recent theoretical development is a shift from deterministic to stochastic models, which do not generally assert that A will be preferred to B, but only indicate a probability of choice between A and B. Two kinds of empirical findings, both of which were quite clear in 1954, underlie and motivate the development of stochastic models. One is the finding that a subject, required to make a choice from the same set of courses of action under the same conditions as a previous choice, may not repeat the previous choice; this is called inconsistency. The other is that sets of choices are often intransitive – that is, a subject may prefer A to B, B to C, and C to A. Non-stochastic models formally exclude both of these empirical facts, and so usually are accompanied by some vague theory about errors. Stochastic models permit both, but put stringent restrictions on them; these restrictions provide the most important empirical tests of the various stochastic models.

Luce's model. – By far the grandest and most complete stochastic theory of choice yet proposed is contained in Luce's book *Individual choice behavior* (87). Luce starts by assuming one strong axiom which is now widely known as Axiom 1; the rest of the book shows how much work that axiom can do. Axiom 1 asserts (for probabilities of choice not 0 or 1) that if set T has a subset S which has a subset R, then the probability of choosing R from T is equal to the product of the probability of choosing R from S and the probability of choosing S from T. From this axiom Luce induces an underlying scale of preference which he calls a v-scale. He then proves several other theorems from Axiom 1; by far the most interesting, because of its ready empirical testability, is the one which asserts that the frequency of intransitive triads of choices of the form $A > B > C > A$ should be equal to the frequency of intransitive triads of choices of the form $A > C > B > A$, which cycle in the opposite direction.

Luce next directs his attention to a series of theorems about the psychophysical applications of the v-scale. He accepts Fechner's assumption that the probability of discriminating between two stimuli is a function of the distance between the stimuli on an underlying continuum (the v-scale), indeed this statement is a consequence of Axiom 1. But he denies the consequent inference that the underlying continuum is 'subjective sensation' and instead accepts the Stevens and Galanter (122) position about prothetic and metathetic continua and also accepts Stevens's power law for prothetic continua.

Finally Luce turns his attention to utility theory. Here he introduces Axiom 2, which appeared (as did the substance of his utility work) in earlier publications (84, 85, 86). Axiom 2 is about two gambles, each of which has the same two possible outcomes a and b, but one of which gives you a if event ρ occurs and b otherwise, while the other gives you a if event σ occurs and b otherwise. Axiom 2 is motivated by the reasonable notion that you will prefer the first of these gambles to the second in either of two cases: if a is better than b and ρ is more likely than σ, or if b is better than a and σ is more likely than ρ. Specifically, Axiom 2 assumes that the probability of choosing the first of these gambles in preference to the second is equal to the following:

$$P(a, b) Q(\rho, \sigma) + P(b, a) Q(\sigma, \rho)$$

where $P(a, b)$ is the probability that a will be preferred to b and $Q(\rho, \sigma)$ is the (presumably subjective) probability that ρ will be considered more likely than σ. Notice that this expression, which looks like something that you might derive from a SEU model, actually is not; it refers to probabilities of preference of a to b and to probabilities that ρ is considered more likely than σ; neither of these kinds of probabilities can be at home anywhere except in a stochastic model. Nevertheless, there is a strong flavor of the SEU model in Luce's Axiom 2, except that it is, according to Luce, much weaker. (Considering the consequences of Axiom 2, this statement deserves a raised eyebrow.)

From Axioms 1 and 2, taken in conjunction, flow a remarkable series of theorems about the limits on the classes of imperfect discriminations permitted by the axioms; the most remarkable (which requires a couple of trivial axioms more) asserts that if any cases of imperfect discrimination ever occur among gambles, then they must occur in clusters each of which is at a specified probability of choice; in other words, the function relating probability of choice to some systematic variation of amount or probability of payoff in gambles must always be a step function. This statement seems very unlikely, but apparently Luce finds it plausible, since he has done an experiment (still unpublished) which he interprets as supporting the prediction. Luce's book goes on to apply the v-scale (but not Axiom 2) to learning, deriving several stochastic learning models with interesting properties; this review will not follow him there.

Abundant evidence, some of which Luce discusses in his book, shows that Axiom 1 is not always correct. Many other stochastic decision theorists consider it too strong, preferring to base their theories on a stochastic equivalent of the notion of cardinal utility. But however vulnerable Axiom 1 and the models erected on it may be, Luce has provided us with one model which certainly will last: his book. Future books of psychological theory (at least in the more mathematizable areas) will have to take serious responsibility for *all* the logical consequences of assumptions made and for the relationships between their own theories and others, as this book does. (Perhaps, though, these future books will contain rather more discussion of data.)

Stochastic transitivity. – Davidson and Marschak (40) generated a rather weaker stochastic model, based on a slight weakening of the stochastic equivalent of the motion of cardinal utility, plus the notion of the subjectively 50–50 bet used by Davidson, Suppes, and Siegel (42). (For closely related work, see [44, 45, 46].) Stochastic choice models may, depending on the strength of their assumptions, predict either of two kinds of stochastic transitivity. Weak stochastic transitivity simply asserts that if the probabilities of preferring A to B and B to C are both equal to or greater than 0·5, then the probability of preferring A to C is also equal to or greater than 0·5. Strong stochastic transitivity asserts that if the probabilities of preferring A to B and B to C are both equal to or greater than 0·5, then the probability of preferring A to C is equal to or greater than the larger of the other two probabilities. Davidson and Marschak (40) predict strong stochastic transitivity from their model both for utilities and for utility intervals; they performed an experiment on choices among bets to examine these predictions. They found percentages of intransitive triples ranging from 7% to 14%, and were easily able to interpret the finding as confirming both predictions. As a final touch, they compared SEU maximization, objective expected value maximization, and variance preferences (see below for definition) as predictors of their data, and found SEU much the best, with 81·6% correct predictions (50% would be chance).

The spirit of this acceptance of strong stochastic transitivity is much like the spirit of Papandreou's similar acceptance (see [96]; his experiment was discussed in 1954 on the basis of a pre-publication draft). That is, both papers report experiments in which transitivity seems quite likely to be true, find an acceptably low percentage of intransitivities, and in effect accept the hypotheses they set out to accept. No experiment yet reported has created conditions deliberately designed to be unfavorable to transitivity, strong or weak, and ended up accepting even weak stochastic transitivity. In short, as a basis for psychological theorizing algebraic transitivity is dead and stochastic transitivity, strong or weak, has yet to be exposed to the adverse climate of hostile experiments. It seems likely that conditions can be designed in which subjects choose intransitively most of the time (unpublished research so indicates); it is even possible that the direction of intransitive cycles can be controlled by experimental manipulation. If so, the question for experimenters to answer is not whether any form of transitivity holds, but rather under what circumstances do various assumptions about transitivity hold and under what circumstances do they not. Flament (63) has made a beginning toward a theoretical attack on this question, but we really haven't advanced much beyond May's (92) speculation that intransitivities occur when inconsistent evaluative dimensions must be simultaneously used in evaluation.

In another experiment directly concerned with transitivity, Davis (43) repeated previous experiments which had found significant numbers of intransitive triads of choices. He too found many intransitive triads, but argues that they were attributable to random choices between pairs of indifferent alternatives. His basis for this argument seems to be that subjects, given the same set of choices a second time, do not repeat the same intransitivities very often (but produce different ones instead). However, his own data raise serious doubts that his subjects were indifferent among the objects involved in intransitive triads – though neither experimental nor statistical procedures encourage the reader to conclude much of anything from this study.

An experiment by Coombs (33, 34) attacks the question of intransitivity from a different angle. He showed sets of four patches of grey to his subjects and asked them to rank order each set in preference. He found that his data did satisfy weak stochastic transitivity, but did not satisfy strong stochastic transitivity. However, he argued that if a subject has an 'ideal' grey, and if a set of three greys are not all on the same side of the ideal, then strong stochastic transitivity need not apply; the underlying interval scale is 'folded' at the ideal, and strong stochastic transitivity need not apply across the fold (essentially because of possible moment-to-moment variation in the location of the folding point). It is hard to see, however, how to apply this defense to the many findings which violate even weak stochastic transitivity.

Other stochastic models exist; for example, Audley (5) has one concerned with decision times.

How well you like the stochastic models depends mostly on whether or not you like to think of choice as a probabilistic phenomenon. It could be argued that inconsistencies and intransitivities should be eliminated from data by careful experimentation or else explained deterministically by more detailed theories about choices, and not accepted and embedded in probabilistic models. But no one has yet been able to use his experimental or theoretical ingenuity to eliminate them, nor are any signs of impending success currently visible. Consequently, it seems likely that stochastic models will become more and more popular – at least among mathematically sophisticated theorists. Their popularity among experimenters remains doubtful.

Applications of Static Decision Models

Though the SEU model has not been applied as yet, numerous applications of the notion of maximizing expected value exist. One, which amounts to a theory in itself, is the application of signal detectability theory to human behavior in psychophysical experiments, especially the work of Tanner and his associates (e.g., 127, 128). Tanner's theorizing centers on the ideal observer, who maximizes expected value in discriminating signals from noise. Many articles reporting work in this context have been published; the more important have been summarized, integrated, and evaluated by Licklider (82).

An important application of expected value maximization is to trouble-shooting of electronic equipment. Gluss (70) has worked out the mathematics for cases in which only trial replacements are possible, and Stolurow, Bergum, Hodgson, and Silva (123) have shown that people do not follow the model. The famous half-split principle, which asserts that checks should be made so that each eliminates half of the still-admissible alternative malfunctions, is another application of expected value maximization; Goldbeck, Bernstein, Hillix, and Marx (71) have shown that people can learn to use this technique only with very simple networks. Dale (39) has examined situations appropriate to both of these kinds of trouble-shooting, with results unfavorable to optimization models. Detambel (48) and Detambel and Stolurow (49) have shown that although optimal behavior may not occur in simulated trouble-shooting, changes are usually in the direction of optimality. Finally, Williams and Hopkins (137) have attempted to analyze an interceptor pilot mission in decision theory terms.

Other applications of static decision theories will probably occur, especially as the probabilistic nature of military information-processing and decision making systems becomes increasingly recognized and the probabilities and values which control the decisions are displayed and used explicitly, instead of being used implicitly as is the case now. But static decision theories have only a limited future. Human beings learn and probabilities and values change; these facts mean that the really applicable kinds of decision theories will be dynamic, not static.

There is an economic and administrative literature on decision making. Wasserman and Silander's (136) annotated bibliography leads into it; Simon's chapter on administrative decisions in his book *Administrative behavior* (118) is a systematic treatment of some of the real-life problems (e.g., what set of possible courses of action does the decision maker really consider) which theories tend to gloss over. In a similar spirit is Lichtenberg and Deutsch's (81) review of research on military staff decision making. Finally, there is the concern of economists with real-life economic decision making; an example is a symposium on expectations, uncertainty, and business behavior (11) held in 1955. A British economist named Shackle has developed a decision model which purports to be especially concerned with such problems; a symposium in which that model figured extensively has been published (15). However, that model turns out to be the non-additive S E U model in a wildly different guise; for a demonstration, see (57).

Variance Preferences

A recurrent theme within static decision theory has been dissatisfaction with S E U models, stochastic or otherwise, because they fail to take into account important properties of static choices. The most common form of this complaint, already clear in 1954, is that the variance of a bet is as important as its SE U in determining its attractiveness. Three major experimental attempts to examine the existence of variance preferences have been made. In 1954 I conducted an experiment (54) using the general technique of previous probability preference experiments (50, 51, 52). Subjects were required to choose between pairs of zero expected value two-outcome bets; one member of each pair had high variance and the other had low variance. Furthermore, conditions were designed to favor high-variance choices at some times and low-variance choices at other times. Little effect of variance on choices appeared. The conclusion from this experiment was that variance preferences are at most a second-order determiner of choices.

Royden, Suppes, and Walsh (105) performed an experiment comparing sure things with 50–50 bets, in an attempt to measure the utility of gambling as an activity. Insofar as the notion of 'utility of gambling' can be given an operational meaning, it must correspond with variance preferences, since clearly any choice whose outcome is uncertain will have a higher variance than the (zero) variance of not gambling at all. Unfortunately, their results indicate a marked utility for gambling only on the assumption that utility of money is linear with dollar value; a nonlinear utility function predicts the results of the experiment some-what better than the notion of variance preferences. This is the first explicit example of the inevitable confounding between utility and variance which must exist in all experiments using two-outcome bets; the same criticism applies to my variance preference experiment, and still another example follows.

Coombs and Pruitt (36) have performed a large experiment concerned with variance and skewness preferences. They pre-pared a square array of two-alternative bets, all of zero expected value, with variance on one dimension and skewness on the other. Variance in such an array is (for any single skewness level) com-pletely confounded with the magnitude of the difference between outcomes; skewness is completely confounded with probability of winning; so these names for the two dimensions of the table are not unique. They examined preferences within certain rows and columns of this table by means of the method of paired com-parisons. The choices were hypothetical, but subjects played one bet at the end of the experiment. Data which failed to satisfy weak stochastic transitivity were rejected; data from the remain-ing subjects were analysed according to Coombs's unfolding technique. The major findings were that most subjects chose con-sistently and transitively and that most subjects exhibited single-peaked variance preferences and (except for an undue preference for 50–50 bets) single-peaked skewness or probability prefer-ences. The consistency found by Coombs and Pruitt was extra-ordinarily high; perhaps it is because their subjects made their choices among bets at rates ranging from 3·4 to 22·4 choices per minute, and so cannot have taken much time for reflection. The two rules 'Always choose the bet with the highest payoff for winning' and 'Always choose the bet with the lowest cost for losing' together account for about 68% of all the rank orderings Coombs and Pruitt obtained; these rules, of course, could be applied simply and mechanically to minimize reflection.

Variance preferences are necessarily confounded with utility, and skewness preferences with probability, for two alternative bets. So all research on variance preferences so far is ambiguous. The remedy is to use more than two alternatives; experiments which do so are in progress.

Personality Variables in Decision Making

In 1954 there was little or nothing to say about how personality variables might influence decision making, except that the theory of level of aspiration which had been developed by Lewin and his collaborators (80) had a substantial resemblance to the SEU model. By 1960 a great deal of work on personality variables in decision making has occurred, most of it expressing Lewinian or Lewin-influenced points of view.

The most important modern version of this point of view is that of J. W. Atkinson, who has discussed in detail his model for risky decision making. Atkinson (3) is primarily concerned with the motive to achieve success (M_s) and the motive to avoid failure (M_f). He is also concerned with the subjective probability of achieving success (P_s), and of failing ($1 - P_s$). Finally, he is concerned with an incentive value of achieving success and an incentive value of avoiding failure; his crucial assumption is that the former is inversely related to the subjective probability of succeeding (and so is given by $1 - P_s$) and the latter is the negative of the subjective probability of succeeding ($-P_s$). He does not do the algebra implied by these definitions, but resultant motivation, as he defines it, is given (after appropriate algebra) by $P_s (1 - P_s) (M_s - M_f)$. For comparison, the variance of a two-alternative bet in which you win A with probability p and win B with probability $1 - p$ is $p (1 - p) (A - B)^2$. The major difference between the two formulas is that Atkinson's quantity can be negative, since the difference term is not squared. Nevertheless, it looks as though there should be a close resemblance between Atkinson's theory and a theory about variance preferences, and indeed there is.

Atkinson proposes that there are two kinds of people, those in whom the motivation to achieve success is greater than that to avoid failure, and those in whom the reverse is true. It is obvious that the function with which Atkinson is concerned has a maximum at $P_s = 0.5$ if M_s is greater than M_f, and a minimum there if M_f is greater than M_s. Consequently Atkinson predicts that subjects of the first kind will prefer bets of intermediate probability of success (and consequently relatively high variance) while subjects of the second kind will prefer bets with probability of success near either 1 or 0 (and consequently relatively low variance). After reviewing experiments which he interprets as showing this, he suggests on the basis of the findings another assumption: 'The relative strength of a motive influences the subjective probability of the consequence consistent with that motive – i.e., biases it upwards' (3, p. 367). He finishes with a discussion of the effect of success or failure on subjective probability.

Atkinson, Bastian, Earl, and Litwin (4) tested Atkinson's model with a shuffleboard experiment in which fictitious probabilities of success were displayed to subjects. Subjects with high M_s stood closer to the target than those with low M_s, and thereby more nearly achieved the intermediate probability levels they are supposed to like. Also, in a replication of my probability preference experiments everyone preferred the sure thing, but after that was excluded from the analysis the subjects with high M_s preferred 2/6, 3/6, and 4/6 probabilities, while those with low M_s preferred 1/6 and 5/6. (See also [93].)

More closely related both to traditional Lewinian theory and to SEU maximization is Siegel's (114) discussion of level of aspiration. On *a priori* grounds, Siegel defines level of aspiration as the least upper bound of that chord connecting two adjacent points on a (discontinuous) utility scale which has the maximum slope. Siegel does not point out that this definition is meaningful only for independent variables measured on at least an interval scale; otherwise the concept of slope is not defined. Becker and Siegel (8) performed an experiment in which they actually gambled with midterm grades in a psychology course as prizes. (Presumably grades are ordinal scale independent variables; Becker and Siegel apply Siegel's definition simply by assuming them equally spaced.) They interpreted the results as confirming Siegel's conception of level of aspiration.

Rotter's social learning theory (103, 104) has inspired a number of Ph.D. theses (e.g., 83, 97, 139) which fit vaguely within the framework of the SEU model. Brehm (13) did a choice experiment which he interpreted in terms of Festinger's cognitive dissonance theory (62). Block and Petersen (10) characterized decision-makers on the basis of various psychological tests; mature subjects made mature decisions. Feather (60, 61), following Lewin and Atkinson, supposes that the harder an objective is to attain, the higher will be its utility, and reports an experiment which he interprets as supporting the hypothesis. Proponents of this hypothesis have not distinguished between two things it might mean. One possibility is that the world is so constructed that more valuable objectives are in fact usually harder to attain; this is obviously true, but does not require postulation of any special psychological interaction between utility and subjective probability. The other possibility is that the same goal becomes more attractive if it becomes harder to attain; this, if true, requires modification of customary SEU models.

Scodel, Ratoosh, and Minas (110) required their subjects to choose among bets. They found that expected value did not control preferences, and reported phenomena analogous to variance preferences. Subjects who chose more conservative bets were higher on need achievement, theoretical and aesthetic values, and fear of failure than those who chose more risky bets.

No coherent picture emerges from this area of study as yet; it is surprising that so few studies explicitly examine utility and subjective probability functions, relating their shapes in different people to personality variables.

Dynamic Decision Making

In real life decisions occur in sequences, and information available for later decisions is likely to be contingent on the nature and consequences of earlier ones. The study of decision processes in such changing situations might be called the study of dynamic decision making. Two cases can be distinguished. In one, the most frequently studied, the environment is (stochastically) unchanging, but the decision maker's information changes as a result of successive decisions, other events, or both. In the other, little studied because it is so complex, the environment changes its characteristics while the decision maker is obtaining information about it.

The distinction between dynamic decision processes and learning is one of emphasis, not content. In particular, probability learning experiments examine a very simple case of dynamic decision making; such experiments are omitted here to avoid overlap with other chapters.

Intuitive statistics. – If the environment is stationary but man's information about it is changing, then a decision task is likely to look very much like a problem in statistics. In fact, most statistical tests can be treated as mathematical models for human behavior, and people can be examined to see if they in fact conform to these models.

Irwin and his collaborators have exploited this possibility in a series of experiments on what they call the 'expanded judgment' situation. Subjects are presented with a sequence of cards, on each of which a number is written. Statistical properties of the sequence of numbers are varied, and subjects are required to make judgments about the population which the numbers represent. In the first of these experiments (78), subjects judged, after seeing each of 20 cards, whether the mean of a 500-card deck was greater or less than zero, and also indicated their confidence in their judgments. The mean confidence ratings (algebraically added so that they also represent judgments of greater or less than zero) were directly related to the mean of the sample; and the absolute magnitude of the confidence ratings increased with sample size and decreased with sample variability. Another part of the same experiment confirmed these results in a slightly different situation in which cards from two decks were simultaneously exposed, and the subject judged which deck had the larger mean. In another experiment (76) subjects were required to look at cards until they had seen enough and then stop; they stopped sooner when the means were more different, and later when variability was larger. In yet another experiment (77), subjects were paid for correct decisions and charged for each card looked at; greater cost and lower prize reduced the number of cards looked at, while lower cost and greater prize increased that number. In addition, the findings of the previous experiment concerning difference between means and amount of variability were confirmed. Unfortunately it is impossible to calculate whether subjects were or were not adopting an expected value maximizing strategy, or something like it. For one thing, a peculiar payoff scheme was used which meant that subjects could not tell the relationship between the amount of imaginary money they had won or lost and the amount of real money they would eventually be paid. Furthermore, subjects had no information about the distribution from which they were sampling, and consequently no optimal strategy can be calculated (except for one unreasonable one based on the peculiarity of the real payoff scheme).

Becker (7) was also concerned with optimal stopping, but he used an experimental design in which the population sampled was binary. Since the population distribution is known except for one parameter, it is easy to calculate optimal strategies in the sense of statistical decision theory. Becker used Wald's model for a two-action decision problem with optional stopping, and compared the behavior of his subjects with the model. He concluded that although people did not perform exactly as the model would require, they came pretty close. He found consistent individual differences which are interpretable as variations in parameters of the model. Unfortunately, Becker used a nonlinear and peculiar payoff scheme similar to the one used by Irwin and Smith (77); it remains unclear what effect variations in real payoff might have on performance.

The upshot of these studies of man (or rather, college student) as statistician is that he makes a fairly good one. In all cases the differences are in the proper directions, though they are not always the proper amounts. (The findings of direct probability estimation experiments discussed earlier are similar.) Of course the only task studied in these experiments is the estimation of the mean. It is an interesting experimental question whether man can perform other statistical tasks well on an intuitive basis. It seems unlikely, for example, that men can estimate variances as accurately as they can means; in fact, some of the minor findings of the Irwin, Smith, and Mayfield (78) experiment suggest this.

Experimental Games

The theory of games has progressed vigorously as an area of mathematical investigation; it would take a book to do justice to its development. Fortunately, just such a book is available, and an extraordinarily thorough and clear one at that: Luce and Raiffa's *Games and decisions* (88). This review will make no attempt to cover the material on games which Luce and Raiffa have so ably covered; instead, it will be confined solely to experiments on game-playing in the spirit of the theory of games. However, attention should be called to discussions of game theory quite different in spirit from Luce and Raiffa's (and quite critical) by Schelling (107) and Rapoport (101), to Braithwaite's curious and ingenious attempt to apply game theory not to behavior but to ethics (12), and to a brilliant exposition by Milnor of the meaning of and relations among various decision criteria which are often spoken of in game-theoretical discussions (95; see also 16 and 99 on the same topic).

Bargaining games. – Most experimental research on games has been concerned with simple bargaining games. A number of experiments by Flood were reviewed in 1954 on the basis of unpublished reports; some of them have now been published (64, 65, 66, 67), along with some other games of the same sort; the main finding from these anecdotal experiments was that people tended to adopt what Flood calls a split-the-difference principle, which distributed gains equitably among participants. Hoffman, Festinger, and Lawrence (73) studied a three-person game in which two subjects and a stooge competed for points. The stooge was given an initial advantage. The main finding was that all subjects sought equity by bargaining in such a way that the stooge was thereafter at a disadvantage; to do so, subjects refused offers which they might profitably have accepted. This tendency was more pronounced under conditions of high task importance ('It is an IQ test') than under conditions of low task importance, and more pronounced when the stooge was perceived as an equal than when the other subjects thought that the stooge was unusually intelligent (because of some ingenious trickery). Kalisch, Milnor, Nash, and Nering (79) similarly found that in a variety of games their subjects were reluctant to exploit advantageous bargaining positions and tended to distribute proceeds as equitably as the rules of the game permitted. Finally, Stone (124) performed an experiment in which subjects unknowingly played against themselves in a variety of well-displayed non-zero-sum games which did not involve negotiation, haggling, or any element of bargaining other than a simple offer. Stone's selection of interesting games is wide, his display technique has intuitive appeal – in short, it looks as though Stone's methods for studying one-offer bargaining approach optimality. Unfortunately, he threw out 61% of his subjects for violating the sure-thing principle one or more times. From the remaining data he concludes only that people who are conservative in some situations are also conservative in others, and that the mathematical models for his particular kind of situation don't fit very well. This startlingly large percentage of rejections probably results from the fact that Stone's subjects had to make rather difficult imaginary judgments at the rate of about one a minute, with no informative feedback. Some of Stone's data also suggest that his subjects pursued equity, though he does not report his results in enough detail to permit any thorough examination of them.

Game theory is not the only kind of theory which can be tested by means of two-person games. Siegel and Fouraker (115) have investigated the traditional economic problem of bilateral monopoly (one commodity, one buyer, one seller), for which a number of models, including the game-theoretical one, are available. Many of these models have in common one important prediction: while the amount of the commodity exchanged will be relatively determinate at the quantity which maximizes joint payoff, the price will not be. Siegel and Fouraker designed an elaborate experiment, in many ways a model of how such experiments should be done, in which pairs of subjects bargained (under very restricted communication rules, and without personal contact or awareness of each other's identities) over prices and quantities of a hypothetical commodity, but with real payoffs contingent on success in bargaining. Their main finding was, as the theories had predicted, that the quantity was determinate at the quantity which maximized joint payoff (and the same for different pairs of subjects) but that the price was not. But in spite of the restricted communication enforced by the experimental design, the pursuit of equity discussed above emerged in this experiment also. 'On the average, negotiated prices do not vary significantly from that price which is associated with a fifty–fifty division of the maximum joint payoff. Dispersion of negotiated prices around the even division price is reduced as the amount of information is increased, approaching the limit under complete information, a condition under which most contracts represented fifty-fifty splits of the maximum joint payoff' (115, pp. 75–76). Furthermore, if one member of a bargaining pair knew the costs, prices, and profits of both, while the other knew only his own costs, prices, and profits, then the member with more information was at a disadvantage, because he more quickly arrived at the equitable offer and consequently was at a disadvantage in subsequent bargaining.

The prisoner's dilemma. – One finding contradicts the hypothesis of desire for equity. Scodel, Minas, Ratoosh, and Lipetz (109) examined a fascinating non-zero-sum non-cooperative game called the prisoner's dilemma (see Luce and Raiffa [88], pp. 94–102). In this frustrating game, if both players choose their optimal strategy, each gets less than if both had chosen a non-optimal strategy. Scodel, Minas, Ratoosh, and Lipetz found that players overwhelmingly tended to choose their optimal but less well-paid strategy, and other unpublished research confirms this finding. Furthermore, players become more rather than less addicted to this uncooperative response as the game progresses. The structure of the prisoner's dilemma makes it very difficult for equity-seeking motives to operate; they almost certainly lead to substantial and inequitable penalties unless they operate in both players at exactly the same time. Scodel *et al.* find that if the players are permitted to discuss the matter, they thereafter do better at choosing the non-optimal but financially more desirable pair of strategies, and of course if this were an unrestricted bargaining game they would easily come to the two-player coalition which would permit them to extract the maximum return from the experimenter. Restraints on communication seem essential to prevent the equity-seeking motive from operating effectively, even in a situation which punishes equity-seeking as effectively as does the prisoner's dilemma.

The main finding from these studies of multi-person games seems to be that people import into bargaining situations a strong desire for equity. Equity-seeking is promoted by effective and free communication and seriously hindered or even prevented by severely restricted communication. Equity-seeking produces results in conflict with those which game theory and similar theories about rapacious economic men imply, except in those games in which equity-seeking and uninhibited rapacity have the same consequences. If this finding stands up under more experimentation, especially with much larger payoffs, theories about multi-person decision situations must either be modified to incorporate such social motives explicitly, or else some means for incorporating them in utility functions must be found.

References

1. ADAMS, E. W., and FAGOT, R., 'A model of riskless choice', *Behav. Sci.*, vol. 4 (1959), pp. 1–10.

2. ARROW, K. L., 'Utilities, attitudes, choices: a review note', *Econometrica*, vol. 26 (1958), pp. 1–23.

3. ATKINSON, J. W., 'Motivational determinants of risk-taking behavior', *Psychol. Rev.*, vol. 64 (1957), pp. 359–72.

4. ATKINSON, J. W., BASTIAN, J. R., EARL, R. W., and LITWIN, G. H., ' The achievement motive, goal setting, and probability preferences', *J. abnorm. soc. Psychol.*, vol. 60 (1960), pp. 27–36.

5. AUDLEY, R. J., 'A stochastic model for individual choice behavior', *Psychol. Rev.*, vol. 67 (1960), pp. 1–15.

6. BATES, J., 'A model for the science of decision', *Philosophy of Science*, vol. 21 (1954), pp. 326–39.

7. BECKER, G. M., 'Sequential decision making: Wald's model and estimates of parameters', *J. exper. Psychol.*, vol. 55 (1958), pp. 628–36.

8. BECKER, S. W., and SIEGEL, S., 'Utility of grades: level of aspiration in a decision theory context', *J. exper. Psychol.*, vol. 55 (1958), pp. 81–5.

9. BLACKWELL, D., and GIRSHICK, M., *Theory of games and statistical decisions*, Wiley, 1954.

10. BLOCK, J., and PETERSEN, P., 'Some personality correlates of confidence, caution, and speed in a decision situation', *J. abnorm. soc. Psychol.*, vol. 51 (1955), pp. 34–41.

11. BOWMAN, M. J. (ed.), *Expectations, uncertainty, and business behavior*, Social Science Research Council, New York, 1958.

12. BRAITHWAITE, R. B., *Theory of games as a tool for the moral philosopher*, Cambridge University Press, 1955.

13. BREHM, J. W., 'Post-decision changes in the desirability of alternatives', *J. abnorm. soc. Psychol.*, vol. 52 (1956), pp. 384–9.

14. BRIM, O. G., and KOENIG, F. W., 'Two aspects of subjective probability among college students', *J. Communication*, vol. 9 (1959), pp. 19–26.

15. CARTER, C. F., MEREDITH, G. P., and SHACKLE, G. L. S. (eds.), *Uncertainty and business decisions: a symposium*, Liverpool University Press, 1954.

16. CHERNOFF, H., 'Rational selection of decision functions', *Econometrica*, vol. 22 (1954), pp. 423–43.

17. CHERNOFF, H., and MOSES, L. E., *Elementary decision theory*, Wiley, 1959.
18. COHEN, J., 'Conjecture and risk', *The advancement of science, Reports of the British Association for the Advancement of Science*, vol. 11 (1954), pp. 333–9.
19. COHEN, J., DEARNALEY, E. J., and HANSEL, C. E. M., 'The risk taken in crossing a road', *Operational Res. Quart.*, vol. 6 (1955), pp. 3–11.
20. COHEN, J., DEARNALEY, E. J., and HANSEL, C. E. M., 'The addition of subjective probabilities', *Acta Psychologica*, vol. 12 (1956), pp. 371–80.
21. COHEN, J., DEARNALEY, E. J., and HANSEL, C. E. M., 'Risk and hazard: influence of training on the performance of bus drivers', *Operational Res. Quart.*, vol. 10 (1956), pp. 67–82.
22. COHEN, J., DEARNALEY, E. J., and HANSEL, C. E. M., 'Measures of subjective probability; estimates of success in performance in relation to size of task', *Brit. J. Psychol.*, vol. 48 (1957), pp. 272–5.
23. COHEN, J., DEARNALEY, E. J., and HANSEL, C. E. M., 'Skill and chance: variations in estimates of skill with an increasing element of chance', *Brit. J. Psychol.*, vol. 49 (1958), pp. 319–23.
24. COHEN, J., DEARNALEY, E. J., and HANSEL, C. E. M., 'The risk taken in driving under the influence of alcohol', *Brit. Med. J.*, vol. 1 (1958), pp. 1438–42.
25. COHEN, J., and HANSEL, C. E. M., 'The idea of a distribution', *Brit. J. Psychol.*, vol. 46 (1955), pp. 111–12.
26. COHEN, J., and HANSEL, C. E. M., 'The idea of independence', *Brit. J. Psychol.*, vol. 46 (1955), pp. 178–90.
27. COHEN, J., and HANSEL, C. E. M., 'Experimental risk-taking', *Jahrbuch für die Psychologie und die Psychotherapie*, Winter, 1955.
28. COHEN, J., and HANSEL, C. E. M., *Risk and gambling: the study of subjective probability*, Philosophical Library, 1956.
29. COHEN, J., and HANSEL, C. E. M., 'La répartition des probabilités subjectives', *J. de Psychologie*, Jan.–March 1957, pp. 10–21.
30. COHEN, J., and HANSEL, C. E. M., 'The nature of decisions in gambling', *Acta Psychologica*, vol. 13 (1957), pp. 357–70.
31. COHEN, J., and HANSEL, C. E. M., 'Subjective probability, gambling, and intelligence', *Nature*, vol. 181 (1958), pp. 1160–1.
32. COHEN, J., and HANSEL, C. E. M., 'Preferences for different combinations of chance and skill in gambling', *Nature*, vol. 183 (1959), pp. 841–2.
33. COOMBS, C. H., 'On the use of inconsistency of preferences in psychological measurement', *J. exper. Psychol.*, vol. 55 (1958), pp. 1–7.
34. COOMBS, C. H., 'Inconsistency of preferences as a measure of psychological distance', in Churchman, C. W., and Ratoosh, P. (eds.), *Measurement: definitions and theories*, Wiley, 1959.
35. COOMBS, C. H., and KOMORITA, S. S., 'Measuring utility of money through decisions', *Amer. J. Psychol.*, vol. 71 (1958), pp. 383–9.
36. COOMBS, C. H., and PRUITT, D. G., *A study of decision making under risk*, Report No. 2900–33-T, Willow Run Laboratories, University of Michigan, April 1960.

37. DALE, H. C. A., 'Subjective probability, gambling, and intelligence', *Nature*, vol. 181 (1958), pp. 363–4.

38. DALE, H. C. A., '*A priori* probabilities in gambling', *Nature*, vol. 183 (1959), pp. 842–3.

39. DALE, H. C. A., 'Strategies of searching in two simple systems', *Amer. J. Psychol.*, vol. 72 (1959), pp. 539–46.

40. DAVIDSON, D., and MARSCHAK, J., 'Experimental tests of a stochastic decision theory', in Churchman, C. W., and Ratoosh, P. (eds.), *Measurement: definitions and theories*, Wiley, 1959.

41. DAVIDSON, D., and SUPPES, P., 'A finitistic axiomatization of subjective probability and utility', *Econometrica*, vol. 24 (1956), pp. 264–75.

42. DAVIDSON, D., SUPPES, P., and SIEGEL, S., *Decision-making: an experimental approach*, Stanford University Press, 1957.

43. DAVIS, J. M., 'The transitivity of preferences', *Behav. Sci.*, vol. 3 (1958), pp. 26–33.

44. DEBREU, G., 'Stochastic choice and cardinal utility', *Econometrica*, vol. 26 (1958), pp. 440–44.

45. DEBREU, G., 'Cardinal utility for even-chance mixtures of pairs of sure prospects', *Rev. econ. Studies*, vol. 71 (1959), pp. 174–7.

46. DEBREU, G., *Theory of value: an axiomatic analysis of economic equilibrium*, Wiley, 1959.

47. DE FINETTI, B., 'Les problèmes psychologiques sur les probabilités subjectives', *J. de Psychologie Normale et Pathologique*, April–June 1955, pp. 253–9.

48. DETAMBEL, M. H., 'Probabilities of success and amounts of work in a multichoice situation', *J. exper. Psychol.*, vol. 51 (1956), pp. 41–4.

49. DETAMBEL, M. H., and STOLUROW, L. M., 'Probability and work as determiners of multichoice behavior', *J. exper. Psychol.*, vol. 53 (1957), pp. 73–81.

50. EDWARDS, W., 'Probability-preferences in gambling', *Amer. J. Psychol.*, vol. 66 (1953), pp. 349–64.

51. EDWARDS, W., 'Probability preferences among bets with differing expected values', *Amer. J. Psychol.*, vol. 67 (1954), pp. 56–67.

52. EDWARDS, W., 'The reliability of probability preferences', *Amer. J. Psychol.*, vol. 67 (1954), pp. 68–95.

53. EDWARDS, W., 'The theory of decision making', *Psychol. Bull.*, vol. 51 (1954), pp. 380–417.

54. EDWARDS, W., 'Variance preferences in gambling', *Amer. J. Psychol.*, vol. 67 (1954), pp. 441–52.

55. EDWARDS, W., 'An attempt to predict gambling decisions', in Dunlap, J. W. (ed.), *Mathematical models of human behavior*, Dunlap and Associates, 1955.

56. EDWARDS, W., 'The prediction of decisions among bets', *J. exper. Psychol.*, vol. 51 (1955), pp. 201–14.

57. EDWARDS, W., 'Note on potential surprise and nonadditive subjective probabilities', in Bowman, M. J. (ed.), *Expectations, uncertainty, and business behavior*, Social Science Research Council, 1958.

58. EDWARDS, W., *Subjective probability in decision theories*, Report No. 2144–361-T, Project MICHIGAN, Willow Run Laboratories, University of Michigan, March 1959.

59. ELLSBERG, D., 'Classic and current notions of "measurable utility"', *Economic Journal*, vol. 64 (1954), pp. 528–56.

60. FEATHER, N. T., 'Subjective probability and decision under uncertainty', *Psychol. Rev.*, vol. 66 (1959), pp. 150–64.

61. FEATHER, N. T., 'Success probability and choice behavior', *J. exper. Psychol.*, vol. 58 (1959), pp. 257–66.

62. FESTINGER, L., *Theory of cognitive dissonance*, Row, Peterson, 1957.

63. FLAMENT, C., 'Analyse pluridimensionelle des structures hiérarchiques intransitives', *Bull. Centre d'Etudes et Recherches Psychotechniques*, vol. 7 (1958), pp. 171–9.

64. FLOOD, M. M., 'Environmental non-stationarity in a sequential decision-making experiment', in Thrall, R. M., Coombs, C. H., and Davis, R. L. (eds.), *Decision processes*, Wiley, 1954.

65. FLOOD, M. M., 'Game-learning theory and some decision-making experiments', in Thrall, R. M., Coombs, C. H., and Davis, R. L. (eds.), *Decision processes*, Wiley, 1954.

66. FLOOD, M. M., 'A group preference experiment', in Dunlap, J. W. (ed.), *Mathematical models of human behavior*, Dunlap and Associates, 1955.

67. FLOOD, M. M., 'Some experimental games', *Management Sci.* vol. 5 (1958), pp. 5–26.

68. FRÉCHET, M., 'Un problème psychologique sur les probabilités subjectives irrationnelles', *J. de Psychologie Normale et Pathologique*, October–December 1954, pp. 431–8.

69. GEORGESCU-ROEGEN, N., 'Choice, expectations, and measurability', *Quart. J. Economics*, vol. 68 (1954), pp. 503–34.

70. GLUSS, B., 'An optimum policy for detecting a fault in a complex system', *Operations Res.*, vol. 7 (1959), pp. 468–77.

71. GOLDBECK, R. A., BERNSTEIN, B. B., HILLIX, W. A., and MARX, M. H., 'Application of the half-split technique to a problem-solving task', *J. exper. Psychol.*, vol. 53 (1957), pp. 330–38.

72. GRIFFITH, R. M., 'Odds adjustment by American horse-race bettors', *Amer. J. Psychol.*, vol. 62 (1949), pp. 290–94.

73. HOFFMAN, P., FESTINGER, L., and LAWRENCE, D., 'Tendencies toward group comparability in competitive bargaining', in Thrall, R. M., Coombs, C. H., and Davis, R. L. (eds.), *Decision processes*, Wiley, 1954.

74. HURST, P. M., and SIEGEL, S., 'Prediction of decisions from a higher ordered metric scale of utility', *J. exper. Psychol.*, vol. 52 (1956), pp. 138–44.

75. IRWIN, F. W., 'Stated expectations as functions of probability and desirability of outcomes', *J. Personality*, vol. 21 (1953), pp. 329–35.

76. IRWIN, F. W., and SMITH, W. A. S., 'Further tests of theories of decision in an "expanded judgment" situation', *J. exper. Psychol.*, vol. 52 (1956), pp. 345–8.

77. IRWIN, F. W., and SMITH, W. A. S., 'Value, cost, and information as determiners of decision', *J. exper. Psychol.*, vol. 54 (1957), pp. 229–32.

78. IRWIN, F. W., SMITH, W. A. S., and MAYFIELD, J. F., 'Tests of two theories of decision in an "expanded judgment" situation', *J. exper. Psychol.*, vol. 51 (1956), pp. 261–8.

79. KALISCH, G. K., MILNOR, J. W., NASH, J. F., and NERING, E. D., 'Some experimental n-person games', in Thrall, R. M.,

Coombs, C. H., and Davis, R. L. (eds.), *Decision processes*, Wiley, 1954.

80. LEWIN, K., DEMBO, T., FESTINGER, L., and SEARS, P. S., 'Level of aspiration', in Hunt, J. McV. (ed.), *Personality and the behavior disorders*, Ronald, 1944, vol. 1, pp. 333–78.

81. LICHTENBERG, P., and DEUTSCH, M., 'A *descriptive review of research on the staff process of decision-making*', AFPTRC-TR-54–129, 1955.

82. LICKLIDER, J. C. R., 'Three auditory theories', in Koch, S. (ed.), *Psychology: a study of a science*, McGraw-Hill, 1958, vol. 1.

83. LOTSOF, E. J., 'Reinforcement value as related to decision time', *J. Psychol.*, vol. 41 (1956), pp. 427–35.

84. LUCE, R. D., 'Semiorders and a theory of utility discrimination', *Econometrica*, vol. 24 (1956), pp. 178–91.

85. LUCE, R. D., 'A probabilistic theory of utility', *Econometrica*, vol. 26 (1958), pp. 193–224.

86. LUCE, R. D., 'A probabilistic theory of utility and its relationship to Fechnerian scaling', in Churchman, C. W., and Ratoosh, P. (eds.), *Measurement: definitions and theories*, Wiley, 1959.

87. LUCE, R. D., *Individual choice behavior*, Wiley, 1959.

88. LUCE, R. D., and RAIFFA, H., *Games and decisions: introduction and critical survey*, Wiley, 1957.

89. MARSCHAK, J., 'Probability in the social sciences', in Lazarsfeld, P. (ed.), *Mathematical thinking in the social sciences*, Free Press, 1954.

90. MARSCHAK, J., 'Toward a preference scale for decision-making', in Shubik, M. (ed.), *Readings in game theory and political behavior*, Doubleday, 1954.

91. MARSCHAK, J., 'Norms and habits of decision-making under certainty', in Dunlap, J. W. (ed.), *Mathematical models of human behavior*, Dunlap and Associates, 1955.

92. MAY, K. O., 'Transitivity, utility, and aggregation in preference patterns', *Econometrica*, vol. 22 (1954), pp. 1–13.

93. MCCLELLAND, D. C., 'Risk-taking in children with high and low need for achievement', in Atkinson, J. W. (ed.), *Motives in fantasy, action and society*, Van Nostrand, 1958.

94. MCGLOTHLIN, W. H., 'Stability of choices among uncertain alternatives', *Amer. J. Psychol.*, vol. 69 (1956), pp. 604–15.

95. MILNOR, J., 'Games against nature', in Thrall, R. M., Coombs, C. H., and Davis, R. L. (eds.), *Decision processes*, Wiley, 1954.

96. PAPANDREOU, A. G., 'A test of a stochastic theory of choice', *University of California Publications in Economics*, vol. 16 (1957), pp. 1–18.

97. PHARES, E. J., 'Expectancy changes in skill and chance situations', *J. abnorm. Soc. Psychol.*, vol. 54 (1957), pp. 339–42.

98. PHILIP, B. R., 'Generalization and central tendency in the discrimination of a series of stimuli', *Can. J. Psychol.*, vol. 1 (1947), pp. 196–204.

99. RADNER, R., and MARSCHAK, J., 'Note on some proposed decision criteria', in Thrall, R. M., Coombs, C. H., and Davis, R. L. (eds.), *Decision processes*, Wiley, 1954.

100. RAMSEY, F. P., 'Truth and probability', in Ramsey, F. P., *The foundation of mathematics and other logical essays*, Harcourt Brace, 1931.

101. RAPOPORT, A., 'Critiques of game theory', *Behav. Sci.*, vol. 4 (1959), pp. 49–66.

102. RILEY, V., and YOUNG, J. P., *Bibliography on war gaming*, Operations Research Office, Johns Hopkins University, 1957.

103. ROTTER, J. B., *Social learning and clinical psychology*, Prentice-Hall, 1954.

104. ROTTER, J. B., FITZGERALD, B. J., and JOYCE, J. N., 'A comparison of some objective measures of expectancy', *J. abnorm. soc. Psychol.*, vol. 49 (1954), pp. 111–14.

105. ROYDEN, H. L., SUPPES, P., and WALSH, K., 'A model for the experimental measurement of the utility of gambling', *Behav. Sci.*, vol. 4 (1959), pp. 11–18.

106. SAVAGE, L. J., *The foundations of statistics*, Wiley, 1954.

107. SCHELLING, T. C., 'The strategy of conflict: Prospectus for a re-orientation of game theory', *J. of Conflict Resolution*, vol. 2 (1958), pp. 203–64.

108. SCHLAIFER, R., *Probability and statistics for business decisions*, McGraw-Hill, 1959.

109. SCODEL, A., MINAS, J. S., RATOOSH, P., and LIPETZ, M., 'Some descriptive aspects of two-person non-zero-sum games', *J. of Conflict Resolution*, vol. 3 (1959), pp. 114–19.

110. SCODEL, A., RATOOSH, P., and MINAS, J. S., 'Some personality correlates of decision making under conditions of risk', *Behav. Sci.*, vol. 4 (1959), pp. 19–28.

111. SHUBIK, M., 'Information, risk, ignorance, and indeterminacy', *Quart. J. Economics*, vol. 68 (1954), pp. 629–40.

112. SHUFORD, E. H., *A comparison of subjective probabilities for elementary and compound events*, Report No. 20, The Psychometric Laboratory, University of North Carolina, 1959.

113. SIEGEL, S., 'A method for obtaining an ordered metric scale', *Psychometrika*, vol. 21 (1956), pp. 207–16.

114. SIEGEL, S., 'Level of aspiration and decision making', *Psychol. Rev.*, vol. 64 (1957), pp. 253–62.

115. SIEGEL, S., and FOURAKER, L. E., *Bargaining and group decision making: experiments in bilateral monopoly*, Wiley, 1960.

116. SIMON, H. A., 'A behavioral model of rational choice', *Quart. J. Economics*, vol. 69 (1955), pp. 99–118.

117. SIMON, H. A., 'Rational choice and the structure of the environment', *Psychol. Rev.*, vol. 63 (1956), pp. 129–38.

118. SIMON, H. A., 'The psychology of administrative decisions', in Simon, H. A., *Administrative behavior*, Macmillan, 2nd edition, 1957.

119. SIMON, H. A., *Models of man, social and rational: mathematical essays on rational and human behavior in a social setting*, Wiley, 1957.

120. STEVENS, S. S., 'On the psychophysical law', *Psychol. Rev.*, vol. 64 (1957), pp. 153–81.

121. STEVENS, S. S., 'Measurement, psychophysics, and utility', in Churchman, C. W., and Ratoosh, P. (eds.), *Measurement: definitions and theories*, Wiley, 1959.

122. STEVENS, S. S., and GALANTER, E. H., 'Ratio scales and category scales for a dozen perceptual continua', *J. exper. Psychol.*, vol. 54 (1957), pp. 377–409.

123. STOLUROW, L. M., BERGUM, B., HODGSON, T., and SILVA, J.,

'The efficient course of action in "trouble shooting" as a joint function of probability and cost', *Educational and Psychological Measurement*, vol. 15 (1955), pp. 462–77.

124. STONE, J. J., 'An experiment in bargaining games', *Econometrica*, vol. 26 (1958), pp. 286–96.

125. SUPPES, P., and WALSH, K., 'A non-linear model for the experimental measurement of utility', *Behav. Sci.*, vol. 4 (1959), pp. 204–11.

126. SUPPES, P., and WINET, M., 'An axiomatization of utility based on the notion of utility differences', *Management Sci.*, vol. 1 (1955), pp. 259–70.

127. TANNER, W. P., Jr, and BIRDSALL, T. G., 'Definitions of d' and η as psychophysical measures', *J. Acoust. Soc. Amer.*, vol. 30 (1958), pp. 922–8.

128. TANNER, W. P., Jr, and SWETS, J. A., 'A decision-making theory of visual detection', *Psychol. Rev.*, vol. 61 (1954), pp. 401–9.

129. THRALL, R. M., COOMBS, C. H., and DAVIS, R. L. (eds.), *Decision processes*, Wiley, 1954.

130. TODA, M., 'Measurement of intuitive-probability by a method of game', *Japanese J. Psychol.*, vol. 22 (1951), pp. 29–40.

131. TODA, M., 'Experimental games for the measurement of subjective probability: I. Introduction and some critical comments on the gambling method', *EPLHU Memorandum Report No. 4*, Experimental Psychology Laboratory, Hokkaido University, Sept. 1956.

132. TODA, M., 'Outline of a theory of decision making', *The Annual Reports on Cultural Science*, Hokkaido University, vol. 5 (1956), pp. 15–37.

133. TODA, M., and OTA, H., 'An experimental study on the interrelationship between the two methods of measuring the sequence of values of subjective inference, i.e., the game-method and the guessing method', *Japanese J. Psychol.*, vol. 25 (1955), pp. 292–63 (sic).

134. VAJDA, S., *Theory of games and linear programming*, Wiley, 1956.

135. VON NEUMANN, J., and MORGENSTERN, O., *Theory of games and economic behavior*, Princeton University Press, 2nd edition, 1947.

136. WASSERMAN, P. S., and SILANDER, F. S. *Decision making: an annotated bibliography*, Graduate School of Business and Public Administration, Cornell University, 1958.

137. WILLIAMS, A. C., Jr, and HOPKINS, C. O., *Aspects of pilot decision making*, WADCTR 58–522, Contract AF 33(616)-5135, Hughes Aircraft Co., Culver City, California.

138. WILLIAMS, J., *The compleat strategyst*, McGraw-Hill, 1954.

139. WORELL, L., 'The effect of goal value upon expectancy', *J. abnorm. soc. Psychol.*, vol. 53 (1956), pp. 48–53.

3 L. J. Savage

Historical and Critical Comments on Utility

Excerpt from L. J. Savage, *The foundations of statistics*, Wiley, 1954, pp. 91–104, Chapman & Hall, 1954.

A casual historical sketch of the concept of utility will perhaps have some interest as history. At any rate, most of the critical ideas pertaining to utility that I wish to discuss find their places in such a sketch as conveniently as in any other organization I can devise. Much more detailed material on the history of utility, especially in so far as the economics of risk bearing is concerned, is to be found in Arrow's review article (2). Stigler's historical study (17) emphasizes the history of the now almost obsolete economic notion of utility in riskless situations, a notion still sometimes confused with the one under discussion.

The earliest mathematical studies of probability were largely concerned with gambling, particularly with the question of which of several available cash gambles is most advantageous. Early probabilists advanced the maxim that the gamble with the highest expected winnings is best or, in terms of utility, that wealth measured in cash is a utility function. Some sense can be seen in that maxim, which will here be called by its traditional though misleading name, the **principle of mathematical expectation.** First, it has often been argued that the principle follows for the long run from the weak law of large numbers, applied to large numbers of independent bets, in each of which only sums that the gambler considers small are to be won or lost. Second, Daniel Bernoulli (4), who was one of the first to introduce a general idea of utility corresponding to that developed in the preceding three sections, made the following analysis of the principle, which justifies its application in limited but important contexts. If the consequences f to be considered are all quantities of cash, it is reasonable to suppose that $U(f)$ will change smoothly with changes in f. Therefore, if a person's present wealth is f_0, and he contemplates various gambles, none of which can greatly change his wealth, the utility function can, for his particular purpose, be approximated by its tangent at f_0, that is,

$$(1) \qquad U(f) \simeq U(f_0) + (f-f_0)\,U'(f_0),$$

a linear function of f. Since a constant term is irrelevant to any comparison of expected values, the approximation amounts to regarding utility as proportional to wealth, that is, to following the principle of mathematical expectation. So far as I know, the only other argument for the principle that has ever been advanced is one concerning equity between two players. As Bernoulli says, that argument is irrelevant at best; and neither of the relevant arguments justifies categorical acceptance of the principle. None the less, the principle was at first so categorically accepted that it seemed paradoxical to mathematicians of the early eighteenth century that presumably prudent individuals reject the principle in certain real and hypothetical decision situations.

Daniel Bernoulli (1700–1782) (4) seems to have been the first to point out that the principle is at best a rule of thumb, and he there suggested the maximization of expected utility as a more valid principle. Daniel Bernoulli's paper reproduces portions of a letter from Gabriel Cramer to Nicholas Bernoulli, which establishes Cramer's chronological priority to the idea of utility and most of the other main ideas of Bernoulli's paper. But it is Bernoulli's formulation together with some of the ideas that were specifically his that became popular and have had widespread influence to the present day. It is therefore appropriate to review Bernoulli's paper in some detail.

Being unable to read Latin, I follow the German edition (6).

Bernoulli begins by reminding his readers that the principle of mathematical expectation, though but weakly supported, had theretofore dominated the theory of behavior in the face of uncertainty. He says that, though many arguments had been given for the principle, they were all based on the irrelevant idea of equity among players. It seems hard to believe that he had never heard the argument justifying the principle for the long run, even though the weak law of large numbers was then only in its mathematical infancy. *Ars conjectandi* (5), then a fairly up-to-date and most eminent treatise on probability, does seem to give only the argument about equity, and that in countless forms. This treatise by Daniel's uncle, Jacob (= James) Bernoulli (1654–1705), incidentally, contains the first mathematical advance toward the weak law, proving it for the special case of repeated trials.

Many examples show that the principle of mathematical expectation is not universally applicable. Daniel Bernoulli promptly presents one: 'To justify these remarks, let us suppose a pauper happens to acquire a lottery ticket by which he may with equal probability win either nothing or 20,000 ducats. Will he have to evaluate the worth of the ticket as 10,000 ducats; and would he be acting foolishly, if he sold it for 9,000 ducats?'

Other examples occur later in the paper as illustrations of the use of the utility concept. Thus a prudent merchant may insure his ship against loss at sea, though he understands perfectly well that he is thereby increasing the insurance company's expected wealth, and to the same extent decreasing his own. Such behavior is in flagrant violation of the principle of mathematical expectation, and to one who held that principle categorically it would be as absurd to insure as to throw money away outright. But the principle is neither obvious nor deduced from other principles regarded as obvious; so it may be challenged, and must be, because everyone agrees that it is not really insane to insure.

Bernoulli cites a third, now very famous, example illustrating that men of prudence do not invariably obey the principle of mathematical expectation. This example, known as the St Petersburg paradox (because of the journal in which Bernoulli's paper was published) had earlier been publicized by Nicholas Bernoulli,[1] and Daniel acknowledges it as the stimulus that led to his investigation of utility. Suppose, to state the St Petersburg paradox succinctly, that a person could choose between an act leaving his wealth fixed at its present magnitude or one that would change his wealth at random, increasing it by $(2^n - f)$ dollars with probability 2^{-n} for every positive integer n. No matter how large the admission fee f may be, the expected income of the random act is infinite, as may easily be verified. Therefore, according to the principle of mathematical expectation, the random act is to be preferred to the status quo. Numerical examples, however, soon convince any sincere person that he would prefer the status quo if f is at all large. If f is $128, for example, there is only 1 chance in 64 that a person choosing the random act will so much as break even, and he will otherwise lose at least $64, a jeopardy for which he can seek compensation only in the prodigiously improbable winning of a prodigiously high prize.

Appealing to intuition, Bernoulli says that the cash value of a person's wealth is not its true, or moral worth to him. Thus, according to Bernoulli, the dollar that might be precious to a pauper would be nearly worthless to a millionaire – or, better, to

1. Daniel refers to this Nicholas Bernoulli as his uncle, but, in view of dates mentioned in the last section of Daniel's paper and the genealogy in Bell, E. T., *Men of mathematics*, Simon & Schuster, 1937, chapter 8, I think he must have meant his elder cousin (1687–1759), perhaps using 'uncle' as a term of deference.

the pauper himself were he to become a millionaire. Bernoulli then postulates that people do seek to maximize the expected value of moral worth, or what has been called moral expectation.

Operationally, the moral worth of a person's wealth, so far as it concerns behavior in the face of uncertainty, is just what I would call the utility of wealth, and moral expectation is expectation of utility. It seems mystical, however, to talk about moral worth apart from probability and, having done so, doubly mystical to postulate that this undefined quantity serves as a utility. These obvious criticisms have naturally led many to discredit the very idea of utility, but (following von Neumann and Morgenstern) there is a more cogent, though not altogether unobjectionable, path to that concept.

Bernoulli argued, elaborating the example of the pauper and the millionaire, that a fixed increment of cash wealth typically results in an ever smaller increment of moral wealth as the basic cash wealth to which the increment applies is increased. He admitted the possibility of examples in which this law of diminishing marginal utility, as it has come to be called in the literature of economics, might fail. For example, a relatively small sum might be precious to a wealthy prisoner who required it to complete his ransom. But Bernoulli insisted that such examples are unusual and that as a general rule the law may be assumed. In mathematical terms, the law says that utility as a function of money is a concave (i.e., the negative of a convex) function.[2] It follows from the basic inequality concerning convex functions (Theorem 1)[3] that a person to whom the law of diminishing marginal utility applies will always prefer the status quo to any fair gamble, that is, to any random act for which the change in his expected wealth is zero, and that he will always be willing to pay something in

2. Often the meanings of 'convex' and 'concave' as applied to functions are interchanged. A function is here called convex if it appears convex in the ordinary sense of the word, when viewed from below. Such a function is, of course, also concave from above, whence the confusion.

3. THEOREM 1. If t is convex and bounded in the interval I, and $x(s) \epsilon I$ for all $s \epsilon S$, then

(4) $$E(t(x)) \geqslant t(E(x)).$$

Equality obtains, if and only if the values of x are with probability one contained in a single interval of linearity of t. Such conditions for equality are to be understood to apply only in the event that either P is countably additive or the random variable is with probability one confined to a finite set of values; the general situation for finitely additive measures is a little more complicated. [Reproduced from *The foundations of statistics*, Appendix 2, p. 268.]

addition to its actuarial, or expected, value for insurance against any loss to himself. The law of diminishing marginal utility has been very popular, and few who have considered utility since Bernoulli have discarded it, or even realized that it was not necessarily part and parcel of the utility idea. Of course, the law has been embraced eagerly and uncritically by those who have a moral aversion to gambling.

Bernoulli went further than the law of diminishing marginal utility and suggested that the slope of utility as a function of wealth might, at least as a rule of thumb, be supposed, not only to decrease with, but to be inversely proportional to, the cash value of wealth. This, he pointed out, is equivalent to postulating that utility is equal to the logarithm (to any base) of the cash value of wealth. To this day, no other function has been suggested as a better prototype for Everyman's utility function. None the less, as Cramer pointed out in his aforementioned letter, the logarithm has a serious disadvantage; for, if the logarithm were the utility of wealth, the St Petersburg paradox could be amended to produce a random act with an infinite expected utility (i.e., an infinite expected logarithm of income) that, again, no one would really prefer to the status quo. To take a less elaborate example, suppose that a man's total wealth, including an appraisal of his future earning power, were a million dollars. If the logarithm of wealth were actually his utility, he would as soon as not flip a coin to decide whether his wealth should be changed to ten thousand dollars – roughly $500 per year – or a hundred million dollars. This seems preposterous to me. At any rate, I am sure you can construct an example along the same lines that will seem preposterous to you. Cramer therefore concluded, and I think rightly, that the utility of cash must be bounded, at least from above. It seems to me that a good argument can also be adduced for supposing utility to be bounded from below, for, however wealth may be interpreted, we all subject our total wealth to slight jeopardy daily for the sake of a large probability of avoiding more moderate losses. But the logarithm is unbounded both from above and from below; so, though it might be a reasonable approximation to a person's utility in a moderate range of wealth, it cannot be taken seriously over extreme ranges.

Bernoulli's ideas were accepted wholeheartedly by Laplace (11), who was very enthusiastic about the applications of probability to all sorts of decision problems. It is my casual impression, however, that from the time of Laplace until quite recently the idea of utility did not strongly influence either mathematical or practical probabilists.

For a long period economists accepted Bernoulli's idea of moral wealth as the measurement of a person's well-being apart from any consideration of probability. Though 'utility' rather than 'moral worth' has been the popular name for this concept among English-speaking economists, it is my impression that Bernoulli's paper is the principal, if not the sole source of the notion for all economists, though the paper itself may often have been lost sight of. Economists were for a time enthusiastic about the principle of diminishing marginal utility, and they saw what they believed to be reflections of it in many aspects of everyday life. Why else, to paraphrase Alfred Marshall (13), does a poor man walk in a rain that induces a rich man to take a cab?

During the period when the probability-less idea of utility was popular with economists, they referred not only to the utility of money, but also to the utility of other consequences such as commodities (and services) and combinations (or, better, patterns of consumption) of commodities. The theory of choice among consequences was expressed by the idea that, among the available consequences, a person prefers those that have the highest utility for him. Also, the idea of diminishing marginal utility was extended from money to other commodities.

The probability-less idea of utility in economics has been completely discredited in the eyes of almost all economists, the following argument against it – originally advanced by Pareto (14) – being widely accepted. If utility is regarded as controlling only consequences, rather than acts, it is not true – as it is when acts, or at least gambles, are considered – that utility is determined except for a linear transformation. Indeed, confining attention to consequences, any strictly monotonically increasing function of one utility is another utility. Under these circumstances there is little, if any, value in talking about utility at all, unless, of course, special economic considerations should render one utility, or say a linear family of utilities, of particular interest. That possibility remains academic to date, though one attempt to exploit it was made by Irving Fisher, as is briefly discussed in the paragraph leading to Footnote 155 in Stigler (17). In particular, utility as a function of wealth can have any shape whatsoever in the probability-less context, provided only that the function in question is increasing with increasing wealth, the provision following from the casual observation that almost nobody throws money away. The history of probability-less utility has been thoroughly reported by Stigler (17).

What, then, becomes of the intuitive arguments that led to the notion of diminishing marginal utility? To illustrate, consider the poor man and the rich man in the rain. Those of us who consider diminishing marginal utility nonsensical in this context think it sufficient to say simply that it is a common observation that rich men spend money freely to avoid moderate physical suffering whereas poor men suffer freely rather than make corresponding expenditures of money; in other terms, that the rate of exchange between circumstances producing physical discomfort and money depends on the wealth of the person involved.

In recent years there has been revived interest in Bernoulli's ideas of utility, that is, as a function that, so to speak, controls decisions among acts, or at least gambles. Ramsey's essays (15) present a relatively early example of this revival of interest. Ramsey improves on Bernoulli in that he defines utility operationally in terms of the behavior of a person constrained by certain postulates. Ramsey's essays, though now much appreciated, seem to have had relatively little influence.

Between the time of Ramsey and that of von Neumann and Morgenstern there was interest in breaking away from the idea of maximizing expected utility, at least so far as economic theory was concerned (cf. 18). This trend was supported by those who said that Bernoulli gives no reason for supposing that preferences correspond to the expected value of some function, and that therefore much more general possibilities must be considered. Why should not the range, the variance, and the skewness, not to mention countless other features, of the distribution of some function join with the expected value in determining preference? The question was answered by the construction of Ramsey and again by that of von Neumann and Morgenstern; it is simply a mathematical fact that, almost any theory of probability having been adopted and the sure-thing principle having been suitably extended, the existence of a function whose expected value controls choices can be deduced. That does not mean that as a theory of actual economic behavior the theory of utility is absolutely established and cannot be overthrown. Quite the contrary, it is a theory that makes factual predictions many of which can easily be observed to be false, but the theory may have some value in making economic predictions in certain contexts where the departures from it happen not to be devastating. Moreover, as I have been arguing, it may have value as a normative theory.

Von Neumann and Morgenstern initiated among economists and, to a lesser extent, also among statisticians an intense revival of interest in the technical utility concept by their treatment of utility (19).

The von Neumann–Morgenstern theory of utility has produced this reaction, because it gives strong intuitive grounds for accepting the Bernoullian utility hypothesis as a consequence of well-accepted maxims of behavior. To give readers some idea of the von Neumann–Morgenstern theory, I may repeat that the treatment of utility as applied to gambles is virtually copied from their book (19). Indeed, their ideas on this subject are responsible for almost all of my own. One idea now held by me that I think von Neumann and Morgenstern do not explicitly support, and that so far as I know they might not wish to have attributed to them, is the normative interpretation of the theory.

Of course, much of the new interest in utility takes the form of criticism and controversy. The greater part of this discussion that has come to my attention has not yet been published. A list of references leading to most of that which has is (1, 3, 7, 9, 16, 20).

I shall successively discuss each of the recent major criticisms of the modern theory of utility known to me. My method in each case will be first to state the criticism in a form resembling those in which it is typically put forward, regardless of whether I consider that form well chosen. I will then discuss the criticism, elaborating its meaning and indicating its rebuttal, when there seems to me to be one.

(a) Modern economic theorists have rigorously shown that there is no meaningful measure of utility. More specifically, if any function U fulfills the role of a utility, then so does any strictly monotonically increasing function of U. It must, therefore, be an error to conclude that every utility is a linear function of every other.

This argument has been advanced with a seriousness that is surprising, considering that it concedes little intelligence or learning to the proponents of the utility theory under discussion and considering that it results, as will immediately be explained, from the baldest sort of a terminological confusion. To be fair, I must go on to say that I have never known the argument to be defended long in the presence of the explanation I am about to give.

In ordinary economic usage, especially prior to the work of von Neumann and Morgenstern, a utility associated with gambles would presumably be simply a function U associating numbers with gambles in such a way that $f \leqslant g$, if and only if

$U(f) \leqslant U(g)$; though economic discussion of utility was, prior to von Neumann and Morgenstern, almost exclusively confined to consequences rather than to gambles or to acts. It is unequivocally true, as I have already brought out, that any monotonic function of a utility in this wide classical sense is itself a utility. What von Neumann and Morgenstern have shown is that, granting certain hypotheses, there exists at least one classical utility **V** satisfying the very special condition

$$(2) \qquad V(\alpha f + \beta g) = \alpha V(f) + \beta V(g),$$

where f and g are any gambles and α, β are non-negative numbers such that $\alpha + \beta = 1$. Furthermore, if I may for the moment call a classical utility satisfying (2) a von Neumann–Morgenstern utility, every von Neumann–Morgenstern utility is an increasing linear function of every other. To put the point differently, the essential conclusion of the von Neumann–Morgenstern utility theory is that (2) can be satisfied by a classical utility, but not by very many. The confusion arises only because von Neumann and Morgenstern use the already pre-empted word 'utility' for what I here call 'von Neumann–Morgenstern utility'. In retrospect, that seems to have been a mistake in tactics, but one of no long-range importance.

(*b*) The postulates leading to the von Neumann–Morgenstern concept of utility are arbitrary and gratuitous.

Such a view can, of course, always be held without the slightest fear of rigorous refutation, but a critic holding it might perhaps be persuaded away from it by a reformation of the postulates that he might find more appealing than the original set, or by illuminating examples. In particular, P1–7[4] are quite different from, but imply, the postulates of von Neumann and Morgenstern. Incidentally, the main function of the von Neumann–Morgenstern postulates themselves is to put the essential content of Daniel Bernoulli's 'postulate' into a form that is less gratuitous in appearance. At least one serious critic, who had at first found the system of von Neumann and Morgenstern gratuitous, changed his mind when the possibility of deriving certain aspects of that system from the sure-thing principle was pointed out to him.

(*c*) The sure-thing principle goes too far. For example, if two lotteries with cash prizes (not necessarily positive) are based on the same set of lottery tickets and so arranged that the prize that

4. [Savage reproduces the seven postulates in the end pages of *The foundations of statistics.*]

will be assigned to any ticket by the second lottery is at least as great as the prize assigned to that ticket by the first lottery, then there is no doubt that virtually any person would find a ticket in the first lottery not preferable to the same ticket in the second lottery. If, however, the prizes in each lottery are themselves lottery tickets, such that the prize associated with any ticket in the first lottery is not preferred by the person under study to the prize associated with the same ticket by the second lottery, the conclusion that the person will not prefer a ticket in the first lottery to the same ticket in the second is no longer compelling.

This point resembles the preceding one in that the intuitive appeal of an assumption can at most be indicated, not proved. I do think it cogent, however, to stress in connection with this particular point that a cash prize is to a large extent a lottery ticket in that the uncertainty as to what will become of a person if he has a gift of a thousand dollars is not in principle different from the uncertainty about what will become of him if he holds a lottery ticket of considerable actuarial value.

Perhaps an adherent to the criticism in question would think it relevant to reply thus: Though cash sums are indeed essentially lottery tickets, a sum of money is worth at least as much to a person as a smaller sum, in a peculiarly definite and objective sense, because money can, if one desires, always be quickly and quietly thrown away, thereby making any sum available to a person who already has a larger sum. But I have never heard that reply made, nor do I here plead its cogency.

(d) An actual systematic deviation from the sure-thing principle and, with it, from the von Neumann–Morgenstern theory of utility, can be exhibited. For example, a person might perfectly reasonably prefer to subsist on a packet of Army K rations per meal than on two ounces of the best caviar per meal. It is then to be expected, according to the sure-thing principle, that the person would prefer the K rations to a lottery ticket yielding the K rations with probability 9/10 and the caviar diet with probability 1/10. That expectation is no doubt fulfilled, if the lottery is understood to determine the person's year-long diet once and for all. But, if the person is able to have at each meal a lottery ticket offering him the K rations or the caviar with the indicated probabilities, it is not at all unlikely, granting that he likes caviar and has some storage facilities, that he will prefer this 'lottery diet'. This conclusion is in defiance of the principle that 'the theory of consumer demand is a static theory.' (Cf. [20].)

I admit that the theory of utility is not static in the indicated sense, as the foregoing example conclusively shows. But there is not the slightest reason to think of a lottery producing either a steady diet of caviar or a steady diet of K rations as being the same lottery as one having a multitude of different prizes almost all of which are mixed chronological programs of caviar and K rations. The fact that a theory of consumer behavior in riskless situations happens to be static in the required sense (under certain special assumptions about storability and the linearity of prices) is no argument at all that the theory of consumer behavior in risky circumstances should be static in the same sense.

(e) If the von Neumann–Morgenstern theory of utility is not static, it is not subject to repeated empirical observation and is therefore vacuous. (Cf. [20].)

I think the discussion in § 3.1[5] of how to determine the preferences of a hot man for a swim, a shower, and a glass of beer, and the discussion in § 5[5] of the practicality of identifying pseudo-microcosms are steps toward showing how the theory can be put to empirical test without making repeated trials on any one person.

(f) Casual observation shows that real people frequently and flagrantly behave in disaccord with the utility theory, and that in fact behavior of that sort is not at all typically considered abnormal or irrational.

Two different topics call for discussion under this heading. In the first place, it is undoubtedly true that the behavior of people does often flagrantly depart from the theory. None the less, all the world knows from the lessons of modern physics that a theory is not to be altogether rejected because it is not absolutely true. It seems not unreasonable to suppose, and examples could easily be cited to confirm, that in the extremely complicated subject of the behavior of people very crude theory can play a useful role in certain contexts.

Second, many apparent exceptions to the theory can be so reinterpreted as not to be exceptions at all. For example, a flier may be observed doing a stunt that risks his life, apparently for nothing. That seems to be in complete violation of the theory; but, if in addition it is known that the flier has a real and practical need to convince certain colleagues of his courage, then he is simply paying for advertising with the risk of his life, which is not in itself in contradiction to the theory. Or, suppose that it were known more or less objectively that the flier has a need to demon-

5. [Paragraphs 3.1 and 5 are not reproduced in this edition.]

strate his own courage to himself. The theory would again be rescued, but this time perhaps not so convincingly as before. In general, the reinterpretation needed to reconcile various sorts of behavior with the utility theory is sometimes quite acceptable and sometimes so strained as to lay whoever proposes it open to the charge of trying to save the theory by rendering it tautological. The same sort of thing arises in connection with many theories, and I think there is general agreement that no hard-and-fast rule can be laid down as to when it becomes inappropriate to make the necessary reinterpretation. For example, the law of the conservation of energy (or its atomic age variant, the law of the conservation of mass *and* energy) owes its success largely to its being an expression of remarkable and reliable facts of nature, but to some extent also to certain conventions by which new sorts of energy are so defined as to keep the law true. A stimulating discussion of this delicate point in connection with the theory of utility is given by Samuelson (16).

(*g*) Introspection about certain hypothetical decision situations suggests that the sure-thing principle and, with it, the theory of utility are normatively unsatisfactory. Consider an example based on two decision situations each involving two gambles.[6]

Situation 1. Choose between

Gamble 1. $500,000 with probability 1; and
Gamble 2. $2,500,000 with probability 0·1,
$500,000 with probability 0·89,
status quo with probability 0·01.

Situation 2. Choose between

Gamble 3. $500,000 with probability 0·11,
status quo with probability 0·89; and
Gamble 4. $2,500,000 with probability 0·1,
status quo with probability 0·9.

Many people prefer Gamble 1 to Gamble 2, because, speaking qualitatively, they do not find the chance of winning a *very* large fortune in place of receiving a large fortune outright adequate compensation for even a small risk of being left in the status quo. Many of the same people prefer Gamble 4 to Gamble 3; because, speaking qualitatively, the chance of winning is nearly the same in both gambles, so the one with the much larger prize seems

6. This particular example is due to Allais (1). Another interesting example was presented somewhat earlier by Georges Morlat (7).

preferable. But the intuitively acceptable pair of preferences, Gamble 1 preferred to Gamble 2 and Gamble 4 to Gamble 3, is not compatible with the utility concept or, equivalently, the sure-thing principle. Indeed that pair of preferences implies the following inequalities for any hypothetical utility function.

U ($500,000) $>$ $0\cdot1 U$ ($2,500,000) $+$ $0\cdot89 U$ ($500,000) $+$
$0\cdot01 U$ ($0),

(3)

$0\cdot1 U$ ($2,500,000) $+ 0\cdot9 U$ ($0) $> 0\cdot11 U$ ($500,000) $+ 0\cdot89 U$ ($0)

and these are obviously incompatible.

Examples[7] like the one cited do have a strong intuitive appeal; even if you do not personally feel a tendency to prefer Gamble 1 to Gamble 2 and simultaneously Gamble 4 to Gamble 3, I think that a few trials with other prizes and probabilities will provide you with an example appropriate to yourself.

If, after thorough deliberation, anyone maintains a pair of distinct preferences that are in conflict with the sure-thing principle, he must abandon, or modify, the principle; for that kind of discrepancy seems intolerable in a normative theory. Analogous circumstances forced D. Bernoulli to abandon the theory of mathematical expectation for that of utility (4). In general, a person who has tentatively accepted a normative theory must conscientiously study situations in which the theory seems to lead him astray; he must decide for each by reflection – deduction will typically be of little relevance – whether to retain his initial impression of the situation or to accept the implications of the theory for it.

To illustrate, let me record my own reactions to the example with which this heading was introduced. When the two situations were first presented, I immediately expressed preference for Gamble 1 as opposed to Gamble 2 and for Gamble 4 as opposed to Gamble 3, and I still feel an intuitive attraction to those preferences. But I have since accepted the following way of looking at the two situations, which amounts to repeated use of the sure-thing principle.

One way in which Gambles 1–4 could be realized is by a lottery with a hundred numbered tickets and with prizes according to the schedule shown in Table 1.

7. Allais has announced (but not yet published) an empirical investigation of the responses of prudent, educated people to such examples (1).

Table 1

Prizes in Units of $100,000 in a Lottery Realizing Gambles 1–4

		Ticket Number		
		1	*2–11*	*12–100*
Situation 1 {	Gamble 1	5	5	5
	Gamble 2	0	25	5
Situation 2 {	Gamble 3	5	5	0
	Gamble 4	0	25	0

Now, if one of the tickets numbered from 12 through 100 is drawn, it will not matter, in either situation, which gamble I choose. I therefore focus on the possibility that one of the tickets numbered from 1 through 11 will be drawn, in which case Situations 1 and 2 are exactly parallel. The subsidiary decision depends in both situations on whether I would sell an outright gift of $500,000 for a 10-to-1 chance to win $2,500,000 – a conclusion that I think has a claim to universality, or objectivity. Finally, consulting my purely personal taste, I find that I would prefer the gift of $500,000 and, accordingly, that I prefer Gamble 1 to Gamble 2 and (contrary to my initial reaction) Gamble 3 to Gamble 4.

It seems to me that in reversing my preference between Gambles 3 and 4 I have corrected an error. There is, of course, an important sense in which preferences, being entirely subjective, cannot be in error; but in a different, more subtle sense they can be. Let me illustrate by a simple example containing no reference to uncertainty. A man buying a car for $2,134.56 is tempted to order it with a radio installed, which will bring the total price to $2,228.41, feeling that the difference is trifling. But, when he reflects that, if he already had the car, he certainly would not spend $93.85 for a radio for it, he realizes that he has made an error.

One further thing that should be mentioned is that the law of diminishing marginal utility plays no fundamental role in the von Neumann–Morgenstern theory of utility, viewed either empirically or normatively. Therefore the possibility is left open that utility as a function of wealth may not be concave, at least in some intervals of wealth. Some economic-theoretical consequences of recognition of the possibility of non-concave segments of the utility function have been worked out by Friedman and myself (10), and by Friedman alone (8). The work of Friedman and myself on this point is criticized by Markowitz (12).

HISTORICAL AND CRITICAL COMMENTS ON UTILITY

References

1. ALLAIS, M., 'Le comportement de l'homme rationnel devant le risque: critique des postulats et axioms de l'école Américaine', *Econometrica*, vol. 21 (1953), pp. 503–46.
2. ARROW, K. J., 'Alternative approaches to the theory of choice in risk-taking situations', *Econometrica*, vol. 19 (1951), pp. 404–37.
3. BAUMOL, W. J., 'The Neumann–Morgenstern utility index – an ordinalist view', *J. polit. Econ.*, vol. 59 (1951), pp. 61–6.
4. BERNOULLI, D., 'Specimen theoriae novae de mensura sortis', *Commentarii academiae scientiarum imperialis Petropolitanae* (for 1730 and 1731), vol. 5 (1738), pp. 175–92.
5. BERNOULLI, J., *Ars conjectandi*, Basel, 1713.
6. *Die Grundlage der modernen Wertlehre. Versuch einer neuen Theorie der Wertbestimmung von Glücksfällen* (German translation of (4) by Alfred Pringsheim, with an introduction by Ludwig Frick), Liepzig, Duncker V. Humblot, 1896.
7. *Fondements et applications de la théorie du risque en économétrie*, Paris, Centre National de la Recherche Scientifique, 1954. (Report on international econometric colloquium, in which there was a discussion of utility, held in Paris, 12–17 May 1952.)
8. FRIEDMAN, M., 'Choice, chance and personal distribution of income', *J. polit. Econ.*, vol. 61 (1953), pp. 277–90.
9. FRIEDMAN, M., and SAVAGE, L. J., 'The expected utility-hypothesis and the measurability of utility', *J. polit. Econ.*, vol. 60 (1952), pp. 463–74.
10. FRIEDMAN, M., and SAVAGE, L. J., 'The utility analysis of choices involving risk', *J. polit. Econ.*, vol. 56 (1948), pp. 279–304. Reprinted with corrections in Stigler, G. J., and Boulding, K. E. (eds.), *Readings in price theory*, Irwin, 1952.
11. LAPLACE, P. S. DE, *Essai philosophique sur les probabilités*, Paris, 1st edition, 1814, and several subsequent editions, of which the 5th, 1825, was the last to be revised by Laplace.
12. MARKOWITZ, H., 'The utility of wealth', *J. polit. Econ.*, vol. 60 (1952), pp. 151–8.
13. MARSHALL, A., *Principles of economics*, Macmillan, 1st edition, 1890, pp. 19 and 95. (Many subsequent editions, of which the 8th, 1927, is standard.)
14. PARETO, V., *Manuel d'économie politique*, Giard, Paris, 2nd edition, 1927, pp. 158–9 and Mathematical Appendix. (1st edition, 1909. Based on a still earlier book in Italian.)
15. RAMSEY, F. P., 'Truth and probability' (1926), and 'Further considerations' (1928), *The foundations of mathematics and other logical essays*, Kegan Paul, 1931, Harcourt Brace, 1931.
16. SAMUELSON, P. A., 'Probability, utility, and the independence axiom', *Econometrica*, vol. 20 (1952), pp. 670–78.
17. STIGLER, G. J., 'The development of utility theory', *J. polit. Econ.*, vol. 58 (1950), Part I, pp. 307–27, Part II, pp. 373–96.
18. TINTNER, G., 'A contribution to the non-static theory of choice', *Quart. J. Econ.*, vol. 56 (1942), pp. 274–306.
19. VON NEUMANN, J., and MORGENSTERN, O., *Theory of games and economic behavior*, Princeton University Press, 2nd edition, 1947.
20. WOLD, H., 'Ordinal preferences or cardinal utility', *Econometrica*, vol. 20 (1952), pp. 661–4.

4 R. D. Luce and H. Raiffa

An Axiomatic Treatment of Utility

Excerpt from R. D. Luce and H. Raiffa, *Games and decisions: introduction and critical survey*, Wiley, 1957, pp. 23–31.

The purpose of this section is to make precise both the consistency requirements and the theorem which have been roughly formulated as follows:

i. Any two alternatives shall be comparable, i.e. given any two, the subject will prefer one to the other or he will be indifferent between them.

ii. Both the preference and indifference relations for lotteries are transitive, i.e. given any three lotteries A, B and C, if he prefers A to B and B to C, then he prefers A to C; and if he is indifferent between A and B and between B and C, then he is indifferent between A and C.

iii. In case a lottery has as one of its alternatives (prizes) another lottery, then the first lottery is decomposable into the more basic alternatives through the use of the probability calculus.

iv. If two lotteries are indifferent to the subject, then they are interchangeable as alternatives in any compound lottery.

v. If two lotteries involve the same two alternatives, then the one in which the more preferred alternative has a higher probability of occurring is itself preferred.

vi. If A is preferred to B and B to C, then there exists a lottery involving A and C (with appropriate probabilities) which is indifferent to B.

We shall adopt a set of axioms which are a bit different from those already available in the literature. At some, but relatively unimportant, expense in generality, we can employ axioms which are extremely simple and which lead to the utility numbers quite directly. For other axiom systems the reader is referred to von Neumann and Morgenstern (1947), Herstein and Milnor (1953), and Hausner (1954).

As we present these axioms, it is well to have some interpretation of them in mind. We suggest the following: suppose that one has to make a choice between a pair of lotteries which are each composed of complicated risky alternatives. Because of their complexity it may be extremely difficult to decide which one is preferable. A natural procedure, then, is to analyze each lottery by decomposing it into simpler alternatives, to make decisions as to preference among these alternatives, and to agree upon some consistency rules which relate the simpler decisions to the more complicated ones. In this way, a consistent pattern is imposed upon the choices between complicated alternatives. Our analysis will follow these lines. At the outset we will not require that a subject choose consistently between all pairs of risky alternatives – just between some of the simpler ones. In the end, we shall show that consistency among the simpler alternatives, plus a commitment to certain rules of composition, implies overall consistency, in the sense that utility numbers can be introduced to summarize choices.

At the same time, as we introduce each assumption (i.e. axiom), we shall view it critically to see just how it will restrict the applicability of the model. Such a model must, inevitably, be a compromise between wider and wider applicability through less restrictive assumptions and richer and more elegant mathematical representation through stronger assumptions.

There is little practical loss of generality if we suppose that all lotteries are built up from a finite set of basic alternatives or prizes, which we denote by $A_1, A_2, \ldots, A_r$. A lottery ticket is a chance mechanism which yields the prizes $A_1, A_2, \ldots, A_r$ as outcomes with certain known probabilities. If the probabilities are $p_1, p_2, \ldots, p_r$, where each $p_i \geq 0$ and the sum is 1, then the corresponding lottery is denoted by $(p_1A_1, p_2A_2, \ldots, p_rA_r)$. We interpret this expression to mean only this: one and only one prize will be won and the probability that it will be A_i is p_i. Operationally, one can think of a lottery as the following experiment: a circle having unit circumference is subdivided into arcs of lengths $p_1, p_2, \ldots, p_r$, and a 'fair' pointer is spun which if it comes to rest in the arc of length p_i means that prize A_i is the outcome.

The meaning of such a lottery bears some consideration. We are definitely assuming that there is no conceptual difficulty in assigning objective probabilities to the events in question by using symmetries of the experiment and past experience with it. That is to say, we are quite willing to admit a frequency interpretation of probability when assigning probabilities to the events. We do not, however, view the lottery itself from a frequency point of view; it is a single entity that will be conducted *once and only once*, not something to be repeated many times. This restriction to events having known objective probabilities will permit us to deal with most of the conceptual problems of game theory.

We shall now be concerned with an individual's choice between a pair of lottery tickets $L = (p_1A_1, p_2A_2, \ldots, p_rA_r)$ and $L' = (p_1'A_1, p_2'A_2, \ldots, p_r'A_r)$. If L is preferred to L', this means that the individual prefers the experiment associated with L to that associated with L'.

Among the basic prizes, we use the symbolism $A_i \gtrsim A_j$ to denote that A_j is not preferred to A_i. Equivalently, we say that A_i is preferred or indifferent to A_j.

Assumption 1 (ordering of alternatives). *The 'preference or indifference' ordering, $\gtrsim$, holds between any two prizes, and it is transitive. Formally, for any A_i and A_j, either $A_i \gtrsim A_j$ or $A_j \gtrsim A_i$; and if $A_i \gtrsim A_j$ and $A_j \gtrsim A_k$ then $A_k \gtrsim A_k$.*

These assumptions can be criticized on the grounds that they do not correspond to manifest behavior when people are presented with a sequence of paired comparisons. This can happen even over time periods when it is reasonable to suppose individual tastes remain stationary. There are several possible rationalizations for such intransitivities. For one, people have only vague likes and dislikes and they make 'mistakes' in reporting them. Often when one is made aware of intransitivities of this kind he is willing to admit inconsistency and to realign his responses to yield a transitive ordering. See Savage (1954, pp. 100–4[1]) for a penetrating discussion of an example due to Allais which traps people, including Savage, into inconsistencies. Once the inconsistency is pointed out, Savage claims that he is grateful to the theory for indicating his inconsistency and he promptly reappraises his evaluations.

A second rationalization asserts that intransitivities often occur when a subject forces choices between inherently incomparable alternatives. The idea is that each alternative invokes 'responses' on several different 'attribute' scales and that, although each scale itself may be transitive, their amalgamation need not be. This is the sort of thing which psychologists cryptically summarize by terming it a multidimensional phenomenon.

No matter how intransitivities arise, we must recognize that they exist, and we can take only little comfort in the thought that

1. [Pp. 107–ʳ in this edition].

they are an anathema to most of what constitutes theory in the behavioral sciences today. We may say that we are only concerned with behavior which is transitive, adding hopefully that we believe this need not always be a vacuous study. Or we may contend that the transitive description is often a 'close' approximation to reality. Or we may limit our interest to 'normative' or 'idealized' behavior in the hope that such studies will have a metatheoretic impact on more realistic studies. In order to get on, we shall be flexible and accept all of these as possible defenses, and to them add the traditional mathematician's hedge: transitive relations are far more mathematically tractable than intransitive ones.

Since the labeling of the prizes is immaterial, we lose no generality in assuming that they have been numbered so that $A_1 \gtrsim A_2 \gtrsim \ldots \gtrsim A_r$ and that A_1 is strictly preferred to A_r. The latter condition is added only to keep things from being trivial.

Suppose that $L^{(1)}, L^{(2)}, \ldots, L^{(s)}$ are any s lotteries which each involve $A_1, A_2, \ldots, A_r$ as prizes. If $q_1, q_2, \ldots, q_s$ are any s nonnegative numbers which sum to 1, then $(q_1L^{(1)}, q_2L^{(2)}, \ldots, q_sL^{(s)})$ denotes a compound lottery in the following sense: one and only one of the given s lotteries will be the prize, and the probability that it will be $L^{(i)}$ is q_i.

Assumption 2 (reduction of compound lotteries). *Any compound lottery is indifferent to a simple lottery with $A_1, A_2, \ldots A_r$ as prizes, their probabilities being computed according to the ordinary probability calculus. In particular, if*

$$L^{(i)} = (p_1^{(i)} A_1, p_2^{(i)} A_2, \ldots, p_r^{(i)} A_r), \text{ for } i = 1, 2, \ldots, s,$$

then

$$(q_1L^{(1)}, q_2L^{(2)}, \ldots, q_sL^{(s)}) \sim (p_1A_1, p_2A_2, \ldots, p_rA_r),$$

where

$$p_i = q_1p_i^{(1)} + q_2p_i^{(2)} + \ldots + q_sp_i^{(s)}.$$

This assumption is deceptively simple. It seems to state that any complex lottery can be reduced to a simple one by operating with the probabilities in what appears to be the obvious way. However, consider the lottery $L^{(1)}$, which we have assumed is described by an experiment $\mathbf{p}^{(1)} = (p_1^{(1)}, p_2^{(1)}, \ldots, p_r^{(1)})$, and the more complex lottery which is described by the experiment $\mathbf{q} = (q_1, q_2, \ldots, q_s)$. It is perfectly possible that these two experiments might not be statistically independent; for example, it might happen that, if the first alternative comes up in experiment **q**, then the third alternative in experiment **p**$^{(1)}$ is bound to occur. If so, the reduction given in assumption 2 makes no sense at all. It must, therefore, be interpreted as implicitly requiring one of two things: either that the experiments involved are statistically independent or that such a symbol as $p_j{}^{(i)}$ actually denotes the conditional probability of prize j in experiment **p**$^{(i)}$ given that lottery i arose from experiment **q**.

Once this interpretation is made, the assumption seems quite plausible. Nonetheless, it is not empty for it abstracts away all 'joy in gambling', 'atmosphere of the game', 'pleasure in suspense', and so on, for it says that a person is indifferent between a multistage lottery and the single stage one which is related to it by the probability calculus. (One neat example of multistage lotteries is found in Paris, as was pointed out to us by Harold Kuhn. Throughout that city are wheels of chance having as prizes tickets in the National Lottery.)

Assumption 3 (continuity). *Each prize A_i is indifferent to some lottery ticket involving just A_1 and A_r. That is to say, there exists a number u_i such that A_i is indifferent to $[u_iA_1, 0A_2, \ldots, 0A_{r-1}, (1 - u_i)A_r]$. For convenience, we write $A_i \sim [u_iA_1, (1 - u_i)A_r] = \bar{A}_i$, but note well that A_i and $\bar{A}_i$ are two quite different entities.*

This is a continuity assumption. If $A_1 > A_i > A_r$, it is plausible that $[pA_1, (1 - p)A_r]$ is preferred to A_i if p is near 1, and that the preference is inverted if p is near 0, so it is also plausible that as p is shifted from 1 to 0 there is a point of inversion when the two are indifferent.

Although this assumption seems plausible, at least as a criterion of consistency, there are examples where it does not seem universally applicable. It is safe to suppose that most people prefer \$1 to \$0.01 and that to death. Would, however, one be indifferent between one cent and a lottery, involving \$1 and death, that puts any positive probability on death? When put in such bald form, some, whom we would hesitate to charge with being 'irrational', will say No. At the same time, there are others who would argue that the lottery is preferable provided that the chance of death is as low as, say, one in 10^{1000}, for such an event is a virtual impossibility. Even though the universality of the assumption is suspect, two thoughts are consoling. First, in few applications are such extreme alternatives as death present. Second, even if assumption 3 is neither explicitly assumed nor a consequence of other assumptions, a utility calculus can be derived. A single number will no longer suffice; rather, an n-tuple is needed; nonetheless, a good deal of game theory can be constructed on this more complicated utility foundation. We will not describe this theory of n-dimensional utilities; the interested reader can consult Hausner (1954).

Assumption 4 (substitutability). *In any lottery L, $\tilde{A}_i$ is substitutable for A_i, that is, $(p_1A_1, \ldots, p_iA_i, \ldots, p_rA_r) \sim (p_1A_1, \ldots, p_i\tilde{A}_i, \ldots, p_rA_r)$.*

This assumption, taken with the third, is reminiscent of what is known in other work as the assumption of the *independence of irrelevant alternatives;* [. . . .]. If one asserts $A_i \sim \tilde{A}_i$, then in view of assumption 4 we also assert that not only are they indifferent when considered alone but also when substituted in any lottery ticket. Thus, the other possible alternatives must be irrelevant to the decision that they are indifferent.

Assumption 5 (transitivity). *Preference and indifference among lottery tickets are transitive relations.*

The comments following assumption 1 apply here even more strongly.

From these first five assumptions it is possible to find for any lottery ticket one to which it is indifferent and which only involves A_1 and A_r. Let $(p_1A_1, p_2A_2, \ldots, p_rA_r)$ be the given ticket. Replace each A_i by $\tilde{A}_i$. Assumption 3 states that these indifferent elements exist, and assumption 4 says they are substitutable. So by using the transitivity of indifference serially,

$$(p_1A_1, \ldots, p_rA_r) \sim (p_1\tilde{A}_1, \ldots, p_r\tilde{A}_r).$$

If now we sequentially apply the probability reduction assumption 2, it is easy to see that we get

$$(p_1A_1, p_2A_2, \ldots, p_rA_r) \sim [pA_1, (1 - p)A_r],$$

where

$$p = p_1u_1 + p_2u_2 + \ldots + p_ru_r.$$

A numerical example illustrating this calculation is given at the end of the section.

We now introduce our final assumption:

Assumption 6 (monotonicity). *A lottery* $[pA_1, (1 - p)A_r]$ *is preferred or indifferent to* $[p'A_1, (1 - p')A_r]$ *if and only if* $p \geqslant p'$.

This seems eminently reasonable: between two lotteries involving only the most and least preferred alternatives one should select the one which renders the most preferred alternative more probable. But is it always? A mountain climber certainly prefers the alternative 'life' to 'death', yet when climbing he prefers some lottery of life and death to life itself, i.e. not climbing. Our trouble here appears to be not so much the assumption but the alternatives we have chosen in the example. A successful climb does not just mean life but also the thrill of the climb, publicity, etc. The real alternative is this 'gestalt' which is completely dependent upon there being the risk of death to be attractive.

As this point is important, let us cite another example where the psychological reaction to an outcome of an experiment depends upon the probabilities in the experiment as well as on the actual outcome. Suppose X and Y are two people who are forced to exchange sums of money depending upon the outcome of an experiment. If X is sensitive to Y's feeling, he may prefer that no money be transferred and his preference may decrease with the amount to be transferred (up to some limit, say \$100) regardless of who pays. Thus, if

$$A_1 \text{ means } X \text{ pays } \$5 \text{ to } Y$$

and

$$A_2 \text{ means } Y \text{ pays } \$10 \text{ to } X,$$

X may well exhibit the following preferences:

$$(^2/_3A_1, \, ^1/_3A_2) > (1A_1, 0A_2) > (0A_1, 1A_2).$$

Such a pattern would violate assumption 6. In other words, X prefers A_2 when it occurs by chance to having it outright.

Although these examples may be a bit strained, they do suggest that, if there is a psychological interaction between the basic alternatives and the probabilities, it may be necessary to use a richer set of basic alternatives in order for assumption 6 to be approximately valid.

With these six assumptions we are done, for if two lotteries L and L' are given, the first five assumptions permit us to reduce them to the form of lotteries in assumption 6, and then we decide between them on the basis of assumption 6. That is, for lotteries $L = (p_1A_1, \ldots, p_rA_r)$ and $L' = (p_1'A_1, \ldots, p_r'A_r)$, we compute

$$p_1u_1 + p_2u_2 + \ldots + p_ru_r \text{ and } p_1'u_1 + p_2'u_2 + \ldots + p_r'u_r,$$

and if the former is larger we prefer L to L', if the latter L' to L, and if they are equal L and L' are indifferent. Put as a formal theorem:

> If the preference or indifference relation $\gtrsim$ satisfies assumptions 1 through 6, there are numbers u_i associated with the basic prizes A_i such that for two lotteries L and L' the magnitudes of the expected values
>
> $$p_1 u_1 + p_2 u_2 + \ldots + p_r u_r \text{ and } p_1' u_1 + p_2' u_2 + \ldots + p_r' u_r$$
>
> reflect the preference between the lotteries.

Let us introduce the following terms which will be used in the rest of the book. If a person imposes a transitive preference relation $\gtrsim$ over a set of lotteries and if to each lottery L there is assigned a number $u(L)$ such that the magnitudes of the numbers reflect the preferences, i.e., $u(L) \geqslant u(L')$ if and only if $L \gtrsim L'$, then we say there exists a *utility function* u over the lotteries. If, in addition, the utility function has the property that $u[qL, (1 - q)L'] = qu(L) + (1 - q)u(L')$, for all probabilities q and lotteries L and L', then we say the utility function is *linear*.[2] The above result can then be stated: if assumptions 1 through 6 are met, then there is a linear utility function over the set of risky alternatives arising from a finite set of basic alternatives.

Specifically, such a utility function u is given by:

$$u(A_1) = 1,$$
$$u(A_i) = u_i, \quad \text{for } 1 < i < r \text{ (see assumption 3)},$$
$$u(A_r) = 0,$$

and

$$u(p_1 A_1, \ldots, p_r A_r) = p_1 u_1 + p_2 u_2 + \ldots + p_r u_r$$

where $u_1 = 1$ and $u_r = 0$ by definition.

If a and b are any two constants such that $a > 0$, then the function u', where

$$u'(L) = au(L) + b$$

for any lottery L, is also a linear utility function, as is easily shown. Technically, we call u' a positive linear transformation

2. Sometimes this property is referred to as the *expected utility hypothesis* since it asserts that the utility of a lottery is equal to the expected utility of its component prizes. Not only is this terminology more explicit (if less brief), but it would help to avoid confusion. The much overworked word 'linear' also arises with a different meaning. We will sometimes assume that the utility of money is linear with money meaning that a plot of utility versus money forms a straight line.

Part Two UTILITY AND SUBJECTIVE PROBABILITY

The central ideas of the static theory of decision making are utility and subjective probability. These ideas have the status of intervening variables. Psychologists have found it tempting to think of them as subjective scales, like scales of loudness of tones or brightness of lights. In decision theory as in psychophysics, one can measure a subjective scale by either of two kinds of procedures. One, illustrated by the magnitude estimation methods in psychophysics and by the Phillips and Edwards paper here, simply asks the subject to report the subjective magnitude under study, and takes the report at face value. This procedure has the advantages of directness, simplicity, and a kind of face validity. It has the disadvantages of depending very heavily on exactly how the subjects are instructed and trained, and of being only indirectly related to the kinds of behaviour that you might wish to predict by means of these scales.

The alternative approach is to assume some model linking the intervening variables of interest with observable behaviour, and then to use that model to calculate the intervening variables. An example from psychophysics is Fletcher and Munson's assumption that the loudness of a tone presented to two ears should be twice that of the same tone heard by only one, which they used as the basis for a loudness scale. The SEU model (defined in Edwards, 1954) is used for this purpose in decision theory. The earliest such use was by Preston and Baratta in 1948, but the experiment that introduced decision theory to psychology as an experimentally accessible topic was Mosteller and Nogee's in 1951. At that time, the relative-frequency identification rules for probabilities were seldom questioned, and so Mosteller and Nogee designed their experiment around the assumption that the probability that could be calculated from their display was the probability that controlled behaviour in the SEU model. This made determination of utility functions for money relatively simple. Mosteller and Nogee were, however, aware of the Preston–Baratta paper, and presented an alternative interpretation of their data in terms of objective values of money and subjective probabilities.

Another continuing issue in utility theory appears for the first time in the Mosteller–Nogee paper: the location of the origin of the utility function. In classical utility theory, you are located at a given point on your utility-of-money scale; if you gain or lose some money, you move to a different point on that scale. But Mosteller and Nogee plotted the utility of gaining $1, $1 away from the origin, regardless of how much money the subject had gained or lost during the course of the experiment. This procedure is clearly inconsistent with classical utility theory: it is less inconsistent with some more recent notions about utility. Some critical arguments about the applicability of all of utility theory grow out of this issue. If the utility function is invariant under changes in financial position it must have a particular and restrictive mathematical form; if it is not, utility theory becomes more difficult to apply.

Two methods for measuring utility for money and subjective probability, among a larger number that have been embodied in experiments, still make sense today. One depends on the discovery of two complementary equally likely events, and is represented here by an excerpt from a monograph by Davidson, Suppes, and Siegel. The other depends on solution of a system of simultaneous inequalities, and is represented here by a paper by Tversky.

Davidson, Suppes, and Siegel used an idea proposed in 1931 by the philosopher F. P. Ramsey. The idea is that if two complementary events (e.g., heads and tails) have equal subjective probability, then you should not care whether you win on heads and lose on tails or vice versa, provided that the sizes of the wins and losses remain fixed. Such events are easy to recognize but may be hard to come by; Davidson, Suppes and Siegel had to reject heads and tails, for example, as not subjectively equally likely. Once they found a suitable pair of events, they used them to determine utility functions for money, and then used these utility functions to determine the subjective probabilities of other events.

Tversky's paper presents a version of the other acceptable procedure, which yields simultaneous estimates of utilities and subjective probabilities from the same set of choices. Every observation of indifference between two bets, or between a bet and an amount of money for certain, specifies an equation via the SEU model. Such a system of simultaneous equations can be solved in any of several ways. Tversky used the data to rank-order the bets in desirability, and then used the independence of utility from subjective probability, perhaps the most fundamental property of the SEU model, to decode the system of inequalities specified by the rank-ordering into utility and subjective probability functions.

Tversky's use of independence between utility and subjective probability is an application of the finite additive conjoint measurement model, a general approach to fundamental measurement in psychology built around the idea of independence.

These studies, combined with others not reprinted here, generally show consistent, orderly, rational performance. The SEU model is clearly wrong in detail; certain invariances, that should exist if it were right, do not exist. But the sizes of the discrepancies indicate that no one is likely to lose his shirt by making bets that grossly deviate from rationality – whether rationality is defined as maximization of SEU or even as maximization of expected money value. Studies like Tversky's look at discrepancies from rationality with sensitive procedures that magnify small discrepancies. It would be completely inappropriate to conclude from them that people are in any major way irrational.

Phillips and Edwards are interested in how people revise probability judgements in the light of new evidence. Their paper introduces to this collection the second model of optimal behaviour that appears in decision theory and in this book: Bayes's theorem. Relative to Bayes's theorem, people are consistently conservative information processors, unable to extract from data anything like as much certainty as the data justify. This finding has been extensively replicated and much extended. These deviations from Bayes's theorem are an order of magnitude larger than the deviations from maximization of expected value found in decision making studies. Apparently the most serious deficiencies in human decision making behaviour arise in processing information, not in making decisions. Why?

5   F. Mosteller and P. Nogee

An Experimental Measurement of Utility

F. Mosteller and P. Nogee, 'An experimental measurement of utility',
J. politic. Econ., vol. 59 (1951), no. 5, pp. 371–404.

I. Introduction

The purpose of this paper is to report a laboratory experiment
that measured in a restricted manner the value to individuals of
additional money income. Although the notion of utility has long
been incorporated in the thinking of economic theoreticians in
the form of a hypothetical construct, efforts to test the validity of
the construct have mostly – and in many cases necessarily – been
limited to observations of the behavior of *groups* of people in
situations where utility was but one of many variables. The
notion of utility is roughly this. Individuals behave as if they had
a subjective scale of values for assessing the worth *to them* of
different amounts of commodities, and this scale is not necessarily merely a stretching or a translation of the 'physical' scale in
use in the market place. First, there is the question of whether
utility can be measured under any circumstances, even in a
laboratory situation, and, second, if utility can be measured, can
it be used to predict behavior in slightly different situations from
those in which it was derived. It should be remarked that, in
advance of this experiment, there was no assurance that utility
curves could be derived in the laboratory by using administra-
tively feasible amounts of money.

Early discussion[1] of methods for constructing utility curves
was given by von Neumann and Morgenstern (1944), and subsequently by Vickrey (1945). The direct antecedent of this experiment is a paper by Friedman and Savage[2] (1948), and the reader
is referred to their paper for an account of the historical background of utility discussions. These authors suggest that reactions

1. The authors are grateful to Professor Armen Alchian and Donald C.
Williams for calling their attention to F. P. Ramsey's 1926 essay, 'Truth
and Probability' (especially the section on 'Degree of Belief', pp. 166–84).
When the experiment began, we were not aware of Ramsey's idea for
measuring degree of belief and utility simultaneously.
2. Plans for this experiment grew directly out of discussions with
Friedman and Savage at the time they were writing their paper. W. Allen
Wallis also contributed to the discussions.

of individuals to risk can be rationalized by a rather simple extension of orthodox utility analysis: individuals in choosing among alternatives involving risk behave in a way to maximize their expected utility (as contrasted with the utility of expected income). Friedman and Savage also admit (indeed, require) the possibility of increasing, as well as diminishing, marginal utility, allowing the introduction of inflection points in utility curves. Two observations are made that seem contradictory when viewed from the standpoint of traditional utility analysis – simultaneous buying of insurance and of lottery tickets. But Friedman and Savage argue that, owing to the peculiar shape of their utility curves, individuals in such cases may be maximizing their expected utilities. Hence the behavior may be consistent with the utility concept. The basic assumptions outlined by Friedman and Savage for constructing utility curves are adopted for the analysis of the present experiment. In a limited experiment such as the present one, we cannot hope to check some of their argument, such as the existence of two or more inflection points in the utility curves of some individuals, because measurement has to be restricted to a rather narrow range of money.

In addition to theoretical material and observational data, there was available a related experiment by Preston and Baratta (1948), dealing with the interrelationship of psychological and mathematical probabilities. The approach of these authors parallels the present one, in that an objective continuum is replaced by a subjective continuum, and it is likewise claimed that people behave as though responding to the subjective continuum exclusively.[3] More remotely related is a large body of data in the domain of psychophysics, where scaling problems having methodological resemblances to the present problem are encountered.

Thus, prior to this experiment, the methodology for constructing utility curves had been worked out in principle, the concept of utility curves had been extensively discussed in the literature, and some related empirical work had been published. With this information at hand, an experimental plan to measure utility was evolved which has four main steps: (a) to have subjects participate in a game with opportunities to take or refuse certain gambles or risks entailing use of *real money*; (b) from behavior in the game to construct a utility curve for each subject; (c) to make predictions from the utility curves about future individual

3. However, Preston and Baratta measure a different variable from the one measured in the present experiment, and an account of the details of their experiment is postponed to our discussion.

behavior toward other and more complicated risks; and (d) to test the predictions by examining subsequent behavior toward more complex risks. It was hoped that this experimental sequence would show whether it was indeed possible to construct utility curves for individuals and, if so, whether these curves could be used to predict future behavior of the same individuals.

II. Theoretical Determination of Points on a Utility Curve

A good description of the assumptions back of the construction of utility curves is provided by a slightly revised version of Friedman and Savage's statement (1948, pp. 287–8). The change is in the second numbered point in the following quotation. An inadequacy in the original version was pointed out by Paul A. Samuelson, but Friedman and Savage were kind enough to supply the present authors with their revision:

In choosing among alternatives open to it, whether or not these alternatives involve risk, a consumer unit (generally a family, sometimes an individual) behaves as if (a) it had a consistent set of preferences, (b) these preferences could be completely described by a function attaching a numerical value – to be designated 'utility' – to alternatives each of which is regarded as certain; (c) its objective were to make its expected utility as large as possible. It is the contribution of von Neumann and Morgenstern to have shown that an alternative statement of the same hypothesis is: An individual chooses in accordance with a system of preferences which has the following properties:

1. The system is complete and consistent; that is, an individual can tell which of two objects he prefers or whether he is indifferent between them, and if he does not prefer C to B and does not prefer B to A, then he does not prefer C to A. (In this context, the word 'object' includes combinations of objects with stated probabilities: for example, if A and B are objects, a 40–60 chance of A or B is also an object.)

2. If the object A is preferred to the object B, then a combination of A and any object C with stated probabilities is preferred to a combination of B and C with the same probabilities, provided that the probability attached to C is less than unity. Conversely, if a combination of A and C with stated probabilities is preferred to a combination of B and C with the same probabilities, then A is preferred to B.

3. If the object A is preferred to the object B and B to the object C, there will be some probability combination of A and C such that the individual is indifferent between it and B.

To bring this discussion back to the experiment, consider the objects A, B, and C in the above quotation as

Object A: receipt of 25 cents,
Object B: neither receipt nor loss of money,
Object C: loss of 5 cents.

Most individuals will prefer A to B, and B to C. Statement 3 of the quotation suggests that, if these preferences hold and the utility rationalization for behavior is correct, there will be some probability combination of A and C such that an individual is indifferent between the A-C combination and B. Writing $U(X)$ for the utility of X, this means there must exist some probability p such that

$$p\, U(A) + (1 - p)\, U(C) = U(B),$$

or, to use our monetary example,

$$p\, U(25\,\cancel{c}) + (1 - p)\, U(-5\,\cancel{c}) = U(0\,\cancel{c}).$$

This equation suggests that three money values be chosen in an experiment and that p then be varied until the indifference point is reached. However, the experimenters preferred to fix two money values – B and C – and the probability p, and search for an A that would bring a balance. This is done partly in deference to the view that most people are more familiar with amounts of money than with probabilities. Thus, for a particular fixed probability p_0, it is necessary to find an A such that, for a given individual,

$$p_0 U(A) + (1 - p_0)\, U(-5\,\cancel{c}) = U(0\,\cancel{c}).$$

An operational definition must be set up for 'indifference' or the ' $=$ ' of the above equation. Let D be the object composed of a p_0 chance of A and a $1 - p_0$ chance of C (losing 5 cents). Then when an A is found such that B and D are chosen *equally often*, i.e., each chosen in half of their simultaneous presentations, the individual is said to be indifferent between B and D, and the utility of B is said to be equal to the utility of D for him.

This formulation must make the reader suspect that an individual cannot tell consistently which of two objects he prefers or whether he is indifferent to them. The present experiment negates the all-or-none assumption implied by von Neumann and Morgenstern (see quotation from Friedman and Savage, the first of the numbered properties) and supports the experience of psychologists with psychological tests showing that a gradation of preference is the rule when persons locate themselves on 'physical' continua. For example, if one were offered one chance in five of winning $5.00 against four chances in five of losing 5 cents, one would almost certainly take the bet. If one were offered the same chance of winning 1 cent against the same chance of losing 5 cents, one would almost certainly not take the

127

bet. However, as the offer increases from 1 cent toward $5.00, vacillation sets in, the bet is taken occasionally, then more and more often, until, finally, the bet is taken nearly all the time. There is not a sudden jump from no acceptances to all acceptances at a particular offer, just as in a hearing experiment there is not a critical loudness below which nothing is heard and above which all loudnesses are heard. This is not to deny that for many purposes and for most individuals the width of a loudness-threshold, over which the chance of hearing a click lies between, say, 1 and 99 per cent, is so small that it can be ignored. However, for certain purposes, such as constructing audiograms to assess auditory deficit, small changes may be important. The importance of this gradation of preference in utility measurement cannot be assessed until it is known to what purpose the analysis will be put. Further, as will be seen later, the width of the discrimination band may be a characteristic that distinguishes groups of people.

At best, utility can be measured only up to a linear transformation. In other words, both a zero point and a unit of measurement are assigned arbitrarily to utility scales. Since 'the loss of 5 cents' and 'neither winning nor losing' are the two anchoring points in the fundamental equation, it is convenient to assign them the following utilities:

$$U(0 \not\!c) = 0 \text{ utile}, \quad U(-5 \not\!c) = -1 \text{ utile},$$

where 'utile' is the arbitrary name of the unit of measurement. Substituting these evaluations in the indifference equation and solving for $U(A)$, we see that, if B and D are found to be indifferent (equal),

$$U(A) = \frac{1 - p_0}{p_0} \text{ utiles}.$$

For any known probability p_0 of winning A, the utility of A is known from the start from the equation just given; but A must be determined experimentally. In other words, the individual by participating in the experiment tells how much a certain number of utiles is worth to him in money. The utility scale has been assigned, and the money scale must be tied to it at different points.

What is the connection between this discussion and the mathematically 'fair' offer? In a mathematically 'fair' situation the money values enter directly into the formula, or, if it is desired to translate into utilities, $U(X \text{ cents}) = X/5$ utiles, so that 10 cents is worth 2 utiles, etc. Thus the 'fair' value is represented by a straight line in the cent-utility plane through the points (0, 0), (−5, −1). One of the points of interest in this experiment is the departure of the observed utility curves of subjects from this straight line. If an individual's utility curve lies consistently below this line, he may be called 'conservative' because he requires more than a mathematically fair offer before taking a risk. Similarly, a person whose utility curve lies above this straight line might be regarded as 'extravagant' because he will give his opponent the mathematically better side of the bet (see Figure 1).

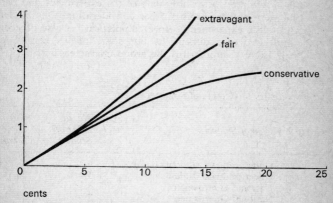

Figure 1   Graph illustrating possible utility curves of conservative, mathe-matically fair, and extravagant players for the units of measurement used in this experiment.

Of course, if the 'extravagant' person bets sufficiently often, he will soon run out of money. A person may not be in any of these three illustrative categories – he can be sometimes conservative, sometimes extravagant, and sometimes 'fair'.

II. Experimental Procedure

The experiment on the measurement of utility was conducted in two parts: a preliminary pilot study and a later experiment incorporating revisions and refinements suggested by the pilot study. The pilot study was conducted in February and March, 1948, and the experiment was conducted from February through May, 1949. The present discussion will be concerned primarily with the experiment, with only a few incidental references to the pilot study.

A. Subjects

There were three groups of subjects. Two groups of five members each were composed of undergraduates attending Harvard College. They were obtained through the Student Employment Office and were concentrators (majors) in various departments of the College. A third group of five subjects was recruited from a regiment of the Massachusetts National Guard. Two additional National Guardsmen originally composed a fourth group, but these men withdrew after only part of the experiment had been run and were omitted from further consideration. One student subject left the experiment before completion because of economic and scholastic difficulties, but some of his results are included. Table 1 summarizes the group characteristics.

Table 1
Characteristics of Groups of Subjects

Group	Type of Subject	No. at Start of Study	No. at End of Study
A	Undergraduate students	5	4
B	Undergraduate students	5	5
C	National Guardsmen	5	5
D	National Guardsmen	2	0

Differences in economic status and personal data of the subjects were revealed through material gathered from special questionnaires. The Harvard students were all unmarried; of the National Guardsmen all but one were married and had at least one child. The students ranged in age from nineteen to twenty-one years; the National Guardsmen ranged in age from twenty-six to thirty-four years, with the exception of the one unmarried man, who was twenty-one. All subjects had had some experience with gambling games previous to joining this experiment, although the amount and kind of this experience was not homogeneous within groups.

All but three of the student subjects were dependent upon their families for the bulk of their financial support, and the three securing the bulk of their finances independently either held large scholarships or were attending school under the G.I. Bill. The students' estimates of their annual expenditures (including tuition expense of $525) ranged from $1,200 to $2,200, with a median estimate of $1,750. The students' estimates of their parents' annual income ranged from $4,000 to $20,000, with a median of $8,000.[4] These students were atypical of the Harvard College population, since they did nonacademic work from 3 to 12 hours per week in addition to time spent on this experiment.

The financial picture of the National Guardsmen, as might be expected, presented a marked contrast to the picture for the Harvard group. All the National Guardsmen were the bread-winners for families of three to four persons, except for the twenty-one-year-old man (he contributed to his parents' support and retained only $36 of his monthly income for his own use). Income for the National Guardsmen was not dependable – two lost positions during the experiment, one falling back on un-employment compensation and the other working as a day laborer. The insecurity of their financial situations is further indicated by the fact that only one man had savings in excess of $100. Monthly incomes for the National Guardsmen were esti-mated by multiplying stated weekly earnings by $4\frac{1}{3}$ and adding pay received for Guard duty; these totals ranged from $162 to

Table 2

Economic Aspirations of Harvard and Non-Harvard Groups

Annual Income Desired at Age Forty	Harvard Students	National Guardsmen
$2,000–$3,000	0	2
$3,000–$4,000	1	3
$4,000–$5,000	0	0
$5,000–$10,000	5	0
$10,000–$20,000	0	0
Over $20,000	3	0

4. From Buck (1948) the following data are available for all Freshmen of 1948 on students' median estimates of their parents' annual income:

	Per Cent of Total	Median Parental Income
Veteran	16	$ 7,400
Nonveterans:		
Scholarship students	27	4,950
Nonscholarship students	57	12,250

$254 per month. Thus the Guardsmen were supporting themselves plus two or three additional persons on very little more than the students were expending for their individual maintenance.

Besides these differences in current economic status, interesting differences between the economic aspirations of the two groups were revealed by answers to the question: 'What income do you feel you would need when you're about forty in order to live comfortably?' Answers to this question are given in Table 2.

In addition to large differences in the amount of income desired, different income units were used by the two groups. The students all stated their desired income in thousands of dollars yearly, while with only one exception the National Guardsmen stated their aspirations in dollars per week. The significance of this use of income units is problematical, but in any case this difference affords additional evidence that the economic values of the two groups are not the same.

B. Preliminary information given to subjects

Before being hired, each prospective subject was interviewed briefly to explain the general conditions of the project. Screening was thought necessary to eliminate persons who might have scruples about participating in gambling games, but none such were interviewed. To help subjects decide whether they would be willing to participate, the following information was given:

(a) The study was to be a series of experiments on the 'theory of games'.

(b) There would be a relatively large number of sessions (approximately three sessions a week for ten weeks), and, once enrolled, subjects would be required to attend all sessions.

(c) Each session would be about an hour long, and the rate of pay would be one dollar per hour.

(d) The payment of one dollar would be given to the subjects at the beginning of each hour's session, and this dollar would be used to participate in the 'games' that would be played. Subjects were informed that it would be possible to complete a session with considerably more than one dollar and that all money on hand at the end of a session would be theirs to keep, that it would also be possible to end up with less than a dollar, or even nothing. They would be required to remain at a session until its completion, even though they had used up their money.

(e) In addition to the 'games', there would be other sessions where psychological tests would be administered, and for these sessions payment would be delayed. The dollar's payment for these sessions would be put into an individual 'reserve fund' for each subject, and he could be required to withdraw this money for use in certain other experiments. The subject was told that whatever balance remained in his reserve would not be paid until the conclusion of the study.

Some reassurance could be given to subjects regarding the possibility of ending up with no money (on the basis of previous experience with the pilot study), and the experimenters thought it expedient to do so. The subjects were told that in a similar study done previously average earnings of subjects had actually turned out to be approximately one dollar per hour. Unknown to the subjects, the experimenters made a commitment to the Student Employment Office and to an officer in the National Guard that, at the end of the study, they would pay any subjects averaging less than a dollar an hour an amount sufficient to bring individual total earnings up to this minimum average hourly rate. (The existence of the reserve fund made possible an unobtrusive payment.) The commitment apparently never became known to the subjects. The forecasting on the basis of the previous year's experiment turned out to be good, since the earnings of only three subjects had to be supplemented at the end of the study (by total amounts of $2.88, $2.17, and $0.42 for from seventeen to twenty-one sessions).

C. Apparatus

The apparatus used in the experiment consisted of: (1) red, white, and blue poker chips; (2) a 'cage', which could be rotated, containing five dice; (3) an Esterline program analyzer for recording most of the data; (4) a series of stimulus cards; (5) a card-holder wired to the recorder, so that time of presentation of the stimulus could be noted; (6) a set of one red and one green button for each subject, wired to an indicator box in front of the experimenter and to the recorder; (7) sheets for manual recording of some of the data by the experimenter.

The cage used for rolling dice is a standard device for playing chuck-a-luck (a three-dice game) and was purchased from a sporting-goods firm. The three original dice were replaced by five new dice, approximately identical to one another in size, weight, and appearance. The cage and dice were checked empirically for bias before the experiment started, and the distribution of results appeared random in about the proportions dictated by theory. Table 5 offers some numerical evidence on this point.

Ten recording pens on the Esterline analyzer were used for

each group of five subjects, one pair of pens per person. Time appears as a linear distance between two pen strokes. For every subject on every play, the time of presentation of the stimulus card, the time of decision to play or not to play, and the nature of the decision were recorded by the Esterline. In addition, the experimenter recorded manually the nature of the decision (a cross-check), whether the subject won when he played, and, if he won, how much. The subject indicated a decision to play by pressing his green button and a decision not to play by pressing his red button.[5]

D. The game

The game used in the experiment was a variation of poker dice. In this game five dice of the ordinary variety, with from 1 to 6 pips on each side, are rolled in a wire cage, and the combination of numbers on the tops of the dice is considered a 'hand'. Each hand can be considered an analogue of a poker hand in a one-suited deck, and so hands can be compared in terms of their relative standing in the game of poker (from lowest to highest: nothing, one pair, two pair, three of a kind, full house, four of a kind, five of a kind). The only departure from the scale of values of hands in poker was that 'straights' – 1, 2, 3, 4, 5 and 2, 3, 4, 5, 6 – were considered of no special value and were classified among the lowest possible hands – indeed, 1, 2, 3, 4, 5 was the lowest. The highest hand is 6, 6, 6, 6, 6. There was no need to distinguish flushes. In the play of the game, the experimenters did not roll but simply displayed a hand on one of the stimulus cards. If a subject elected to play, he rolled the five dice once. If a subject secured a hand higher than that displayed by the experimenters, he won; if he secured a hand that was the same or poorer than that displayed by the experimenters, he lost. In brief, one round consisted of the experimenters' displaying a hand on a stimulus card, each subject choosing to play or not to play, and indicating his decision by pressing a button, the playing subjects individually rolling the cage once in an attempt to beat the displayed hand, and the experimenter either paying the amount of the offer or collecting 5 cents.

E. Procedure of play

Chips of different colors were used instead of money for transactions during the play. The subjects were each given chips worth

5. We are deeply indebted to Mr Henry Gerbrands, of the Laboratory of Social Relations, for the design and construction of the apparatus.

$1.00 at the beginning of a session, and at the end of a session all chips were refunded with money. Red chips were worth 1 cent, white chips 5 cents, and blue chips 50 cents.

As stated before, each subject had two buttons – a red and a green – in front of him. At the start of each session he was instructed to indicate his decision to play or not to play as quickly as possible after the presentation of the stimulus card. He pressed the green button if he wished to play or the red button if he did not wish to play. When a subject made his decision, a light corresponding to the color of the button he pushed flashed in the indicator box in front of the experimenter. The lights in the indicator box served as visual aids for the experimenter: from the lights he could record the type of decision made and, with this immediate information concerning decisions, was able to guide the play smoothly and efficiently.

Subjects (usually five) sat around a long table where they could all see one another, the experimenter, and the stimulus-card holder at the head of the table. Twenty white chips (5 cents each) totaling $1.00 were given to each subject before the game started. A series of stimulus cards was then shown. On each card was a notation like the following:

$$44441$$
$$\$10.00 : : 5 ¢$$

This meant: you have your choice of betting or not betting 5 cents against $10.00 that you can roll five dice once and get a better poker hand than 44441 (examples of hands that would win: 22222, 55551, 44442). The only wager permitted was one of 5 cents by each subject.

No play started until every subject had made his decision to play or not to play. If no one chose to play, the next card was presented immediately. If some or all subjects chose to play, the dice cage was passed, and each player rolled once to try to beat the displayed hand. No attempt was made to control the order in which the players rolled, so that order varied from round to round. If a player lost, the experimenter immediately collected a white chip worth 5 cents from him; if a player won, the experimenter paid him in chips the value of the offer shown on the card. All transactions connected with one card were made before the subsequent card was shown. The experimenter recorded the outcome of each person's play. Since each subject rolled independently, he played only for himself and against the experimenter (the machine) and not against any other subject, it was possible for all subjects to make exactly the same decisions, but for all to finish with different amounts of money. When questioned, the subjects stated that they felt their decisions were only slightly affected by those of the other subjects, and observations by the experimenters of the marked differences in the play of different subjects in the same group partly confirms these verbal statements.

No play started on any round until all subjects had indicated their decisions. Once one subject started to roll, the others were not allowed to change their decisions. If a subject made a mistake and pressed the wrong button, he so informed the experimenter before any play took place. To insure care, a subject had to accept the decision he had made when he pressed the button. In the analysis of results, however, his stated intent was accepted. (The decision to play or not to play was the authors' chief interest, and the winning or losing was of interest only in so far as it affected future decisions to play or not to play.) The actual number of claimed mistakes was small – less than 2 per cent for the most careless subject – and insistence on adherence to first decisions seemed to minimize the subjects' carelessness in pressing buttons. There was occasional byplay during the experiment, when subjects who were not playing took the cage to roll and see 'how it would have come out if I had played'. Occasionally also, a subject would request in advance that his second rather than his first roll be counted. This was allowed.

From this description of the game, it can be judged that the experimenter had many tasks to perform and that these tasks had to be performed rapidly in order for subjects not to become bored from too much dead time. Something like $1\frac{1}{2}$ cards and the play connected with them, on the average, consumed about one minute. Check on the experimenter's recording of decisions was made possible through the double recording of these decisions. The subjects themselves checked the accuracy of the money transactions.

F. Hands

All hands displayed on stimulus cards and their corresponding fair bets are shown in Table 3. These hands were selected by the experimenters from all possible hands after a complete table of odds had been computed. Criteria determining selection were such things as the fair offer being approximately an integral multiple of 5 cents at the lower end of the scale, and getting fairly good representation of hands of different expected frequencies.

Table 3

True Odds for Hands Played

Rank of Hand	Hand	Approximate True Odds against 5 Cents
1	44321	2½ ¢—5 ¢ or 0·50—1
2	66431	5 ¢—5 ¢ or 1·01—1
3	55221	10 ¢—5 ¢ or 2·01—1
4	22263	25 ¢—5 ¢ or 5·00—1
5	55562	51 ¢—5 ¢ or 10·17—1
6	22255	$1.01 —5 ¢ or 20·24—1
7	44441	$5.07 —5 ¢ or 101·32—1

With each of these hands, a varying group of offers was used, ranging from extremely poor in terms of the fair bet to extremely good. An arbitrary group of different hands plus the different offers combined with them form a 'series'. For instance, a series might be hands 1, 2, 3, 4, and 7 of Table 3 with four different offers per hand, making a total of twenty combinations. Several series differing in composition and length were used, for reasons to be given below in the section on 'Experimental Design'. The order within a series was randomized before its initial presentation. Two to five repetitions of a single series make one session. The subjects' participation as well as the length of a series governed how many repetitions were carried through in one session.

Table 4

List of Hands Displayed and Offers Made in Uncertainty and Learning Sessions

(Number in Parentheses is Serial Order of Hand in Series)

	Hand						
	44321	66431	55221	22263	55562	22255	44441
	¢	¢	¢	¢	¢	$	$
Offers	(14) 7	(42) 10	(11) 16	(39) 43	(24) 72	(41) 1.42	(46) 8.00
	(6) 6	(32) 9	(21) 13	(44) 37	(48) 61	(12) 1.21	(16) 7.50
	(47) 5	(9) 7	(23) 12	(15) 31	(7) 56	(49) 1.11	(8) 7.00
	(25) 4	(19) 6	(30) 11	(2) 28	(13) 53	(20) 1.05	(29) 6.00
	(17) 3	(45) 5	(38) 10	(10) 25	(18) 50	(4) 1.00	(26) 5.50
	(36) 2	(27) 4	(43) 9	(22) 22	(35) 45	(28) 0.90	(3) 5.00
	(34) 1	(1) 3	(5) 7	(31) 19	(40) 39	(33) 0.79	(37) 4.00

There were no 'breaks' between series, and play went on continuously. Once a series was begun, it was completed within the session.

It would have been preferable to randomize each series each time it was used. Unfortunately, practical difficulties concerned with the experimenter's recording of the outcome of individual plays made continuing randomization difficult. The one initial order was kept for all occasions when a series was used, both for different sessions and for different groups of subjects. In Table 4 are all the hands used, all the offers used, and the order within the series used in the Uncertainty situation and the learning sessions.

G. Experimental design

A number of different experimental conditions was used within the framework of the game and procedure of play described. These conditions were structured (1) to teach the subject about the game and give him an opportunity to gain experience in the play, (2) to derive experimentally utility curves for each individual, and (3) to check experimentally predictions about the sub-

Table 5

Comparison of Actual Wins with Expected Wins (Uncertainty Sessions)

Hand (And Fair Bet)	No. of Times Played	No. of Times Won	No. of Expected Wins	Per Cent Times Won	Per Cent Expected Wins
44321 2·5 ¢—5 ¢	255	173	170	67·8	66·67
66431 5 ¢—5 ¢	269	132	134	49·0	49·75
55221 10 ¢—5 ¢	279	88	93	31·5	33·22
22263 25 ¢—5 ¢	302	49	50	16·2	16·67
55562 51 ¢—5 ¢	261	17	23	6·5	8·95
22255 $1.01—5 ¢	284	12	13	4·23	4·71
44441 $5.07—5 ¢	339	3	3·3	0·88	0·98

jects' behavior based on the utility curve constructed from previous sessions.

The first sessions for all groups are classed as 'Uncertainty' sessions because during these the subjects did not know and, questioning revealed, could not calculate the true probabilities or mathematically fair bet for any hand. The Uncertainty situation consisted of three sessions, and the series used (Table 4) contained forty-nine combinations – seven hands with seven offers each. The series used was the same for all three groups of subjects.

At the end of the three Uncertainty sessions, each group met to learn how to calculate the true odds for any hand. In addition, each subject was given a sheet with the true odds for all hands used (like Table 3) and *was required to keep this sheet in front of him in all future sessions*. At this instruction meeting the subjects were also shown copies of Table 5 – giving the number of times each hand had been played during the previous sessions, the number and percentage of wins expected if the information of Table 3 were correct. Subjects were given an opportunity to discuss results and to ask the experimenter about probability problems. The instruction may have been convincing, for, when questioned at the end of the experiment, all subjects said that they accepted as true the information given them in the instruction session.

At this stage the subjects had before them the true odds for each hand; so the next group of sessions was called the 'Known-risk' situation. For each group the series used in the first few sessions (the learning sessions) of the Known-risk situation was exactly the same as the series used for that group in the Uncertainty situation. Following the instruction meeting, four learning sessions were used for each of the two student groups, and the National Guardsmen had three sessions. It should be emphasized that the *hands* were not changed throughout the experiment, so the odds sheets continued to be pertinent.

The data obtained from the learning sessions were analyzed before proceeding further with the Known-risk situation. The purpose of the analysis was to ascertain how extant offers had to be changed to produce the kind of information desired by the experimenters. To derive the utility curve of a subject, it is necessary that for each hand the offers range from some so low that the subject will refuse to play most or all of the time to some so high that he will play most or all of the time. Since the utility curves – and, consequently, what is high and what is low – are expected to vary from subject to subject, a wide range of offers is needed for group coverage. This range can be determined only from the actual play of the subjects. (For some subjects, the amount of money required to induce play against a hand may be so large that a project such as this one cannot afford the information. The only information to be gained in such cases is that the subject's 'indifference point' – 50 per cent acceptance and 50 per cent rejection – for these hands is beyond a certain amount.)

After the analysis the offers for the remaining sessions of the Known-risk situation were adjusted to try to maximize the amount of information to be obtained from each group. The series used then varied from group to group. The data secured from the postlearning sessions were used to derive a utility curve for each subject.

An important part of the work is to obtain an independent check on the use of the utility curve to predict other behavior. To check the information contained in the individual utility curves, the Known-risk situation was modified by the introduction of a more complex bet. This modified procedure was termed the 'Doublet' situation. Combination offers using two of the previous hands were devised. The stimulus cards carried a notation like this:

$$22263 : : 20 \, ¢$$
$$66431 : : \ \ 3 \, ¢$$

This meant: 'You have the opportunity of betting or not betting 5 cents against this double offer: if you beat 22263 you will receive 20 cents; if you do not beat 22263 but do beat 66431, you will receive 3 cents; if you do not beat either, you will lose the 5 cents you must risk to play. You will roll the dice only once.' During the Doublet sessions the subject had in front of him a new sheet giving the fair bet for each double combination presented. These data were for use in checking behavioral predictions growing out of the data from which the utility curve was constructed. This point will be expanded later.

Among the criticisms offered of attempts to measure utility in risk situations is that participation in the gambling situation may have utility. To obtain some information on this point an 'Investment' session was held. In the Investment situation the subject himself did not play but wrote out a set of instructions to be followed by an agent. This agent in the absence of the subject would rigidly follow the subject's instructions in playing with a dollar of the subject's money. The instructions given to subjects for these investment sessions were:

One dollar ($1.00) will be taken from your reserve fund and given to some person whom you will designate. This person will use instructions which you are to write out for him below.

Below is a list of the hands against which you've played. Opposite each hand you are to check or to write in the lowest offer for which your representative may wager five cents (5 ¢) against beating the hand with one roll of the dice. He will play against any hand only when the amount you indicate, *or more*, is offered. After he plays, *the total proceeds* of his playing will be given to you. You may not be present, however, when he is playing.

As a matter of fact, the agent never did play for the subjects in the experiment proper, although this had been done in the pilot study. Although this omission seemed sensible at the time, in retrospect the authors view it as a procedural error.

For other purposes, not the subject of this paper (although a brief report will be included later) a 'Paired-comparison' situation was used. Two bets were presented on a single card, and the subject *had* to choose to play against *one* of the offers.

In Table 6 is a summary of the experimental design, listing the kind and number of sessions. For each session the number of rounds (one hand with one offer) and the average earnings for the three groups of subjects are listed.

IV. Analysis of Results

A. Utility curves

As the first step in the analysis of the data, it was necessary to find the 'indifference offer' to each subject on every hand. For each hand a range of offers had been made (see Table 7). The proportion of times the subject elected to play each offer was calculated (see example for subject B–I in Table 8), and these points were plotted on ordinary arithmetic graph paper with vertical axis as per cent participation and horizontal axis as amount of offer in cents (see Figure 2). A freehand curve or a broken-line curve was then fitted to the points.[6] The abscissa value of the point where this curve crossed the 50 per cent participation line gave in cents

6. Various procedures were tried for smoothing the points: plotting on probability paper and on arithmetic paper, drawing freehand curves and broken-line segments. Fortunately, no dilemma arose, because the results were much the same no matter what techniques of plotting and fitting were used.

the subject's indifference offer for that hand. In other words, for that hand this calculation yielded an interpolated offer which the subject would be equally likely to accept or reject if given the opportunity.

Since the probability p of winning is fixed for a given hand, the utility of the indifference offer is just $(1 - p)/p$, as described

Table 6

Summary of Experimental Sessions

Type of Session in Chronological Order	Group A Harvard Undergrads.		Group B Harvard Undergrads.		Group C National Guardsmen	
	No. of Rounds*	Av. Earnings per Subject	No. of Rounds	Av. Earnings per Subject	No. of Rounds	Av. Earnings per Subject
Uncertainty	49	$0·96	49	$0·45	49	$1·02
Uncertainty	98	1·05	98	0·87	98	0·47
Uncertainty	98	3·01	98	1·48	98	1·44
Paired comparison	42	0·90	42	0·90	42	0·53
Investment Instruction	Subjects told odds and instructed in calculating these odds					
Known risk	49	0·78	49	1·07	49	0·73
Known risk	98	0·87	98	1·78	98	1·34
Known risk	98	1·44	98	1·31	98	2·49
Known risk	98	2·66	98	1·72	Omitted	
Known risk	*94*	2·98	Omitted		*111*	1·54
Known risk	*92*	1·68	*99*	1·65	*129*	3·41
Known risk	*92*	2·11	*140*	1·41	*129*	0·26
Known risk	*138*	1·02	*140*	1·33	*132*	0·03
Known risk	*92*	2·34	*102*	0·89	*88*	0·47
Investment						
Known risk	Omitted		Omitted		*132*	1·47
Known risk	Omitted		Omitted		*132*	1·50
Doublet	100	0·91	100	2·11	90	0·45
Doublet	100	1·14	100	2·74	90	1·25
Doublet	110	1·21	100	1·60	110	1·07
Doublet	Omitted		Omitted		50	0·25
Paired comparison	60	1·04	60	1·05	60	0·50
Doublet	100	2·75	100	2·32	100	1·31

* Italicized rounds are ones used for constructing utility curves.

in Section II. For example, the data of Figure 2 yield an indifference offer of 10·6 cents. Hand 55221 has a probability of 0·332 of being beaten. Therefore, the utility is about 2 utiles, and the utility curve of subject B–I will pass through the point (10.6, 2).

Table 7

The Entries Show for Each Group and Each Hand the Range of Monetary Offers Made in the Course of the Experiment

(The Subject Puts Up 5 Cents)

Hand	Group A		Group B		Group C	
44321	1 ¢–	7 ¢	1 ¢–	7 ¢	1 ¢–	7 ¢
66431	3 ¢–	10 ¢	3 ¢–	10 ¢	3 ¢–	10 ¢
55221	7 ¢–	16 ¢	5 ¢–	16 ¢	3 ¢–	16 ¢
22263	19 ¢–	43 ¢	13 ¢–	43 ¢	10 c–	43 ¢
55562	39 ¢–	72 ¢	28 ¢–	72 ¢	11 ¢–	72 ¢
22255	79 ¢–$1.42		79 ¢–$ 1.63		23 ¢–$1.42	
44441	$4.00 –$8.00		$4.00 –$10.00		25 ¢–$8.00	

Table 8

This Table Shows for Subject B–I and Hand 55221 the Basic Information Required To Estimate His Indifference Point*

Offer (Cents)	No. of Times Presented	No. of Times Played	Per Cent (Times Played/ Times Presented)
16	14	14	100
12	14	13	92·9
11	14	9	64·3
10	14	4	28·6
9	14	1	7·1
7	14	0	0
5	11	0	0

* Here only data from the italicized Known-risk sessions indicated in Table 6 are used.

The number of points on the utility curve which can be determined in this fashion equals the number of different hands which were used in the experiment. In the present experiment the value in cents of $\frac{1}{2}$, 1, 2, 5, 10, 20, and 101 utiles was determined (these are rounded values). These, and the arbitrarily defined points $[U(0 \text{¢}) = 0$ utiles and $U(-5 \text{¢}) = -1$ utiles] can be connected by straight-line segments to form the utility curve of a subject. In Figure 3, illustrations of the utility curves are given for a few subjects. For reasons of scale we have shown values for only a few different utile positions. Logarithmic scales would be somewhat misleading because some interest attaches to the curvature.

It was not possible to secure utility curves as complete as those in Figure 3 for all subjects. The behavior of one subject in the

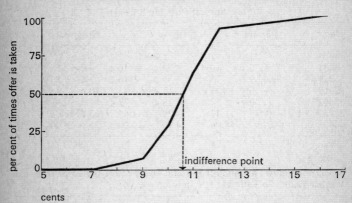

Figure 2   In this graph the data of Table 8 for subjects B–I, hand 55221, are plotted to show how the indifference point is actually obtained.

pilot study was so erratic that no utility curve at all could be derived for him. For two student subjects in the experiment it was possible to derive only a short section of the curve. Their indifference points for the high hands (i.e., those in which the probability of winning was small and which gave the values for 10, 20, and 101 utiles) were so high that the experimenters felt they could not afford to make the offers necessary to get the subjects to choose to play (if such offers existed).

There was nothing in the experimental procedure which coerced any subject to play at any time. It was possible for a subject to take his dollar at the beginning of a session and not play, thus assuring himself of $1.00. It is interesting that this never happened.

One subject showed markedly superstitious behavior toward one hand. He seldom played against it for any of the offers made, even though he would accept the same, or even smaller, offers against a hand which was less likely to be beaten. When asked about this after the project was completed, the subject said that he had been aware of his behavior but that he simply felt that the particular hand was unlucky for him and that he 'just didn't like it'.

In Table 9 are the indifference offers corresponding to each utility. When these are graphed, a rough utility curve is obtained. Figure 3 shows such utility curves plotted for a few subjects. The straight line on each plot represents the 'fair' curve. Casual investigation of Table 9 will show that the students (Groups A and B) tended to be 'conservative', while the National Guardsmen

Table 9

Amount of Money in Cents Corresponding to Values on the Utile Scale for All Subjects*

Subjects	'Fair' Offer Utiles	−5¢ −1	0 0	2.5 0.5	5 1	10 2	25 5	51 10	101 20	507 101
A–I		−5¢	0	4.8	8.2	12.4	24.8	55.0	108	580
A–II		−5¢	0	3.8	5.2	9.9	28.5	58.0	121	583
A–III		−5¢	0	3.7	6.1	11.9	29.5	60.3	118	570
A–IV		−5¢	0	4.2	5.8	11.7	29.3	64.5	119	560
A–V†		−5¢	0	2.5	4.5	9.5	19.0	53.0	103	545
B–I		−5¢	0	4.8	5.0	10.6	28.5	60.0	163‡	1,000‡
B–II		−5¢	0	3.8	5.0	10.1	22.0	72.0‡	163‡	1,000‡
B–III		−5¢	0	5.0	6.5	16.0	22.0	44.5	163‡	990
B–IV		−5¢	0	4.5	5.4	11.2	20.0	42.0	139	657
B–V		−5¢	0	4.2	10.0	14.4	20.0	36.5	134	590
C–I		−5¢	0	4.1	6.2	§	12.7	22.5	66	92
C–II		−5¢	0	3.4	3.9	6.5	10.8	12.4	35	85
C–III		−5¢	0	4.7	7.8	9.0	21.6	23.5	55	175
C–IV		−5¢	0	3.9	4.7	9.5	20.6	28.0	62	103
C–V		−5¢	0	4.0	7.3	9.0	11.4	14.2	36	90

* The italicized Known-risk sessions of Table 6 were used in calculating these points of the utility curves. Columns for −5¢ and 0¢ are assigned, not measured.

† Data for three of five sessions. Subject left experiment.

‡ This number is the highest offer made, and it was refused by this subject more than 50 per cent of the time. Thus it is known only that the utility expressed in monetary units is larger than the value given.

§ Subject refuses all offers up to and including 16 cents. See discussion of superstitious behavior in text. (Sec. IV*A*.)

were 'extravagant'. If support is desired for classical diminishing-returns curves, the student groups supply it. Support for the notion of increasing utility of money is given by the Guardsmen. It must be remembered, however, that this curve covers only ranges from −5 cents to about $5.50 for the students and only up to about $1.00 for the Guardsmen. It should be remembered, further, that all subjects had had instruction in the fair odds and in their computation and had before them at all times sheets giving them the fair odds for each hand played.

It seems clear that student Groups A and B differed in their reactions to the high-valued, low-probability hands. Every B subject wants more money to play the 20 to 1 and 100 to 1 hands than any A subject. Since there was no known selective factor between these two groups, supposedly this systematic difference between groups is a result of running the subjects as groups rather than individuals (see Sec. VI*D*).

B. Investment sessions

In the Investment sessions the subjects wrote instructions for an agent to use in playing for them. The second such session was given immediately after the Known-risk sessions used to determine the utility curves (i.e., the numbers of Table 9). On the basis of the instructions to the agent, it is possible to obtain approxi-

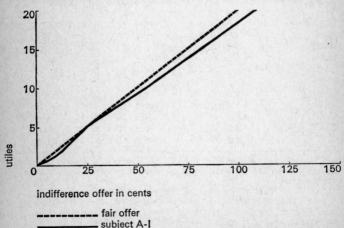

Figure 3a   Utility curve for subject A–I and straight line showing mathematically fair offer. Offer for 101 utiles not shown.

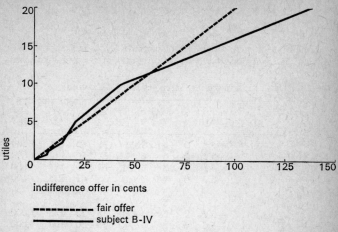

Figure 3b   Utility curve for subject B–IV and straight line showing mathematically fair offer. Offer for 101 utiles not shown.

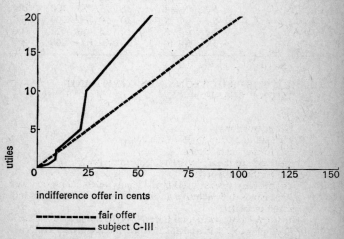

Figure 3c   Utility curve for subject C–III and straight line showing mathematically fair offer. Offer for 101 utiles not shown.

Table 10

Amount of Money in Cents Corresponding to Values on the Utile Scale for All Subjects Based on Information of Second Investment Session

(Columns for −5 ¢ and 0 ¢ Are Assigned, Not Measured)

Subjects	'Fair' Offer Utiles	−5 ¢ −1	0 0	2·5 0·5	5 1	10 2	25 5	51 10	101 20	507 101
A–I		−5 ¢	0	6	9	16	31	60	121	600
A–II		−5 ¢	0	4	6	11	31	70	142	1,000
A–III		−5 ¢	0	3	6	12	28	61	121	600
A–IV		−5 ¢	0	4	7	12	30	61	125	600
A–V					Subject left experiment					
B–I		−5 ¢	0	5	5	10	35	72	125	1,000
B–II		−5 ¢	0	5	5	10	25	50	100	1,000
B–III		−5 ¢	0	5	7	20	25	50	142	1,000
B–IV		−5 ¢	0	5	5	10	25	50	121	700
B–V		−5 ¢	0	5	7	12	25	50	121	750
C–I		−5 ¢	0	5	8	16	21	40	90	500
C–II		−5 ¢	0	4	9	16	25	50	100	200
C–III		−5 ¢	0	5	10	10	30	60	100	400
C–IV		−5 ¢	0	5	9	12	25	50	121	600
C–V		−5 ¢	0	10	13	20	50	100	200	600

FURTHER INSTRUCTIONS TO AGENT FOR INVESTMENT SESSION

STUDENTS

A–I No instructions.

A–II Play till you drop to 75 ¢ then *stop!!*

A–III No further instructions.

A–IV Just stick to these; go above, but not below.

B–I No further instructions.

B–II Do not play against two highest hands unless doing *very* well.

B–III Play hands 1–5 inclusive at all times when odds are as indicated or better.

Play 6 & 7 only when total *EARNINGS* are in excess of $1.00.

B–IV Only play to 22255 and 55221 when you are ahead. Otherwise instructions are the same.

B–V Keep away from double pairs, full house, and four of a kind, except when very good odds and when you think you can win. If you get low, play only very good odds.

GUARDSMEN

C–I   If you are ahead you may play the four 4's for as low as $3.00.

C–II   Just play according to what I checked off.

C–III   If player finds that he is winning, he shall go ahead and bet at his discretion.

C–IV   If his winnings exceed $2.50 he may play any and every hand as he so desires, but if his amount should drop below $0.60, he should use discretion in regard to the odds and hands that come up.

C–V   Just play as if it was your own money.

mate utility curves which should be experimentally independent of utility of participation (but not necessarily of utility of gambling, whatever this means). Comparison of Tables 9 and 10 shows that subjects in the student groups had about the same or a little higher indifference offers in the Investment session. But the Guardsmen group in every case had vastly higher indifference offers for the Investment sessions than for the Known-risk sessions. If one accepts the vertical difference between utility curves constructed from Known-risk sessions and Investment sessions as a measure of the value of participation, then the Guardsmen find participation more and more valuable as the sums involved increase. Compared with the Guardsmen, the students are relatively unaffected by participation.

It was originally planned to have the second Investment session follow the last Known-risk session for all groups. When the Investment records of Group C were checked, however, the instructions for play written by these subjects appeared remarkably different from their actual behavior in the risk sessions. They seemed much less prone to accept offers on any hand which were less than the fair bet for that hand. The problem arose as to whether this new behavior was specific to an Investment session or whether it would persist if Group C were given further opportunities to play. To check this, two more Known-risk sessions were run with this group. Their behavior in these two sessions was approximately the same as that in the earlier Known-risk sessions, so the data of the italicized Known-risk sessions of Table 6 were used to construct utility curves for Group C, after all.

This paper-and-pencil method of testing has been criticized on the grounds that we are measuring what the subjects think is the socially accepted or proper thing to do or what they think we think they should do, rather than giving information on how the subjects really want their broker to play. The critic points out that the paper and pencil may lend an air of formality and finality that is not present in the regular sessions, making the subjects more aware of being observed and therefore pushing them in the direction of conforming to a norm – say, the norm of the odds sheets. This may be the explanation of the Guardsmen's behavior. We are not in a position to check this view.

C. Utility-participation graphs

After the results of the behavior are reduced to the forms shown in Table 9 or Figure 3, the question of predicting future behavior of the same individuals arises. According to the strict consistency assumption, the only predictions that can be made are that offers (or objects or probability combinations of objects) whose expected utilities are positive will always be taken, and those whose expected utilities are negative will never be taken. As the discussion of Section II indicates and as the data show, such an assumption is invalidated by the experiment. Failing such an

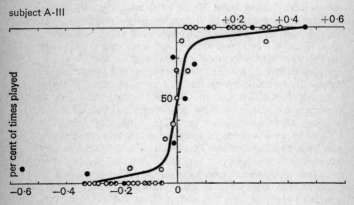

subject A-III

per cent of times played

expected utility

o known-risk hands
● doublet hands
◐ two known-risk hands
◒ three known-risk hands

Figure 4a Percentage times played plotted against expected utility for subject A–III. Curve is freehand fit to Known-risk points. The fit of this curve to the Doublet points shows roughly how good predictions of subsequent behavior are.

assumption, the natural next-best prediction would be to say that offers whose expected utilities are positive will be taken more than 50 per cent of the time. Such a prediction is not so quantitative as could be desired, and it would seem to waste a good deal of the information contained in the data. One further possibility for unifying the data suggests itself. Since utility curves for individuals are now available, most offers used in the experiment involve amounts of money whose utility has been measured; exceptions are offers on the 44441 hand beyond the individual's indifference point and certain offers for subjects B–I, B–II, and B–III that were not measured, as explained above. Thus for most hands and offers used it is possible to compute the expected utility of a bet for a particular subject. From this information and the data on participation (per cent of all opportunities that the hand is played at the offer), a graph can be made for an individual showing a scatter of points for each expected utility, and a curve may be passed through these points. This was done by eye, with only points for Known-risk sessions plotted on the graphs (see Figure 4, a, b, c, and d, showing four typical scatters). These four subjects were chosen to represent the student with least spread

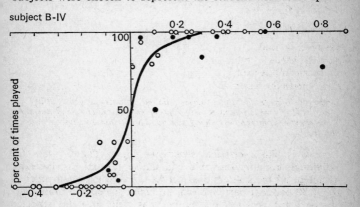

subject B-IV

per cent of times played

expected utility

o known-risk hands
• doublet hands

Figure 4b   Percentage times played plotted against expected utility for subject B–IV. Curve is freehand fit to Known-risk points. The fit of this curve to the Doublet points shows roughly how good predictions of subsequent behavior are.

(A–III) and a medium-spread student (B–IV), the Guardsman with least spread (C–I), and a Guardsman with large spread (C–III). Such a curve is reminiscent of dosage-mortality curves in pharmaceutical work, where participation corresponds to mortality and expected utility to dosage, or, more generally, such

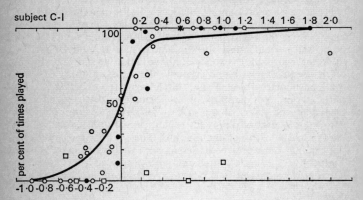

subject C–I

Figure 4c Percentage times played plotted against expected utility for subject C–I. Curve is freehand fit to Known-risk points. The fit of this curve to the Doublet points shows roughly how good predictions of subsequent behavior are.

a curve is like a classical sensitivity curve. These curves for individuals roughly resemble cumulative normal distributions. Although all the scatters pass across the zero expected utiles at about 50 per cent participation, no credit for such a uniformity can be given because this finding was built into the expected utilities by the construction leading to the utility curves. However, it is pleasant to find a fairly uniform rise and drop of the points on the right and left of the origin, and it is still more gratifying to find that each subject has quite a decent-looking scatter of points. The general uniformity of such scatters suggests that, if one knew the expected utility of an offer for a subject, one could estimate approximately the proportion of times the offer would be taken.

152

In Table 11 is given half the estimated distance in expected utiles from the 16 per cent participation point to the 84 per cent participation point, subject by subject, as estimated from a rough graph of the subject's utility-participation curve. This quantity is roughly the standard deviation of the density function whose

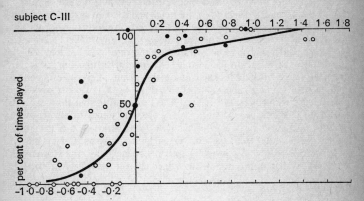

subject C-III

per cent of times played

expected utility

o known-risk hands
• doublet hands

Figure 4d   Percentage times played plotted against expected utility for subject C-III. Curve is freehand fit to Known-risk points. The fit of this curve to the Doublet points shows roughly how good predictions of subsequent behaviur are.

Table 11

Index of Discrimination for Subjects*

Subject	Group A	Group B	Group C
I	0·05	0·97	0·18
II	0·07	0·06	0·23
III	0·03	0·06	0·31
IV	0·03	0·06	0·18
V	0·07	0·10	0·36
Average	0·05	0·07	0·25

* This is half the distance in expected utiles between estimated 16 per cent and 84 per cent participation from utility-participation curve.

cumulative is represented by the scatter of points. Or, to provide a more palatable description, this index is a measure of the discrimination used by the subject – the smaller this index, the more nearly the subject approaches the ideal of the man who always knows which of A and B he prefers or whether he is indifferent between them. A rough-and-ready interpretation would regard one utile as equal to 5 cents in the neighborhood of zero expected utilities. Furthermore, since the discrimination index is roughly a standard deviation, four standard deviations might be taken as the band width of the general indifference region or, better, 'inconsistency zone' of an individual. Within this range the subject may regularly both take and refuse the same offer on different presentations, but to the right of this zone he will almost invariably accept the wager, while to the left he will almost invariably decline. Thus for student subjects the 'inconsistency zone' in the neighborhood of zero is roughly 4×0.06 utiles $\times$ 5 ¢/utile = 1.2 ¢ long, while that for the Guardsmen is about 4×0.25 utiles $\times$ 5 ¢/utile = 5 ¢ long. To put it another way, the students have an eye for differences little larger than a penny when small

Table 12a

Predicted and Actual Participation Percentages for Doublet Hands and Number of Participation Opportunities by Subject*

Doublets	Subject A–I			Subject A–II			Subject A–III			Subject A–IV		
	P	A	N	P	A	N	P	A	N	P	A	N
1	100	85	27	100	98	41	100	100	41	100	100	41
2	75	52	27	72	7	41	84	54	41	87	83	41
3	0	4	28	3	2	41	0	5	41	0	10	41
4	98	63	27	94	98	41	98	100	41	94	100	41
5	64	32	28	44	7	41	16	15	41	13	10	41
6	2	0	28	7	0	41	3	0	41	2	2	41
7†	99	95	21	100	100	31	99	100	31	99	87	31
8†	1	81	21	88	13	31	30	82	31	87	84	31
9	8	21	28	93	100	41	91	78	41	89	93	41
10	99	54	28	100	100	41	99	100	41	99	95	41
11‡	0	33	6	0	0	10	0	10	10	0	10	10
12‡	100	100	7	100	90	10	98	100	10	98	70	10

* Letters in columns have following meanings: P = predicted per cent participation; A = actual per cent participation; and N = number of observations upon which A is based.

† Used in all Doublet sessions but the first.

‡ Used only in first Doublet session.

amounts are involved, while the Guardsmen react about as frequently to differences amounting to a nickel.

D. The Doublet situation

To see whether more complicated offers than those used in constructing the utility curve would be handled by the subjects in a way that could be predicted from their expected utilities, the Doublet situation was used. Since there were two hands, there were three outcomes: (1) beat the high hand and receive A_1 cents; (2) beat the low hand but not the high one and receive A_2 cents; and (3) not beat either hand and lose 5 cents. So the expected utility of a Doublet hand is

$$E(U) = p_1 U(A_1 \cent) + (p_2 - p_1) U(A_2 \cent) + (1 - p_2) U(-5 \cent),$$

where

$p_1 = $ probability of beating the higher hand,

$p_2 = $ probability of beating the lower hand,

and the utilities of A_1 and A_2 are read from the subject's previously constructed utility curve. In Figure 4 the solid circles are the results for the Doublet hands. In Tables 12a, b, c, and d are given

Table 12b

Predicted and Actual Participation Percentages for Doublet Hands and Number of Participation Opportunities by Subject*

Doublets	Subject B–I			Subject B–II			Subject B–III			Subject B–IV			Subject B–V		
	P	A	N	P	A	N	P	A	N	P	A	N	P	A	N
1	†	98	40	†	10	40	95	100	40	99	85	40	93	83	40
2	26	75	40	†	8	40	87	98	40	92	50	40	88	40	40
3	6	43	40	†	5	40	14	3	40	17	3	40	50	3	40
4	90	35	40	†	83	40	96	98	40	100	98	40	94	100	40
5	41	10	40	†	80	40	94	98	40	98	98	40	92	98	40
6	1	0	40	0	10	40	3	5	40	12	10	40	30	85	40
7	100	100	40	100	100	40	97	100	40	100	100	40	89	100	40
8	91	100	40	94	100	40	7	28	40	81	95	40	23	78	40
9	92	98	40	96	100	40	75	33	40	97	98	40	15	33	40
10	95	100	40	†	100	40	100	100	40	100	78	40	100	98	40

* For meanings of letters in columns see note * to Table 12a.

† Would require extrapolation of utility curve to determine the expected values of the hand.

Table 12c

Predicted and Actual Participation Percentages for Doublet Hands and Number of Participation Opportunities by Subject*

Doublets	Subject C–I			Subject C–II			Subject C–III			Subject C–IV			Subject C–V		
	P	A	N	P	A	N	P	A	N	P	A	N	P	A	N
1	†	100	35	†	98	42	87	95	44	96	94	33	†	97	39
2	†	60	35	†	19	42	11	5	43	29	36	33	†	23	39
3	84	91	35	100	83	42	85	95	43	84	91	33	91	72	39
4	35	11	35	89	40	43	54	77	44	43	61	33	82	54	39
5	12	0	35	55	5	41	7	43	42	3	10	32	22	8	39
6	90	97	35	95	100	43	86	59	44	82	85	33	87	100	39
7	42	29	35	88	78	41	13	56	43	4	66	32	83	85	39
8	98	100	35	100	100	42	95	100	43	91	100	33	92	100	39
9‡	100	100	35	100	100	35	93	91	35	100	100	23	97	97	30
10‡	97	100	35	98	100	35	87	89	35	89	100	24	86	100	30
11§	—	—	‖	99	100	6	36	100	8	43	89	9	90	100	9
12§	—	—	‖	14	100	7	11	67	9	3	56	9	13	100	9

* For meanings of letters in columns see note * to Table 12a.

† Would require extrapolation of utility curve to determine the expected values of the hand.

‡ Used in all Doublet sessions but the first one.

§ Used in the first Doublet session only.

‖ Absent.

Table 12d

Summary of Tables 12a, b, and c for Doublet Hands with More than 20 Observations

Table	Frequency Tabulation of Difference between Predicted and Observed Results for Doublet Hands in Percentages					
	0–9	10–19	20–29	30–39	40 and Over	Total
12a	25	5	1	4	5	40
12b	22	9	2	2	8	43
12c	24	11	4	1	4	44

predictions of per cent participation in Doublet hands by subjects (based on the utility-participation curves previously presented), along with the observed frequencies. Here the fact that hands with positive utility are usually played is *not* an artifact of the computation scheme, as it was in the original utility-participation graphs.

As was to be expected, the Doublet sessions caused considerable confusion, which is reflected in a larger inconsistency zone. On the other hand, the predictions from the Known-risk to the Doublet sessions seem rather satisfactory to the authors. It should perhaps be mentioned that most of the small percentage differences in Table 12d come from the extremes of the scale.

E. The paired-comparison situation

In the paired-comparison situation the subjects were forced to choose between two hands. Each of these hands, of course, had its own expected utility for the subject, based on his previously derived utility curve. The utility-curve method, then, might be

Table 13

Comparison of Predictions of Preferences Made by the Expected Utility and the Expected Money-Value Methods in the Paired-Comparison Situation*

Utility Value	Money Values			Utility Value	Money Value		
	R	W	Total		R	W	Total
	Group A				Group B		
R	15	7	22	R	20	21	31
W	5	10	15	W	2	9	11
?	1	2	3	?	3	1	4
Imp.	0	0	0	Imp.	1	3	4
Total	21	19	40	Total	26	34	50
	Group C				All Groups Combined		
R	23	9	32	R	48	37	85
W	9	8	17	W	16	27	43
?	1	0	1	?	5	3	8
Imp.	0	0	0	Imp.	1	3	4
Total	33	17	50	Total	70	70	140

* The letters 'R' and 'W' stand for 'right' and 'wrong' predictions, '?' for equality of the hands, and 'Imp.', for impossibility of prediction. A case represents the preference displayed by one subject for one pair of offers.

compared with the money-value method in predicting which choice would be made by the subject. In other words, the utility-curve method would predict that the hand with the larger expected utility would be preferred, while the money-value method would predict that hands with the higher expected money value would be preferred. In Table 13 these results are compared. Here a case means one pair of offers presented to one subject. Of course, each pair was presented several times, and the subject's over-all preference is being compared with the prediction. The letters 'R' and 'W' stand for 'right' and 'wrong' predictions. The ' ?' means that expected utility is identical for the two hands as nearly as we were able to tell, while 'Imp.' means 'impossible' to tell because the expectancy in utiles could not be calculated for one of the hands. This calculation difficulty did not destroy the usefulness of these hands for their original purpose, which is not reported here. As a matter of fact, the present comparison is an afterthought and was not originally envisaged in the experimental design. In groups A and C the money-value and utility predictions are about equally accurate. But in Group B, of the 23 cases of disagreement, the utility computation is correct 21 times.

Two further computations of interest show the percentages correct as a function of the difference between the offers in a pair measured in expected utiles and in expected money value. The lines of the table roughly correspond. Thus the 54 per cent correct for the utility method corresponds approximately to the 42 per cent correct for the money-value method. In Table 14 the same 12 cases are missing from the summary of the utility method that are shown as ' ?' or 'Imp.' in Table 13. If the reader feels that any injustice has been done, he may split the 8 ' ?' entries 4 and 4 in the 0·01 to 0·15 line of the utility table. He will then find only 53 per cent correct instead of 54 per cent for the utility method. This leaves only 4 cases unaccounted for.

This comparison suggests that the utility method can be used to compare two offers and that it is somewhat more successful as a predictor than the expected money-value method.

F. The decision times

An extended discussion of the times taken by subjects to decide to play or not to play will be given elsewhere. It is of interest, however, to know that these decision times have some relation to the notion of utility. In particular, as the expected utility goes from negative to positive, the average time taken by a subject to decide *to play* decreases. Similarly, as the expected utility goes from negative to positive, the average time taken by a subject to decide *not to play* increases. If straight lines are plotted to represent the decision times as a function of expected utility, the line representing 'play' will have a negative slope, and the line representing 'not play' will have a positive slope. Computations reveal that the utility co-ordinate of the intersection of these lines, which represent the relation between time measurements and expected utility, comes rather close to the zero point of the expected utility scale. Such computations supply an independent check on the reasonableness of the utility measurements and, moreover, give an additional way of thinking about the concept of indifference. This phenomenon is not an artifact of the experimental design but is a bona fide experimental finding. It could just as well have happened that the 'play'-'not play' lines would not have intersected at all, or at least that they would not have intersected in any reasonable neighbourhood of the zero point of expected utility. It is true, of course, that common sense suggests that the slopes of the lines would be as they are.

V. Psychological Probability

Preston and Baratta (1948) reported an experiment designed to study the notion of *psychological* probabilities in relation to mathematical probabilities through the medium of a game. Participants used play money to bid for gambles. A gamble is a

Table 14

Number and Percentage of Cases* Correctly Predicted as a Function of Difference in Expected Utility and of Difference in Expected Money Value

Prediction by Expected Utility Value				*Prediction by Expected Money Value*			
Difference in Expectancies in Utiles of the Two Offers	*All Groups Combined*			*Difference in Actuarial Values (in Cents) of Two Offers*	*All Groups Combined*		
	No. Right	No. Wrong	Per Cent Right		No. Right	No. Wrong	Per Cent Right
0·01–0·15	37	32	54	$0.02–$0.50	34	46	42
0·16–0·30	21	7	75	0.55– 1.55	17	13	57
0·31–0·45	13	3	81	1.80– 2.20	9	6	60
0·46 and above	14	1	93	2.50 and above	10	5	67

* A 'case' represents the preference displayed by one subject for one pair of offers.

prize with a certain probability of winning attached. Example: prize of $500 play money with probability of winning 0·75. The mathematical expected value is $375, and the average successful bid was $305. From such information Preston and Baratta estimated what psychological probability was needed to correspond to the mathematical probability of 0·75. In the example given, it would be about 305/500 = 0·61. On the basis of such data, the authors graph an average relation between mathematical and psychological probability. Using the data of the present article, similar psychological probabilities can be derived for comparison with Preston and Baratta's results. This is done in Table 15,

Table 15

Comparison of True and Psychological Probabilities from Preston and Baratta and for the Student and Guardsmen Groups of the Present Experiment

Approximate True Probability	P and B*	Students N = 10	Guardsmen N = 5
0·667	0·55	0·54	0·56
0·498	0·42	0·47	0·50
0·332	0·26	0·30	0·36
0·167	0·15	0·16	0·28
0·090	0·14	0·081	0·18
0·047	0·12	0·038	0·083
0·010	0·07	0·0085	0·052

* Preston and Baratta.

where the Preston and Baratta numbers are read from their Figure 1, and student and Guardsmen results are medians from the present study.

There certainly is general agreement between the Preston and Baratta data and the numbers of the present study. On the other hand, one of their findings is that the 'indifference point on the scale of probabilities' (psychological probability *equals* mathematical probability) is in the neighborhood of 0·20. For students, no such point was discovered, but for Guardsmen there is such a point in the neighborhood of $p = 0·5$. An explanation that immediately leaps to mind is that Preston and Baratta have mixed subjects, naïve and sophisticated in knowledge of probability. This happy explanation falls to the ground when it is discovered that knowledge of probability is one of the variables which those authors controlled in their experiment. Thus no ready explanation of the discrepancy between the results is available. It is also interesting to note that Griffith (1949), through a study of horse-racing odds (after correction for track take), found a corresponding indifference point at about $p = 0.16$ (although he is unwilling to go along with Preston and Baratta's complete interpretation). The results of the present study seem not to agree too well with either Preston and Baratta or Griffith in this respect.

In the actual play of the game, participants bid many times, and the winning bidder drew essentially from a table of random numbers to decide whether he won the particular gamble or not. The funds of subjects depleted or piled up as the game progressed. At the end the participant with the most play money received a prize. This would suggest that the auctioning system might not be independent from hand to hand but that bidding behavior should depend drastically on an over-all strategy designed to get the single prize, since it does not matter by how much one loses if he loses. Such a strategy might be much in evidence toward the end of the game, when it became clear that the losing members must gamble or lose the prize. Preston and Baratta kindly made available to us information about the sequences in which their gambles were presented. Our analysis of their results by sequences did *not* reveal to us any evidence of differential bidding for gambles at the beginning and end of the game; therefore, the strategy explanation does not seem adequate. There are further conjectures available as to why such an effect would *not* be found, but it seems best to get off the conjecture train here.

The present authors find some difficulties in the notion of psychological probabilities that need to be cleared up. First, is the total psychological probability in a situation to be fixed at unity, and does additivity hold? If so, just how is this done? To give an illustration, suppose the mathematical probability of A happening is 0.5, and that of not-A happening is also 0.5; then, using Preston and Baratta's curves, the psychological probability of A is 0.42. The same psychological probability value would hold for not-A, and, assuming additivity, the total probability would be 0.84, which is less than unity. The failure of the total probability to be unity seems unsatisfactory.

By using a many-choice situation and small mathematical probabilities, a situation could be constructed in which the total psychological probability would be greater than unity on the basis of Table 15, because for small mathematical probabilities Preston and Baratta find that the psychological probabilities exceed the mathematical, as we do for the Guardsmen. In a two-choice (A, not-A) situation, these troubles could be partly avoided. It could be argued that an individual orients himself psychologically to a particular outcome – say, A – and splits the total probability into $P_s(A)$ and $1 - P_s(A)$, where $P_s(A)$ means psychological probability of A. Such an approach might handle two-choice situations, but it is difficult to see how probabilities derived from two-choice situations could be used to predict in the Doublet situations (where three probabilities must be known).[7] This kind of difficulty makes it impossible to compare some results of the present study with theirs.

Such criticisms do not affect the importance of Preston and Baratta's experiment, but they do call for some further discussion of one of their interpretations.

VI. Discussion

A. General results

From the material of Section IV, we conclude that for simple wagers it is possible to construct utility curves experimentally. There are considerable individual differences in the utility curves, as indicated by the results of Table 9, but the great difference is between the student groups and the Guardsmen group. The former, by and large, behave in accordance with classical diminishing-returns notions, while the latter do not, at least over the range of values measured. In so far as both increasing and diminishing returns have been observed, there is some experimental support for Friedman and Savage's arguments about inflection points in the utility curve, although it is true that such inflection points have not been very reliably observed within single subjects.

The utility curves were used to predict future behavior on more complicated wagers. These predictions are not so good as might be hoped, but their general direction is correct.

The notion that subjects would consistently prefer A to B or consistently be indifferent to A or B was not supported.

7. Ramsey (1926) seems to be able to avoid the problem of setting up a correspondence between empirical (or mathematical) probabilities and psychological probabilities by introducing the concept of 'degree of belief' in a proposition p. If several propositions have equal empirical probabilities, their degrees of belief apparently need not be the same in Ramsey's system.

B. Some criticisms: experience

One of the uncontrolled factors in the experiment was the amount of experience a subject had in playing against each hand. This experience depended upon the number of times which a subject and the other members of the group with which he met had elected to play against each hand. The number of times a subject could see what happened when either he or other members of the group played against a particular hand could vary widely from group to group. The only hands on which very large differences did occur, however, were the two for which the probability of winning was least (44441 and 22255). For example, in all Known-risk sessions, Group B played against hand 22255 only 73 times, while Group A played against it 341 times, and Group C 520 times.

Professor John Tukey, of Princeton University, has suggested that this problem be handled by making every subject roll at every opportunity, whether or not he had elected to bet. The result, of course, would not count, either for or against him, if he had not elected to bet. The only disadvantage of this procedure is the amount of extra experimental time it would require. Both the greater amount of experience and the greater uniformity of experience which the subjects would get on each hand would be marked advantages. This suggested procedure might well be adopted in any further experimentation.

C. Effect of the amount of money in front of subject upon his decisions

In evaluating results, one difficulty stems from the fact that the subject had differing amounts of money in front of him when he made decisions. In both the pilot study and the experiment a subject 'rolled' immediately after making a decision to play. If he won, he was immediately given an amount of chips corresponding to the offer; and, if he lost, he had to give the experimenter a white chip worth 5 cents. Each time he played, then, the amount of money he had on hand changed before his next decision.

One possible criticism could be that the subject changes his utility curve with these changes in capital, so that each decision he makes depends upon the amount of money he has on hand at that particular moment. Such a criticism is not unreasonable – indeed, there are some data available from the pilot study to support this criticism. Furthermore, written instructions for the

Investment session (Table 10) are in some cases contingent on the total amount of money on hand. An analysis of frequency of play broken down by amount of money on hand and by monetary offer is quite expensive to make. This analysis was carried out for some subjects in the pilot study but not for subjects in the experiment. The pilot-study subjects had utility curves similar to those of the student subjects in the experiment.

Some of the results of this analysis are shown in Table 16. Rather than use space for all the data, a systematic sample will be given. Subjects were arbitrarily numbered from 1 to 8, and the first two subjects displayed for the lowest hand, the second two for the next lowest, etc. The best information on this is obtained from an examination of the middle offers. Subjects P–I, P–VI, and P–VIII seem to show a clear trend of being more likely to accept an offer as their money on hand increases, as examination of Table 16 reveals. In this table notice that subject P–I, in playing against the even-money hand, played against offers from $5\frac{1}{2}$ to 6 cents, with frequencies depending on the amount before him. When he had 75 cents or less, he played 24 per cent of the 21 times he could have; with 76–175 cents he played 59 per cent of the 17 times he could have; and with more than 175 cents on hand he took all but one of the 14 offers.

One way to handle this problem would be to change the experimental procedure. Instead of having the subject roll immediately after each decision to determine the outcome, one could have him first make all decisions for the entire series of offers used in any session. After he had completed this part, he would then roll against those offers where he had decided to play. If he ran out of money at any point during this second part, he would, of course, be required to stop; but all his decisions could still be used for calculating his utility curve. This change in procedure would have at least two marked advantages. All decisions of the subject would be made while he had a constant amount of money in front of him – his original endowment for the session of $1.00. And his decisions would be uninfluenced by experience of success or failure during that session. On the other hand, by interposing a relatively long delay between the decision and knowledge of the outcome of that decision, this procedure might make the events seem more mechanical and less 'realistic' to the subject, and so affect the results detrimentally. As a matter of fact, there is some evidence that the Guardsmen would be affected by such a procedure. In the Investment session their written decisions did not correspond to their behavior in the actual play of the game. This may be a much more serious factor than the influence of the amount of money on hand.

In the pilot study, offers involving half- and even quarter-cents were tried, as Table 16 suggests. It was thought that finer measurements could be obtained by using a finer scale. Such wagers turned out miserably. For example, a subject in possession of a chip worth half a cent would take another offer involving half a cent at odds much worse than those he had consistently refused. He was merely trying to get an integral number of cents. Thus the half-cent chip in front of the subject influenced his behavior unduly, from the point of view of the experimenters. In the experiment proper, fractions of cents were not used in any offers.

D. Effect of group participation

Ideally, each subject should have been put through the procedure individually, but this would have required an excessive amount of experimental time. Therefore, the compromise procedure of using small groups of five subjects was adopted (see last paragraph of Sec. IV*A*).

At the first session of each group, the subjects were strongly warned not to make any comments about any other person's decisions. Throughout all the sessions this rule was rarely – in fact, almost never – violated. The strongest desires to violate this rule developed in the pilot-study group, which contained the one subject for whom no utility curve could be calculated. His unusual behavior apparently deeply offended the sensibilities of the other subjects, particularly since he did not always lose his money as a result of such behavior. In private interviews after the study was completed, the other subjects were sarcastic and contemptuous of his style of play. Yet they never commented upon his decisions during the actual sessions.

It might be thought that the subjects would form coalitions against the experimenters. If all subjects had consistently refused to accept a series of offers, the experimenters would have been forced to raise the offers in order to get information. A group coalition could have determined the limits of the offers made on any hand. That such coalitions did not occur was probably due to at least two reasons: first, the rule that the subjects were not to discuss the experiment either among themselves or with other persons and, second, the subjects seemingly never became aware of the reasons for changing offers to a hand. So far as they could see, this was independent of their own play. Within any one

Table 16

The Relation between Amount of Money on Hand and Frequency of Participation for Selected Hands and Subjects Stratified by Offer*

Amount on Hand (Cents)	Offer in Cents			Total Per Cent	Offer in Cents			Total Per Cent
	Subject P–I				Subject P–II			
	1–5·25	5·5–6	6·5–10		1–4	5–6·5	7–10	
Hand 66431								
5–75	3, 36	24, 21	92, 13	30	0, 2	39, 28	71, 7	43
76–175	0, 28	59, 17	97, 29	51	5, 22	25, 16	84, 25	41
Over 175	0, 7	93, 14	100, 12	76	0, 6	31,16	88, 8	40

Amount on Hand (Cents)	Subject P–III			Total Per Cent	Subject P–IV			Total Per Cent
	4–11	12	13–25		1–5·5	6–10		
Hand 55221								
5–75	0, 25	44, 9	100, 24	48	0, 16	80, 20	—	44
76–175	0, 12	25, 8	77, 22	45	0, 42	89, 46	—	47
Over 175	0, 7	—	100, 7	50	0, 2	100, 4	—	67

Amount on Hand (Cents)	Subject P–V			Total Per Cent	Subject P–VI			Total Per Cent
	5–50	60–100			5–51	52–55	48–100	
Hand 55526								
5–75	0, 11	80, 27	—	63	0, 21	14, 14	95, 22	40
76–175	4, 27	86, 42	—	54	0, 30	24, 29	100, 34	44
Over 175	0, 7	64, 11	—	39	0, 7	58, 12	100, 28	75

Amount on Hand (Cents)	Subject P–VII			Total Per Cent	Subject P–VIII			Total Per Cent
	25–150	175–200			25–100	103–150	175–200	
Hand 22255								
5–75	0, 3	0, 2	—	0	0, 43	23, 86	75, 8	19
76–175	2, 89	20, 30	—	7	0, 11	63, 24	100, 3	47
Over 175	0, 3	33, 3	—	17	0, 10	92, 24	100, 4	68

* The second entry gives the *number* of times the offer was made, while the first entry gives the *percentage* of times that the offer was taken.

session no offers were changed at all by the experimenter, no matter what the subjects did. From session to session not all offers to a hand were ever changed, and often no changes were made.

E. The utility of gambling

The notion of utility of participation has already been discussed (see Tables 9 and 10), but there still is the criticism that gambling itself may have utility. The authors have no good experimental method of approaching this problem. Some attempts in the pilot study came to nothing. Nonetheless, this criticism has a tendency to be overworked – especially by people who have no notion how to measure such a utility. Mere exhilaration over winning is not enough to imply that gambling has utility; behavior must be changed before we shall be interested in this effect. Furthermore, there is no reason to assume that utility of gambling has a large effect, compared, say, to utility of participation, as discussed earlier. Indeed, the writers would prefer to defer discussion of this point until a way of testing arguments about it is provided.

F. Triviality of sums involved

Some persons with whom the pilot study was discussed commented that the results might not be meaningful because the amounts of money which the subjects could obtain were trivial.

To meet this criticism, emphasis was placed on selecting for the experimental study subjects who needed money. All student subjects were selected from rosters kept by the Student Employment Office. While participating in the experiment, these students had to give up other opportunities for part-time employment at which they could earn approximately a dollar for an hour's work. The National Guardsmen were selected as subjects to insure having a group with a less favored economic status than the student subjects.

In those Known-risk sessions from which the data for calculating the utility curves were obtained, the largest amount which a subject could win on a single round (i.e., the highest offer for beating hand 44441) represented a sizable fraction of his regular weekly income or expenditures. For the student subjects this offer amounted to approximately 30–50 per cent of their monthly room rentals and was generally either equal to, or more than, their average weekly earnings from other part-time work. For the National Guardsmen this offer amounted to 16–43 per cent of their monthly home rental and was equal to approximately 11–14 per cent of their weekly take-home pay from their regular jobs.

During the final interview all subjects were asked the uses they had made of their earnings from this study. Most students reported that they had used the earnings to pay for general living expenses, recreation, and books and other school supplies. One student, however, reported that he had used his earnings to repay some old debts incurred when he had owned a car. Most of the National Guardsmen also said that they had used their earnings for everyday living expenses. One, however, reported that he had saved his earnings to buy a layette for an expected baby. Another, who became unemployed during the course of the study remarked that his winning a sizable amount in one session was very opportune, since it gave him the means of paying some overdue insurance premiums.

Although the amounts of money involved were small in comparison to those involved in many situations considered by economists, it seems apparent that both the possible and the actual earnings were not entirely trivial from the point of view of the subjects. On the other hand, from any long-run point of view the amounts were indeed trivial. No windfall from this experiment would be enough to buy a house or a new car or enough 6 per cent bonds to defray regularly the cost of the daily newspaper. Perhaps one can never meet this point squarely. As Ramsey says, 'Since it is universally agreed that money has a diminishing marginal utility, if money bets are to be used, it is evident that they should be for as small stakes as possible. But then again the measurement is spoiled by introducing the new factor of reluctance to bother about trifles' (1926, p. 176).

VII. Conclusion

On the basis of the results of the experiment described in this paper, the authors conclude:

1. That it is feasible to measure utility experimentally.

2. That the notion that people behave in such a way as to maximize their expected utility is not unreasonable.

3. That on the basis of empirical curves it is possible to estimate future behavior in comparable but more complicated risk-taking situations.[8]

4. That there is some support for the inflection-point analysis offered by Friedman and Savage, although this support is not

8. Professor Armen Alchian, who discussed the present paper at the joint session of the American Statistical Association, the American Economic Association, the Econometric Society, and the Institute of Mathematical Statistics, suggested that conclusions 1 and 2, in so far as they mean anything, mean the same thing as conclusion 3.

wholly satisfactory – i.e., there is no contradiction, but the support is meager.

5. That subjects are not so consistent about preference and indifference as postulated by von Neumann and Morgenstern but have a graded response, gradually increasing the frequency of risks taken as the value of the risk increases.

6. That this effect may be negligible in the practical situations which economists wish to consider.

7. That, in spite of extensive instruction and experience, some individuals continue to take wagers which lead to monetary losses in the long run.

References

BUCK, P. H., 'Who comes to Harvard?' *Harvard Alumni Bulletin*, 10 January 1948.

FRIEDMAN, M., and SAVAGE, L. J., 'The utility analysis of choices involving risk', *J. polit. Econ.*, vol. 56 (1948), pp. 279–304.

GRIFFITH, R. M., 'Odds adjustments by American horse-race bettors', *Amer. J. Psychol.*, vol. 62 (1949), pp. 290–94.

PRESTON, M. G., and BARATTA, P., 'An experimental study of the auction-value of an uncertain outcome', *Amer. J. Psychol.*, vol. 61 (1948), pp. 183–93.

RAMSEY, F. P., 'Truth and probability' (1926), *Foundations of mathematics and other logical essays*, Humanities Press, 1950.

VICKREY, W., 'Measuring marginal utility of reactions to risk', *Econometrica*, vol. 13 (1945), pp. 319–33.

VON NEUMANN, J., and MORGENSTERN, O., 'Theory of games and economic behavior', Princeton University Press, 1944.

6 D. Davidson, P. Suppes and S. Siegel

Decision-Making: An Experimental Approach

Excerpts from D. Davidson, P. Suppes and S. Siegel, *Decision-making: an experimental approach*, Stanford University Press, 1957, chapter 2, pp. 19–30, 49–81.

Experimental Test of the Basic Model

1. Introduction

This chapter offers an explicit theory for the explanation and prediction of individual decision making under conditions of risk, and reports in some detail an experiment designed to test the adequacy of that theory in certain limited situations. The theory represents one possible implementation of the general strategy for the simultaneous measurement of utility and subjective probability. The chief experimental result may be interpreted as showing that for some individuals and under appropriate circumstances it is possible to measure utility on an interval scale. The experiment is concerned with decisions made in situations involving the loss and gain of small amounts of real money.

The following section of the present chapter (Section 2) contains a summary and critical analysis of earlier experimental work on the measurement of utility and subjective probability. Section 3 gives a precise statement of the hypotheses to be tested. An axiomatic formulation of the theory is given in Section 4[1]; it is shown that if the hypotheses of Section 3 are verified, the axioms hold (for the appropriate set of alternatives), and it is pointed out (but not proven) that the axioms are adequate to insure the existence of a utility function unique up to a linear transformation and an absolutely unique, nonadditive subjective probability function. Section 5[1] explains and justifies the method of approximation which creates the necessary bridge between formal theory and experimental technique. In Section 6 the details of the experimental procedure are given. Section 7 summarizes the experimental results, while Section 8 discusses these results in the light of various considerations.

1. [Sections 4 and 5 have been omitted in this edition.]

170

2. Previous work

Theoretical discussion of the interval measurement of utility based upon theories of decision making under conditions of risk has been voluminous and will not be reviewed here. Those interested will find extensive bibliographies in Edwards (4) and Savage (12). Much of this discussion bears on empirical matters in the sense that it contains armchair speculation concerning the behavior of individuals in decision-making situations.

To date, the only published report of an experiment directly designed to derive an interval measurement of utility from actual decisions is contained in an article by Mosteller and Nogee (9). Since the theory and experiment reported in this chapter were originally inspired by the desire to see whether it was possible to improve on Mosteller and Nogee's results, frequent reference will be made to their experiment. Here we may summarize the essential design. Following a suggestion made previously by Friedman and Savage (7), Mosteller and Nogee decided to test the empirical validity of the von Neumann and Morgenstern axiomatization of utility as applied to alternatives consisting of winning and losing small amounts of money, and probability combinations of such alternatives. A total of fourteen subjects completed the experiment, of whom nine were Harvard undergraduates and five were from the Massachusetts National Guard. The testing took place over a period of about four months. Subjects were given one dollar at the beginning of each hour of play and used the dollar to gamble. The subjects were presented with bets which they could accept or refuse; the bets were presented to four or five subjects at a time, but each subject made his own decisions. When an offer was made him, a subject had two options: Option 1 was to refuse the bet, in which case no money changed hands; Option 2 was to accept the bet, in which case the subject either lost 5 ¢ or won some stipulated amount of money (x) depending upon whether or not a specified chance event (E) occurred. When the subject was indifferent between Option 1 and Option 2 (i.e., when he accepted the bet half the time), then the following equation could be used to calculate the relative utilities of the outcomes:

$$(2.1) \qquad \phi(0 \; ¢) = s(E) \, \phi(-5 \; ¢) + [1 - s(E)] \, \phi(x).$$

Here ϕ is the utility function, e.g., $\phi(x)$ is the utility of x; $s(E)$, the probability of E, i.e., a real number between 0 and 1; $0 \; ¢$, the outcome if Option 1 is taken; $-5 \; ¢$, the outcome if E occurs;

and x, the outcome if E does not occur.[2] Since Option 1 and the losing amount (5 ¢) were fixed throughout the experiment, the utilities $\phi(0 ¢) = 0$ and $\phi(-5 ¢) = -1$ were arbitrarily assigned. By selecting events with appropriate probabilities, and varying x until the subject was indifferent between the options, it was possible to find the amounts of money corresponding to various points on the utility scale. In all, nine points in the utility curve of each subject were determined, running from the arbitrary points $\phi(-5 ¢) = -1$ and $\phi(0 ¢) = 0$ to the experimentally found x such that $\phi(x) = 101$. Using information derived from the utility curves, predictions were then made concerning the choices of each subject among somewhat more complex options, and the predictions were tried against the facts.

There seem to us to be three important respects in which the formal side of Mosteller and Nogee's experimental design may be criticized.

1. Their procedure did not provide a systematic check on whether or not the numbers assigned as utility measures were unique up to a linear transformation; it is therefore uncertain to what extent the claim is justified that they 'measured' utility in the sense of an interval scale.[3] The point under discussion is frequently treated in a confused manner in both theoretical and experimental work in fundamental measurement. Since it is essential to be clear about it in order to grasp the rationale of the experiments described here, it seems worth some preliminary clarification.

Mosteller and Nogee write: 'First, there is the question of whether utility can be measured under any circumstances, even in a laboratory situation, and second, if utility can be measured, can it be used to predict behavior in slightly different situations from those in which it was derived' (9, p. 371; cf. p. 403). In this passage and elsewhere in their article Mosteller and Nogee speak of 'measuring utility' in a sense which must be distinguished from the sense in which we use this phrase in the present monograph. Mosteller and Nogee considered that they had measured the utility of a given alternative to a subject when (a) they had empirically found a pattern of responses which could be interpreted as

2. It should be emphasized that '0 ¢' and ' −5 ¢' are in this context used as names, not of amounts of money, but of specific outcomes of the play (neither winning nor losing money; losing 5 ¢).

3. In formulating the present paragraph, we have benefited by some comments on an earlier draft which Professor Mosteller was kind enough to make in a private communication. This does not imply, of course, that he would agree with our analysis.

showing that the subject was indifferent between two options of the kind mentioned above, and (b), using Equation (2.1), they had assigned a number to the alternative. Since there was no guarantee in advance that pattern of responses of the sort demanded in (a) would be found, it must be agreed that 'measurement' in the sense under discussion is not trivial.

On the other hand it must be emphasized that the meaningful use of Equation (2.1) to assign numbers (rather than some other way of assigning numbers), and consequently drawing a graph on which slopes may be meaningfully compared, is justified only if it is experimentally determined for the situation covered by the theory that the numbers assigned are unique up to a linear transformation. The procedure outlined in (a) and (b) gives no evidence one way or the other that this is the case.

An example will illustrate the point. Suppose, on the basis of the choices of an individual, the alternatives a, b, c, and d are assigned the utilities 0, 1, 2, 3, using Equation (2.1). That the ratios of the differences in utility between a, b, c, and d are reflected by the assignment of numbers is, so far, an assumption. If the assignment is unique up to a linear transformation, however, then it follows that the interval between a and b is the same as the interval between c and d; that the intervals between b and c, and c and d are the same; that the interval between a and c is twice the interval between c and d; and so on. Each of these consequences can be translated into a statement about the preferences the individual will reveal through his choices, and can therefore be tested. If these predictions are not verified, then it is hard to say what significance to attach to the numbers originally assigned the alternatives; at any rate they do not measure utilities in an interval scale in the sense demanded by von Neumann and Morgenstern. And until a representative sample of such predictions is verified, there is no reason to say that it is possible to achieve *interval* measurement of utility by Mosteller and Nogee's method.[4]

Mosteller and Nogee did test some predictions based on their original utility assignments. Unfortunately, however, they did not specify precisely what these predictions were, so that it is impossible to tell to what extent a claim of interval measurement would have been supported if the predictions had been verified. It is also very difficult to assess how well the facts bore out their

4. This discussion oversimplifies a very complicated matter. Exactly what predictions must be checked will vary with the particular axiomatic analysis of utility adopted.

predictions; as they point out, the results seem somewhat inconclusive (9, p. 395). The major criticism, however, is not that the results are inconclusive, but that the experiment was not designed to yield a clear test of whether interval measurement of utility is possible.

2. A second criticism of Mosteller and Nogee's experimental design is that almost every choice offered the subjects (including most of the situations for which predictions were made[5]) was a choice between accepting or rejecting a gamble. Thus one option always involved playing and taking a risk, while the other resulted in not playing and in neither gaining nor losing money. If there is a (negative or positive) utility of participation in the play, as seems likely *a priori*, the experiment was designed in such a way that this factor would produce the maximum distortion. In the experiments reported in the present book, the utility measure was largely derived from choices between two gambles, thus for the most part canceling out distortion due to the utility of participation. This approach also allows for the possibility of separately measuring a specific utility of gambling if this concept is analyzed in a certain way.

3. The third criticism of Mosteller and Nogee's experimental design is that they had to assume that the degree of expectation or subjective probability of an event is equal to its objective probability. This criticism may be understood in the following way. At the time he made each decision, a subject could, if he had wished, have chosen the option with the higher actuarial value, for he was informed of the money values of the alternatives and the objective probabilities of the events involved; in fact he also had in front of him at all times a card which told him, in effect, whether any given offer had an actuarial value above, below, or equal to the actuarial value of the fixed option of not playing, namely, 0 ¢. If two assumptions could be made, then the theory of decision concerning money gambles would be very simple. The assumptions are (*a*) psychological probability (degree of expectation) is equal to objective probability and (*b*) utility is linear in money, i.e., if ϕ is a utility function, then there are numbers α and β with $\alpha > 0$ such that for any amount of money x in the range being considered,

$$\phi(x) = \alpha x + \beta.$$

5. Some predictions were made for 'paired comparisons' in which each option involved uncertainty. These predictions were slightly better than predictions based on expected money-value. See Mosteller and Nogee (9, p. 395).

The theory would in this case plausibly predict that a person will always choose the option with the higher actuarial value. None of Mosteller and Nogee's subjects did this. The von Neumann and Morgenstern approach to decision theory drops assumption (b) and derives a subjective utility scale from decisions on the basis of assumption (a). But as Mosteller and Nogee point out (9, Section V), it is perhaps as plausible to drop assumption (a) and on the basis of assumption (b) to use the same data to compute subjective probabilities.

Failing reliable empirical evidence, there seems no more reason to accept one assumption than the other. What enters an actual decision is the believed or felt likelihood of an outcome rather than the (perhaps unknown or imponderable) actual probability; and it is the relative attractiveness of the alternatives to the subject rather than their worth on some arbitrary, conventional scale which weighs with the decision maker. The theory of decision must begin, at least, without unwarranted presumptions concerning either subjective probabilities or utilities.

The little experimental work done to date on the measurement of psychological probability is uniformly based on the untested and unlikely assumption that utility is linear in money. Ward Edwards (4, 5) did not make this assumption, but he attempted no numerical measurement of probabilities (cf. 6, p. 396). Edwards does claim, however, to have shown that, independent of utility considerations, people 'prefer' some probabilities to others. It is not clear whether this merely means that subjective probabilities are not equal to objective probabilities, or something more; nor is it obvious that the conclusion really can be drawn at all independent of utility considerations. Coombs and Milholland (1) have reported an experiment which tests both utilities and subjective probability, but the methods were not behavioristic in the sense of dealing exclusively with actual decisions involving risk. The same remark applies to the earlier work of Preston and Baratta (10) who, like Mosteller and Nogee, depended in any case on the usual assumption concerning utility. Thus the experiment reported in this chapter, while extremely tentative in character, actually represents the first attempt to measure subjective probability behavioristically on the basis of empirically determined utilities.

It was remarked by von Neumann and Morgenstern (13, p. 19), that probability could be axiomatized along with utility; this would yield a theoretical model in which probability could be interpreted as a subjective magnitude. Such a model has in fact been developed by Savage (12). The theory developed here, which also leads to the measurement of both utility and subjective probability on behavioristic grounds, was suggested informally and in outline by F. P. Ramsey (11). A proposal for using this method as the basis for an experiment was first made in Davidson, McKinsey, and Suppes (2). A discussion of the theory (in a form somewhat different from that presented here) and a formal proof of its adequacy for interval measurement of utility is given in Davidson and Suppes (3).

3. Formal statement of the hypotheses tested

In this section we state formally the hypotheses tested. Since the aim of these experiments was primarily to develop a psycho-metric technique for measuring utility, no attempt was made to sample any population systematically: the hypotheses apply to any arbitrary individual, but there is no implication that they apply to most, or many, individuals. It may be considered that the hypotheses are restated for each subject and therefore that the results obtained for each subject constitute, in effect, the outcome of a separate experiment.

The underlying thesis is that an individual makes choices among alternatives involving risk as if he were trying to maximize expected utility. In practice we test whether an individual's decisions over a brief period of time, with respect to an extremely limited and special set of alternatives, and under carefully con-trolled conditions, are consistent with the thesis. Obviously, un-less we can find an empirical interpretation for the theory under such circumstances, there is little point in making, or testing, broader claims.

The basic set of alternatives among which subjects were asked to choose consisted of the loss or gain of small amounts of money. Two alternatives were arbitrarily determined, namely, losing 4 ¢ (alternative a) and winning 6 ¢ (alternative b). To alternatives a and b the utilities -1 and $+1$ respectively were assigned. Four more amounts of money were then determined experimentally such that $\phi(f) = -5$, $\phi(c) = -3$, $\phi(d) = 3$, and $\phi(g) = 5$. In other words, six amounts of money were found which could be considered as equally spaced on the utility scale, provided interval measurement was obtained.

We may now state the hypotheses. The first is empirically trivial and is included only for formal completeness.

Hypothesis H0. $x P y$ if and only if $x > y$.

The interpretation of this hypothesis is that the subject prefers more money to less, i.e., if x is a greater amount of money than y, he prefers x to y. A first condition for the measurement of utility is that the basic alternatives should be ordered under the relation of preference. In the case where the alternatives are winning and losing amounts of money, it is natural to assume that any gain will be preferred to any loss and that the larger gain, or the smaller loss, will be preferred to the smaller gain or larger loss. The transitivity of preference with respect to the basic alternatives is thus assured. It also follows from H0 that if x and y are different amounts of money, one will be preferred to the other. It was not considered necessary to test H0 in a systematic way; it may be remarked, however, that if this hypothesis had not been true for some subject, it is extremely unlikely that the remaining hypotheses would have been verified.

In order to explain the second hypothesis it is necessary to refer to the device of a one-person game, the general format of which may, for experimental purposes, be represented as follows:

	Option 1	Option 2
If event E happens, you get	outcome x	outcome u
If event E does not happen, you get	outcome y	outcome v

Figure 1

The subject chooses the column; whether event E happens or not determines the row, and thus the outcome. Suppose, for example, that event E is a coin coming up heads on a given toss; then not-E ($\bar{E}$) is the coin coming up tails. We take outcomes x, y, u, and v as winning 5 ¢, losing 10 ¢, winning 16 ¢, and losing 22 ¢. Then we have:

	Option 1	Option 2
E (heads)	5 ¢	16 ¢
$\bar{E}$ (tails)	−10 ¢	−22 ¢

Figure 2

This means: if the subject chooses Option 1, then he will win 5 ¢ or lose 10 ¢ depending upon whether the coin comes up heads or tails; if the subject chooses Option 2, he wins 16 ¢ or loses 22 ¢ depending upon whether the coin comes up heads or tails.

In the subsequent hypotheses it is necessary to deal with the situation in which the subject is indifferent between two options such as Option 1 and Option 2 in Figure 1. In order to have a compact notation, we introduce the five-place relation $\approx$ to represent this situation:

$x, y \approx (E) u, v$ *if and only if the subject is indifferent between* (a) *the option of receiving amount x if E happens and y if E does not happen, and* (b) *the option of receiving u if E happens and v if E does not happen.*

If, as before, we suppose that ϕ is a utility function unique up to a linear transformation, and s is a subjective probability function which assigns to an event a unique real number between 0 and 1, then we may consider that the following equation represents the situation where $x, y \approx (E) u, v$:

$$(3.1) \qquad s(E) \phi(x) + s(\tilde{E}) \phi(y) = s(E) \phi(u) + s(\tilde{E}) \phi(v).$$

In particular, if the subject is indifferent between the options shown in Figure 2, we would have:

$$s(\text{heads}) \phi(5 \ \cent) + s(\text{tails}) \phi(-10 \ \cent) =$$
$$s(\text{heads}) \phi(16 \ \cent) + s(\text{tails}) \phi(-22 \ \cent).$$

Obviously we may use (3.1) to calculate utilities only if we know the probabilities involved, or the probabilities only if we know the utilities; the problem is to find one without knowing the other. The next hypothesis accomplishes this for a special case.

Hypothesis H1. *There exists a chance event E^* such that for every two amounts of money x and y*

$$x, y \approx (E^*) y, x.$$

The interpretation of this hypothesis is that the subjective probability of E^* is equal to the subjective probability of $\tilde{E}^*$ – i.e., $s(E^*) = s(\tilde{E}^*)$ – and this subjective probability is independent of any particular outcomes (i.e., amounts of money). Mathematically the reasoning is simple: if the assumptions are valid which justified (3.1), we may represent the case where H1 holds as follows:

$$(3.2) \qquad s(E^*) \phi(x) + s(\tilde{E}^*) \phi(y) = s(E^*) \phi(y) + s(\tilde{E}^*) \phi(x).$$

But from (3.2), we see that if $\phi(x) \neq \phi(y)$, $s(E^*) = s(\tilde{E}^*)$. The intuitive interpretation of H1 may be made reasonable by an example. Suppose the subject is indifferent between the options shown in Figure 3:

	Option 1	Option 2
Heads	$-7 \ \cent$	$13 \ \cent$
Tails	$13 \ \cent$	$-7 \ \cent$

Figure 3

178

It is plausible to infer that $s(\text{heads}) = s(\text{tails})$, since if the subject deemed heads more probable than tails, he would presumably prefer Option 2, which would give him a better chance (in his opinion) to obtain the preferred outcome (receiving 13 ¢). On the other hand, if he thought it more likely that tails would come up than heads, Option 1 would, by similar reasoning, be preferred.

When the game is played using the event E^*, for which it is known that $s(E^*) = s(\tilde{E}^*)$, equation (3.1) can, as we have seen, be simplified and transformed into:

$$(3.3) \qquad \phi(x) - \phi(u) = \phi(v) - \phi(y).$$

Thus (to recapitulate) when the subject is indifferent between the options:

	Option 1	Option 2
E^*	x	u
$\tilde{E}^*$	y	v

Figure 4

we may reasonably interpret this result as meaning that the difference in utility between x and u is equal to the difference in utility between v and y. The next hypothesis takes advantage of the special form of the game shown in Figure 4 to find six amounts of money equally spaced in utility; it also (as we shall later show) verifies that interval measurement has been obtained, thus justifying the use of (3.3) in calculating utilities. In the statement of H2 and henceforth we write simply ' $\approx$ ' for ' $\approx(E^*)$ '.

Hypothesis H2. *Let a and b be two amounts of money such that $a < b$. Then there are unique amounts of money c, d, f, and g such that*

  (i) $b, c \approx a, a$ (viii) $g, f \approx b, a$
 (ii) $b, a \approx d, c$ (ix) $g, f \approx d, c$
(iii) $d, f \approx b, c$ (x) $g, c \approx d, a$
 (iv) $b, f \approx a, c$ (xi) $g, a \approx d, b$
  (v) $d, f \approx a, a$ (xii) $g, c \approx b, b$
 (vi) $a, d \approx b, b$ (xiii) $g, b \approx d, d$
(vii) $a, f \approx c, c$

The interpretation of this hypothesis is that the outcomes a, b, c, d, f, and g are equally spaced (in utility) in the following order:

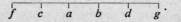

$$f \quad c \quad a \quad b \quad d \quad g.$$

179

The last two hypotheses deal with the measurement of subjective probability by using a utility function ϕ determined by H2 and with values interpolated for all outcomes between f and g for which the utility was not directly found. These hypotheses are stated for the set K of outcomes x such that $f \leqslant x \leqslant g$, and a set S of chance events, none of which are certain.

Hypothesis H3. *For all outcomes x, y, and z in K and every chance event E in S, if there is an outcome w in K such that*

$$x, y \approx (E) z, w,$$

then w is unique.

The significance of H3 is that when we have found the unique outcome w we may then use (3.1) to compute the subjective probability of E. It is necessary, in addition, to assume that for every event E in S, $s(E) + s(\tilde{E}) = 1$.

Hypothesis H4. *Let ϕ be a utility function determined by* H2. *For all outcomes x, y, z, w, x', y', z', and w' in K and every chance event E in S, if $x, y \approx (E) z, w$, $\phi(y) \neq \phi(w)$, and*

$$\frac{\phi(x) - \phi(z)}{\phi(y) - \phi(w)} = \frac{\phi(x') - \phi(z')}{\phi(y') - \phi(w')}$$

then $x', y' \approx (E) z', w'$.

Hypothesis H4 asserts that the measurement of subjective probability is independent of the particular outcomes used. It is clear that for a given subject H3 may be true and H4 false, and that in such a situation we have not actually obtained a subjective probability function. Further hypotheses concerning subjective probability are easily generated, but these two are the ones explicitly tested in the experiment reported here.

[. . . .]

6. *Experimental Procedure*

The subjects were nineteen male students hired through the Stanford University Student Employment Service. Subjects were hired and tested individually, and none of them, so far as we know, was acquainted with any of the others. The subjects hired were drawn from those who answered an Employment Service request for people willing to work at comparatively unattractive labor (e.g., yard cleaning) or mundane office work (e.g., stapling or filing) for $1.00 an hour. Those hired were told they were to do stapling. There was no way in which a subject could volunteer or choose to be a subject for the experiment. The first session with each subject lasted about two hours; at the end of the first session, we took his address and telephone number and told the subject he might be recalled if he were willing. Most subjects were recalled for a second or third session, the sessions being spaced from a few days to a month apart for any one subject.

When a person hired through the Employment Service came to us for work, he was informed that a subject for an experiment had canceled his appointment, and that he could, if he wished, serve as the experimental subject instead of doing the work he was hired to do. But he was told that he would have to gamble with his wages, and might lose them all. He was told that if he did lose all of his wages before the time was up (the time being two hours, for which $2.00 was paid), he would then have to work at the labor for which he was originally hired (for no pay) for the duration of the unexpired time. However, he was told that, on the basis of past experience, his chances of coming out at least even were extremely good. If the person was interested, the game was explained to him and he became a subject. If the person refused, he was given stapling work at $1.00 per hour. Only one person declined to become a subject. Without the knowledge of the subjects, a promise was made to the Employment Service that no subject would average less than $2.00 for a two-hour session. This was easy to arrange because the basic game is such as to admit cases where all four outcomes are positive, and such offers could be inserted into the testing sequence at will.

When someone agreed to become a subject, he was told that the experiment has been designed to test human behavior in gambling situations, and that whatever he did would be equally valuable to the experimenters. He was assured that no particular behavior was demanded or expected of him, and that the experiment in no way tested intelligence. Few subjects asked for additional information. He was then told that the games he was to play would last about two hours, and the rate of pay would be $1.00 per hour; the payment of $2.00 would be given to him at the beginning of the session, and this money would be used to participate in the games. The subject was informed again that it would be possible to complete a session with considerably more money than $2.00, and that all of the winnings at the end of the session would be his to keep. He was also told that it would be possible to end up with less than $2.00 or even with no money at all. Subjects were permitted to gamble with only the $2.00 given them in payment for their participation.

The apparatus used consisted of red, white, and blue poker chips, a circular green gambling table, a leather dice shaker-cup, a timing clock, scratch paper (for the subject), scoring sheet, and dice. The dice will be described presently.

In general the game was played as follows: the subject was seated opposite the 'croupier' (the experimenter), who presented him verbally with the options between which he was to choose. The subject was always required to choose one of the two options. During some sessions a third person was present who recorded the time taken in making each decision. The subject was urged to ponder each choice as long as he pleased.

The first step in the experiment required that, for each subject, an event E^* be found such that

$$x, y \leqslant (E^*) y + 1 \not{c}, x \text{ and } x, y - 1 \not{c} \leqslant (E^*) y, x,$$

where x and y are taken as several different pairs of outcomes. Actually, a single chance event was found during pilot studies which proved to satisfy the conditions for every subject. This chance event was not easily found, however. A coin was tried and the subject given the opportunity to bet on heads (E) or tails ($\tilde{E}$); a die was used with odd numbers as E and even numbers as $\tilde{E}$; two coins were tried, with match (two heads or two tails) as E and non-match as $\tilde{E}$; and some other equally simple or more complex games were tried. In every case, most subjects showed a preference for either E or $\tilde{E}$. Finally an event was found which satisfied the conditions. This event was produced by means of a specially made die. On three faces of the die, the nonsense syllable 'ZOJ' was engraved, on the other three faces 'ZEJ'. Two more similar dice were made with 'WUH' and 'XEQ', 'QUG' and 'QUJ' on their faces. These syllables are ones which according to Glaze (8) and others have practically zero association value. The hope was that subjects would have no prejudice in favor of one such syllable over another. All three dice were tested with each subject and in every case Hypothesis H1 held (within the 1 $\not{c}$ limits set by the method of approximation), taking as the event E^* throwing the die so that a face showing 'ZOJ' (or 'WUH' or 'QUG') came up and $\tilde{E}^*$ throwing the die so that a face showing 'ZOJ' (or 'WUH' or 'QUG') did *not* come up. (In explaining the game to the subject, $\tilde{E}^*$ was indicated positively in terms of the syllable on the remaining faces of the die.)

Before the play began, the game was explained to the subject in these words:

Instructions to subject:

The game we will play will take the following form. You will shake this die in the shaker-box, and then toss it onto the table. As you may see, there are two different syllables on the die. Three sides of the die have ZOJ on them, and the other three sides have ZEJ. Sometimes we will play with this die, and sometimes with other dice just like this except that their syllables will be WUH and XEQ, or QUG and QUJ. These dice have been made especially for us, and they are as fair as dice can be. In fact, they have been ground to specifications accurate to 1/10,000th of an inch.

Before each shake, I'll present you with two alternatives; you must choose one of them. Here is a pencil and paper which you may wish to use. Take whatever time you wish in order to make your choice.

Here, for example, is the die with ZOJ and ZEJ on it. If you want to bet on ZOJ, you will win five cents if you are right (i.e., if ZOJ comes up when you toss the die) and you will lose five cents if you are wrong (if ZEJ comes up). If you want to bet on ZEJ, you will win six cents if you are right, and lose five cents if you are wrong. Which is your choice? [*The subject chooses*.] O.K.

Before starting, I want to suggest that you write down each offer in this form:[6]

ZOJ	ZEJ
+5	+6
−5	−5

This means: if you bet on ZOJ, you'll win five cents if it comes up and lose five cents if it doesn't. If you bet on ZEJ, you'll win six cents if it comes up and lose five cents if it doesn't. Are you ready to proceed?

The pilot study had revealed a number of difficulties, the solutions to which were incorporated into the final experimental design.

First, it was necessary to control the effects of cumulative and immediate reinforcement. Winning or losing several times in a row made subjects sanguine or pessimistic and tended to produce altered responses to the same offers. Increases and decreases in the size of stake also had distorting effects. To control the effects of reinforcement, the following procedure was used: In testing Hypothesis H1 the house gambler offered about fifteen bets to the subject. When the first set of alternatives was offered to the subject, he chose one alternative, shook the die in the shaker-box, tossed the die, and either collected or paid out. The same sequence occurred for the next two or three sets of alternatives.

6. It was found experimentally simpler to present the options in this form. The situation represented here corresponds to the matrix:

	Option 1	Option 2
ZOJ	+5	−5
ZEJ	−5	+6

Then the subject was asked whether he minded, in the interest of saving time, being given two or three sets of alternatives in succession, making choices for each set as it was given, then rolling the die and paying or collecting for each. That is, a pair of alternatives was presented to him and he made his choice, which was noted, then immediately another pair of alternatives was offered him. The subject was told that the choices he made at this time were binding and that when he had made his choices on the two or three pairs of alternatives successively, he would roll for them each, one at a time, at which time he could not change his mind. In other words, the subject was committed to the choice he made when the alternatives were offered, even though he did not roll the die to see whether a particular choice paid off until after all of his choices were made. The experimenter gave the subject the pairs of alternatives in groups of three and four until all of the trials for testing H1 had been exhausted. The experimenter was then ready to measure the subject's utility (H2).

At this point, the experimenter told the subject that there were only about twenty-five or thirty more choices he would have to make, and asked him whether he would be willing to make all of his choices before rolling the die to see what the pay-offs would be. (In fact, there were usually more than twice that many bets remaining, but no subject seemed to notice this.) All of our subjects agreed to this plan readily. There was no indication that interest lagged under these conditions of postponed pay-off; subjects apparently continued to feel that they were in fact gambling, inasmuch as each choice they made was binding and would eventually reward or cost them.

A second problem concerned the recency effect of seeing a particular syllable on a die turn up, or fail to turn up, through a number of throws. If the same syllable came up three times in succession, for example, the subjective probability would temporarily decrease for most subjects. This effect was partly eliminated by postponing the pay-off. This procedure could not help in the testing of H1, however, for at the start the subject had to roll after each choice to acquaint him with the game; nor could it help with the fact that merely having the same nonsense syllable coupled in the offers with attractive outcomes several times in succession was enough to influence the response of some subjects. The problem was effectively solved by using three dice instead of one. The die in use was changed after each toss, and the choice of winning nonsense syllable was randomized. In this way no particular syllable could win or lose, or even be chosen, twice in succession. By the time the same die was used again, the subject had forgotten, or was not influenced by, his previous experience. In practice, the problem tended to solve itself relatively early in the game since subjects quickly learned to attend only to the four outcomes and to ignore the matching events (since these all had the same subjective probability). The experimenter therefore did not announce the matching events until just before the dice were rolled.

The third problem was more complex and received only a partial solution. In the testing of H2, it will be remembered that two amounts of money, $a = -4\cent$ and $b = 6\cent$, are arbitrarily chosen; on the basis of these, an amount c is found such that b, $c \approx a$, a (or its approximation analogue); on the basis of a, b, and c, a further amount is found, and so forth. Thus the value of each point on the utility scale depends on those found before. A distortion in the value c is therefore crucial, since it will distort all the further values; such distortion will in the end result in a failure of the checks contained in H2 which justify interval measurement. But relation (i), which determines the value of c, is open to a distorting force which does not enter any of the other relations which are essential to determining further points, for one of the options (a, a) is not a gamble but a sure thing – whatever happens, the subject loses $4\cent$ if he chooses (a, a) – while the other option is a gamble. If a subject has a high (positive) utility of gambling, he will have to be offered a spuriously low c before he will switch his choice to the option (a, a); this will in turn make the value for d spuriously high, and so forth.

Aside from relation (i), the problem was not met, but neglected; we did not test the other consequences of the axioms which led to relations in which one option was a sure thing. In this we felt partly justified by the fact that an axiomatization can be produced leading to interval measurement which excludes *all* such offers. What was lacking for complete justification at the time these experiments were performed was a method of approximation based on such an axiomatization (one has since been devised).

The method employed in the present experiments to offset possible distortion in the determination of the money value of c will be given only in outline. For simplicity, we assume perfect measurement; the reader can easily construct the analogue for the method of approximation. Using the value of c found in relation (i), an amount d is found; using d, f is found. Now a c' is found such that b, $f \approx a$, c'. If $c' = c$, no distortion due to the utility of gambling has apparently entered the original determination of c (we assume throughout this discussion that no distortion due to the utility of gambling enters into choices between two options each of which is a gamble). If $c' < c$, an obvious line of reasoning leads to the conclusion that the original c was set too low. The experimenter therefore arbitrarily raises the original c by 1 ¢, determines a new d and a new f (call them $c + 1$ ¢, d', and f') and checks whether b, $f' \approx a$, $c + 1$ ¢; if so, $c + 1$ ¢ is the correct value. If not, a further adjustment is indicated. A similar procedure is followed if $c < c'$.

For only one-third of our subjects did we have to make compensations. For all but one subject of those who required compensations for their utility of gambling, only one compensation was necessary. For the one subject, two compensations sufficed. We believe it is possible to interpret these results as showing that distortion due to the utility of gambling is not as strong or as prevalent as has often been surmised, at least for small amounts of money. These results are, however, very tentative.

The final problem we wish to mention is that it was felt to be expedient to obtain all the data relevant to the measurement of utility in a single session, since no evidence prior to this experiment ensured the stability of an individual's utility function over extended periods of time. With this in mind, we judged that speed and simplicity were worth some sacrifice of completeness in certain aspects of the experiment, at least until there was good evidence that the utility function was relatively stable over time. In the final design, we were able to gather the necessary information for H2 in a little less than one hour (on the average).

A. Final experimental procedure. – We may now describe the experimental procedure followed. Subjects were brought into the experimental situation and instructed as described above. The first sequence of offers had a double purpose: to test H1 and to familiarize the subject with the game. Table 1 shows a typical opening sequence of offers. In this sequence, all offers except numbers 3, 12, and 14 test H1; these are inserted entirely for the purpose of exposing the subject to offers of the kind he will find in the subsequent part of the experiment. The responses to these offers were not directly relevant to testing H1 or H2. To verify H1, the subject had to make the choices marked in the last column. Occasionally a subject was confused in the first few plays; in these cases a few offers were added to see whether H1

Table 1
Typical Sequence of Offers Testing H1

Offer number	Events	Option 1	Option 2	Correct choice to confirm H1
1	ZOJ	5 ¢	−5 ¢	Option 2
	ZEJ	−5	6	
2	QUG	17	−11	Option 1
	QUJ	−10	17	
3	ZOJ	24	13	
	ZEJ	−3	5	
4	WUH	10	3	Option 1
	XEQ	4	10	
5	ZEJ	4	5	Option 2
	ZOJ	−5	−5	
6	QUG	−4	−2	Option 2
	QUJ	−3	−4	
7	ZOJ	13	−3	Option 1
	ZEJ	−2	13	
8	XEQ	7	−6	Option 2
	WUH	−6	8	
9	QUJ	−2	−4	Option 2
	QUG	−4	−1	
10	WUH	5	10	Option 1
	XEQ	10	4	
11	ZOJ	−4	13	Option 2
	ZEJ	13	−3	
12	XEQ	−3	8	
	WUH	−5	−19	
13	QUJ	−9	17	Option 1
	QUG	17	−10	
14	ZOJ	15	22	
	ZEJ	−10	−19	
15	WUH	−6	8	Option 1
	XEG	9	−6	

would then be verified, and the first responses were considered as training.

The subject was given $2.00 worth of chips at the beginning of the play, and all the choices made in testing H1, including the training offers, were resolved before going further by having the subject cast the appropriate die and paying him or collecting from him the amount of money he lost or won (in chips). He understood, of course, that at the end of the session the chips in his possession would be redeemed in cash.

When H1 had been adequately tested the experimenter made the offers necessary to test H2 and determine (in case H2 was verified) the utility curve of the subject for the amounts of money involved. [. . . .] The following comments and details suffice to give a clear idea of the experimental procedure.

The base points $a = -4 ¢$ and $b = 6 ¢$ were chosen so that the totality of offers (with two amounts above and two below the base points) would tend to have an expected (actuarial) value near $0 ¢$. Thus the subject was inclined to sense (even when the pay-off was postponed) that his losses and winnings would probably be nearly equal. The amounts a and b were skewed slightly in the favorable direction partly in order to make the expected value of the totality of offers slightly positive (at least for most subjects) and partly to avoid possible distorting effects which might result from an obvious symmetry about $0 ¢$.

To illustrate the method with an example, let us suppose an upper and a lower bound for c and for d have been found for a given subject, such that $c_l = -11 ¢$, $c_h = -10 ¢$, $d_l = 11 ¢$, and $d_h = 12 ¢$. The next step is to find bounds for f on the basis of these values. The basic relation is $d, f \approx b, c$. The lower bound of f will be the *highest* amount f such that $d_h, f_l \leqslant b, c_l$. [. . . .] This amount was found by making a series of offers of the following sort:

Option 1	Option 2
$(d_h =) 12 ¢$	$(b =) 6 ¢$
x	$(c_l =) -11 ¢$

In a table, we show the amounts tried for x and the subject's responses:

Offer number	x	Responses
1	$-16 ¢$	Option 1
2	$-20 ¢$	Option 2
3	$-18 ¢$	Option 2
4	$-17 ¢$	Option 1

Since the subject shifted from Option 2 to Option 1 when $x >$ -18 ¢, we conclude that $f_i = -18$ ¢. A similar series of offers, actually interlarded with those shown, finds f_h on the basis of d_l, b, and c_h. Upper and lower bounds for the other points on the utility scale were found in an analogous fashion. Obviously the actual number of offers necessary to find a given bound might vary depending on how soon the exact point was found at which the subject changed his choice from one option to the other. The experimenter decided what offers were appropriate in each phase of the experiment only when he knew the values found in the preceding steps. In consequence, different offers, and different numbers of offers, were made to different subjects. Although in the pilot experiments various means were tried to mask from the subject the fact that we were attempting to locate the point at which the shift took place, these were rejected in the final design as too time-consuming. What masking took place was accomplished in general by presenting the series of offers which determined the high and low values of a given point simultaneously and by interjecting an occasional dummy offer when a series became too long. The best practical protection against distortion due to the subject noticing the pattern of offers was the shrewdness with which the experimenter could guess the approximate change-over point. Problems raised by the method we used are discussed in the final section of this chapter.

The final stage of the experiment concerned the measurement of subjective probability for a single chance event. If time was left, this phase of the experiment followed directly upon the verification of H2. If not, the subject was hired for a second session. When this was done, a large sample of the offers previously made in testing H2 was made again to determine whether the utility curve had remained constant. If it had not, a new utility curve was determined experimentally as before. Only subjects for whom H2 had been successfully tested could be used in this phase of the experiment.

For this part of the study, another special die was made. The die had two opposite ends rounded so that when it was tossed it could land on one of only four sides. (Thus, for a fair die, the objective probability of any particular face coming up was $\frac{1}{4}$.) Each side of the die had a different nonsense syllable engraved on it: ZEJ, WUH, XEQ, VAF.

Instructions were given to the subject informally, in words like these:

Now we will play a game which is slightly different from the one which we have been playing up until now, although the general form is the same: I will still present you the opportunity of choosing between two gambles. Here is a four-sided die. When you toss this die, only one of four sides can come up, instead of one out of six. That is because two of the sides of the die are rounded and therefore the die cannot rest on them. You will be given the opportunity of betting on the occurrence of one of these sides, say ZEJ, or of betting on the 'field'. Betting on the field means that you bet that ZEJ will *not* come up, but one of the other three will. Obviously, the 'field' will come up more often than ZEJ, inasmuch as this is a fair die. This die has been made especially for us, and it is as fair as a die can be; in fact, this die was ground to specifications accurate to 1/10,000th of an inch.

As in the first game we played, I'll present you with two alternatives. You are to choose one of them. For example, if you want to bet on ZEJ against the field, you will win 18 ¢ if ZEJ comes up when you toss the die, but you will lose 4 ¢ if the field comes up (that is, if any side but the ZEJ side comes up). On the other hand, if you want to bet on the field, you will win 6 ¢ if the field comes up, but you will lose 12 ¢ if ZEJ comes up.

For this game also, I suggest that you write down each offer in this form:

$$\begin{matrix} 18\,¢ & & 6\,¢ \\ -4\,¢ & & -12\,¢ \end{matrix}$$

I think it would be to your advantage if I first gave you a few sets of practice alternatives for you to make your choices on, without any money being involved. That is, I'll give you a set of alternatives, you pick the one that you prefer to gamble on, and then you roll the die to see what the pay-off is. But for these first few trials, no money will be involved. In other words, I want to give you a chance to get used to this new game before you begin gambling with money.

After the instructions were given, three or four sets of alternatives were offered to the subject as a learning period. When the subject seemed to understand that the game was no longer a fifty-fifty one, the experimenter proceeded to test the subject's subjective probability. [. . . .]

7. Summary of results

For all nineteen subjects tested, H1 was verified. For fifteen subjects, H2 was verified (in the approximate sense explained above), and for these fifteen it is therefore possible to conclude (*a*) their behavior is consistent with the claim that there exists a real-valued function ϕ unique up to a linear transformation defined over the basic alternatives involved and (*b*) if there is such a real-valued function, and we set $\phi(a) = -1$ and $\phi(b) = 1$, then the c, d, f, and g such that $\phi(c) = -3$, $\phi(d) = 3$, $\phi(f) = -5$, and $\phi(g) = 5$ lie within the intervals stated.

Table 2

Summary of Data Determining Bounds in Cents for Fixed Points on the Utility Scale

Subject	Bounds for f where $\phi(f) = -5$	Bounds for c where $\phi(c) = -3$	$\phi(a) = -1$ (arbitrarily set)	$\phi(b) = 1$ (arbitrarily set)	Bounds for d where $\phi(d) = 3$	Bounds for g where $\phi(g) = 5$
	¢	¢	¢	¢	¢	¢
1	-18 to -15	-11 to -10	-4	6	11 to 12	14 to 18
2	-34 to -30	-12 to -11	-4	6	12 to 18	31 to 36
3	-18 to -11	-8 to -7	-4	6	10 to 13	14 to 22
4	-29 to -24	-15 to -14	-4	6	14 to 17	25 to 31
5	-21 to -14	-10 to -9	-4	6	10 to 12	16 to 24
6	-25 to -21	-14 to -13	-4	6	13 to 15	19 to 23
7	-18 to -14	-7 to -6	-4	6	7 to 14	10 to 23
8	-25 to -21	-14 to -13	-4	6	14 to 17	23 to 28
9	-35 to -29	-12 to -11	-4	6	16 to 18	43 to 50
10	-26 to -20	-15 to -14	-4	6	14 to 15	20 to 27
11	-22 to -19	-14 to -13	-4	6	11 to 13	18 to 22
12	-21 to -13	-12 to -11	-4	6	8 to 12	11 to 15
13	-34 to -23	-14 to -13	-4	6	13 to 17	23 to 32
14	-16 to -13	-10 to -9	-4	6	12 to 15	20 to 24
15	-12 to -8	-8 to -7	-4	6	8 to 10	11 to 15

Table 2 summarizes the utility data for the fifteen subjects who were successfully measured. Figures 5, 6, and 7 show these results graphically for subjects numbered 1, 8, and 9 in Table 2. Since the amounts of money corresponding to c, d, f, and g were not precisely determined, Table 2 gives, instead of the precise amount, the upper and lower bounds between which the precise

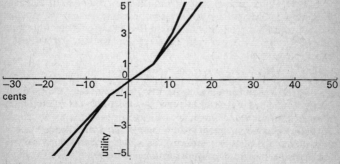

Figure 5   Bounds for utility curve of subject 1 (Table 2).

191

amount must lie. The graphs reflect this fact by showing *two* curves between which the true utility curve (provided there is one) must lie. Even this claim may be precisely maintained only for the points directly tested, of course. The bounds for the true utility curve between the points experimentally determined must

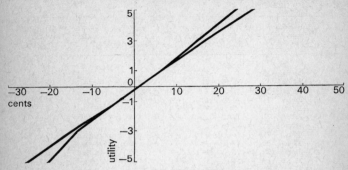

Figure 6   Bounds for utility curve of subject 8 (Table 2).

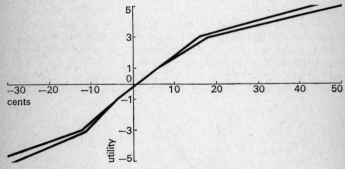

Figure 7   Bounds for utility curve of subject 9 (Table 2).

be inferred by interpolation. As can be seen, the points were simply connected by straight lines; no attempt was made to fit more elegant curves.

It is instructive to remark that there is no simple way to describe the results for those subjects for whom H2 was not verified. The first part of the testing of H2 is concerned simply with *finding* upper and lower bounds on amounts of money with fixed utilities. Barring very unusual behavior (which occurred with no subject), no result can falsify H2 up to this point. Furthermore, *if* the subject has a utility curve, the bounds found in this first part of the test of H2 are the bounds used to approximate the true curve. But it cannot be claimed that there is serious evidence for the existence of a utility function until the checks described in Section 5 [not included in this edition] have been run. From the experimenter's viewpoint the testing of H2 breaks down as soon as a check fails; that is, the failure of at least one check is sufficient evidence to reject H2. However, it is important to emphasize that the failure of a check is not to be interpreted as meaning that the subject was erratic or inconsistent in this particular response. Rather the failure is to be interpreted as meaning that the *total pattern* of the subject's responses was inconsistent; no special significance can be attached to any arbitrary consistent subset of the total set of responses (for example, those that come first).

Some very brief remarks may be made concerning the four subjects whose utility was not measured. Two of these subjects showed considerable disinclination to gamble with their pay and would have preferred to do the work for which they thought they had been hired. In retrospect it seems a mistake to have tried to

Table 3

Summary of Data on Subjective Probability of Chance Event E'

Subject Number from Table 2)	Bounds within which $s(E')$ lies							
	As determined by $d, a \approx (E') c, b$		As determined by $g, c \approx (E') a, a$		As determined by $f, d \approx (E') b, b$		Intersection	
	Lower bound	Upper bound	Lower bound	Upper bound	Lower bound	Upper bound	Lower bound	Upper bound
3	0·23	0·36	0·16	0·32	0·13	0·27	0·23	0·27
5	0·19	0·21	0·10	0·25	0·13	0·27	0·19	0·21
6	0·17	0·28	0·11	0·18	0·14	0·25	0·17	0·18
7	0·09	0·23	0·13	0·26	0·00	0·27	0·13	0·23
9	0·20	0·24	0·21	0·26	0·15	0·24	0·21	0·24
2	0·41	1·00	0·28	0·67	0·16	0·35	empty intersection	
4	0·20	0·21	0·25	0·30	0·08	0·22	empty intersection	

persuade these individuals to be subjects. The two remaining subjects were extremely tense during the experiment, asked for advice, commented on their own lack of system, and seemed aware that they were making their decisions erratically. It would, of course, be very interesting to explore the possible connections between 'rationality' in decision making of the sort tested here and other personality traits.

Table 3 summarizes the data on subjective probability. Seven subjects for whom utility curves had been derived were tested for subjective probability with the chance event E' described above. H3 was verified for all subjects. H4, which requires that the subjective probability of an event be the same no matter what the outcomes with which it is matched may be, was verified (in the sense demanded by the method of approximation) for five of the seven subjects, using three sets of outcomes. In the cases of the two subjects for whom H4 was not verified, two of the three intervals derived had a non-empty intersection, but all three did not.

For the five subjects for whom H4 was verified, it is possible to conclude (a) their behavior is consistent with the claim that there exists a subjective probability function with the properties specified in Theorem 4.7[6] and (b) if there is such a subjective probability function s, then $s(E')$ lies within the bounds shown in the last two columns of Table 3.

Table 4 gives in detail the results obtained when subjects were rerun after a period varying from a few days to several weeks. Eight subjects were run twice, and two of these three times. It was not thought necessary to repeat the test of H1; otherwise the experimental procedure was identical. Three subjects performed

6. Theorem 4.7. If $<T, X, \mathscr{F}, \approx>$ is a weak subjective probability structure, then there is a unique function s defined on $\mathscr{F}$ such that for every E and F in $\mathscr{F}$:

   (i) $s(E) \geqslant 0$,
   (ii) $s(X) = 1$,
   (iii) $s(E) + s(\tilde{E}) = 1$,
   (iv) if $E \subseteq F$ then $s(E) \leqslant s(F)$,
   (v) $x, y \approx (E) u, v$ if and only if $xs(E) + ys(\tilde{E}) = us(E) + vs(\tilde{E})$.

This theorem shows in an exact way how a weak probability structure differs from a probability space. Essentially (iii) and (iv) replace Axiom 4 of Definition 4.5, i.e. the very special additive property of (iii) and the monotonic property of (iv) replace the standard additive property. Without an addition law there is no need for $<X, \mathscr{F}>$ to be a field, and in Definition 4.6 we have accordingly weakened the requirements to closure under complementation (Axiom 2) and Axiom 3. [Definitions 4.5 and 4.6 are not included in this edition.]

194

Table 4

Summary of Data on Remeasurement of Utility Function
(Data for Session 1 same as in Table 2)

Subject (number from Table 2)	Session number	Bounds for f	Bounds for c	Bounds for d	Bounds for g
		¢	¢	¢	¢
2	I	−34 to −30	−12 to −11	12 to 18	31 to 36
	II	Exact duplication			
3	I	−18 to −11	−8 to −7	10 to 13	14 to 22
	II	−15 to −10	−8 to −7	9 to 12	12 to 19
	III	Exact duplication of II			
4	I	−29 to −24	−15 to −14	14 to 17	25 to 31
	II	−14 to −8	−8 to −7	7 to 11	7 to 20
5	I	−21 to −14	−10 to −9	10 to 12	16 to 24
	II	Exact duplication			
6	I	−25 to −21	−14 to −13	13 to 15	19 to 23
	II	−23 to −19	−14 to −13	10 to 12	21 to 25
7	I	−18 to −7	−7 to −6	7 to 14	10 to 23
	II	−10 to −7	−8 to −7	7 to 8	7 to 12
	III	Exact duplication of II			
9	I	−35 to −29	−12 to −11	16 to 18	43 to 50
	II	Exact duplication			
12	I	−21 to −13	−12 to −11	8 to 12	11 to 15
	II	−29 to −18	−14 to −13	9 to 12	13 to 18

the rather astonishing feat of exactly duplicating their first
choices (they were given no hint as to what their earlier choices
had been). Both subjects who were run a third time exactly
duplicated their second choices on the third trial although their
second choices had not duplicated their first. There is no obvious
generalization to make about the changes in choice. Of those who
made substantial changes, only one moved closer to the linear
in money utility curve (Subject 12).

Altogether the ten reruns afforded 48 possible comparisons of new with earlier pairs of bounds for the four experimentally determined points (f, c, d, g). As Table 5 shows, in 23 out of these 48 cases, the earlier results for bounds were precisely duplicated. More significant, in 42 cases there were non-empty intersections;

Table 5

Analysis of Results on Remeasurement of Utility Function

Sessions compared	Number of exact duplications	Number of non-empty intersections (including exact duplications)	Number of empty intersections	Totals (columns 3 and 4)
Sessions I and II	14	26	6	32
Sessions II and III	8	8	0	8
Sessions I and III	1	8	0	8
Totals	23	42	6	48

where this happened there is no direct evidence that the true utilities have altered at all. Of the six times that a second run yielded bounds which did not intersect the bounds found earlier, four are due to the same subject (Subject 4). This subject was a foreign student with some language difficulty, and it seems possible this may have affected his behavior. The other two cases of failure of intersection (one for Subject 6, one for Subject 12) fall short of intersection by 1 cent.

8. Discussion

A. The utility curves. – For fifteen out of the nineteen subjects tested, every prediction which followed from the theoretical model (with the exception of predictions involving sure-thing options) was verified within the limits of accuracy set by the method used. One reasonable way of thinking about the significance of these results is to compare the predictions actually made with the predictions which would have been made on the assumption that subjects choose the offer with the larger actuarial value. (For all options in the present experiment using the special event E^*, actuarial value equals half the sum of the money value of the two basic alternatives.) This comparison is not statistical but precise, in the following sense: for any given subject, we can say with respect to *every* pair of options for which the theory and data allow a prediction, how the actual choice compares with the choice that would have been made if the subject were maximizing actuarial value. A single example will illustrate the general method. For Subject 1 (Table 2), a prediction is possible for all options of the following form, no matter what amount of money x may be:

	Option 1	Option 2
E^*	$-4 \cent$	$6 \cent$
$\tilde{E}^*$	x	$11 \cent$

The prediction is as follows: if $x \geqslant 18 \cent$, the subject will choose Option 1; if $x \leqslant 14 \cent$, he will choose Option 2; if x is between $14 \cent$ and $18 \cent$, no prediction can be made. These predictions were all verified in the sense that for some amount y such that $14 \cent \leqslant y \leqslant 18 \cent$ the subject chose Option 1 (and for every amount larger than y tested, chose Option 1); and for some amount z such that $14 \cent \leqslant z \leqslant 18 \cent$ the subject chose Option 2 (and for every amount larger than z tested, chose Option 2). (Clearly $z \leqslant y$.) For the same pairs of options, choices predicted on the basis of actuarial values would be: if x exceeds $21 \cent$, Option 1 will be chosen; if x is less than $21 \cent$, Option 2 will be chosen: if x is less than $21 \cent$, Option 2 will be chosen: if $x = 21 \cent$, no prediction is possible. A comparison of the two methods for this case may be summarized:

Values of x	Above 21 ¢	21 ¢	20 ¢	19 ¢	18 ¢	17–15 ¢	14 ¢	Below 14 ¢
Actuarial prediction	Option 1	?	2	2	2	2	2	2
(Verified) prediction of present hypothesis	Option 1	1	1	1	1	?	2	2

It is obvious how to extend this type of comparison to a large number of further cases.

Clearly much of the interest of the empirical data lies in the extent to which the choices of a subject, while consistent with the assumption of a subjective utility scale, differed from the choices the subject should have made if he had wanted to maximize actuarial value. One way of judging the extent of such deviations is by comparing the intervals shown in Table 2 with the amounts of money which would have been found for the actuarial chooser. Disregarding the fact that indifference between options was ruled out, these amounts are $f = -24 ¢$, $c = -14 ¢$, $d = 16 ¢$, $g = 26 ¢$. (Let us call these 'linear money values'.) Table 6 shows the

Table 6

Comparison of Intervals with Linear Money Values

	f	c	d	g	Total
Number of intervals entirely above linear money value	8	9	0	2	19
Number of intervals including linear money value	5	6	5	4	20
Number of intervals entirely below linear money value	2	0	10	9	21

number of empirically found intervals for which the lower bound is above the linear money value, the number of intervals which include the linear money value, and the number of intervals for which the upper bound is below the linear money value. As can be seen, out of sixty intervals only one-third include the linear money value.

It seems reasonable to call a subject conservative who is willing to choose an offer with a smaller actuarial value provided it is less risky. A subject who did this over the entire range of options would have a utility curve which was convex from above through its length. There were no such subjects. Nor were any subjects extravagant for all offers (willing to accept an option with a smaller actuarial value provided it entailed a greater risk). Indeed this can be seen at once from the zero entries in Table 6, for these entries show that no subject was clearly conservative for the range a, b, d, and no subject was clearly extravagant for the range c, a, b. Perhaps not very surprisingly, most subjects were somewhat sanguine about small wins and conservative with respect to small losses. In most cases, the larger losses represented by the money values of f were treated conservatively relative to a and b but neither conservatively nor extravagantly relative to c and a.

The larger gains tied to *g* were generally held worth spending something for when compared with *a* and *b* but not when compared with *b* and *d*. Two mavericks, Subjects 2 and 9, were extravagant with respect to the largest loss and conservative when it came to the largest win (comparing both to the base *a*, *b*) but agreed, for some reason, to pay to avoid the smaller loss tied to *c*. Three subjects, 4, 8, and 13, had bounds for their utility curves which were consistent with the assumption that they made their choices on an actuarial basis.

It is perhaps of some passing interest to note that most of our subjects had a utility curve which looks like a miniature version of the curve hypothesized by Friedman and Savage in (7). Most of our subjects were in a position at the start of each play where it would have been rational for them, on the basis of their subjective utilities, to pay something in the form of insurance against the risk of small losses, and also to pay something for the privilege of a chance on a small win. On the other hand, most subjects would pay more, proportionately, for a lottery ticket paying 6 ¢ than one paying *d* provided the actuarial values were the same. Friedman and Savage predicted such a falling off in marginal utility, but of course at some point on the utility curve involving very much larger amounts of money.

B. Comparison with the Mosteller and Nogee experiment. – Before making a brief comparison of our empirical results with those reported by Mosteller and Nogee in (9), it seems worth while to summarize the main respects in which the two experiments were similar and dissimilar. Both had the same over-all aim: to test the adequacy of the expected utility decision model with respect to gambles involving small wins and losses of money. Both experiments derived utility curves for fifteen subjects; due to differences in method and the details of the hypotheses tested, we simply failed to derive any utility curve for four subjects while Mosteller and Nogee report incomplete results for two of their fifteen subjects.

In point of theory, Mosteller and Nogee relied upon the von Neumann and Morgenstern axiomatization while we developed a finitistic model which differs from that of von Neumann and Morgenstern in several essential respects. Perhaps the most important difference is that our method measures utility using a single chance event with a subjective probability experimentally determined. Thus we are able to dispense with the dubious assumption basic to the von Neumann and Morgenstern model

DECISION-MAKING: AN EXPERIMENTAL APPROACH

that subjective probabilities equal objective probabilities. Compared to the Mosteller and Nogee experiment, the choices we offered to subjects (to measure utility) were simple in that only one chance event was used, and no option involved more than two possible outcomes. We made no basic distinction between those offers used to make tentative assignments of utilities to alternatives and those offers which tested the transformation properties of the assignments; in particular, the *sorts* of offers were the same from the subjects' point of view. Mosteller and Nogee tested whether interval measurement had been achieved by presenting the subject with new sorts of decisions. These tests were limited to a very special subset of the consequences of their model, namely, choices between options with an expected utility nearly or exactly equal to the utility of 0 ¢. We were able to test all the consequences of our finitistic model (with exceptions noted) for the alternatives involved; this would not be possible of course for the von Neumann and Morgenstern model. Our subjects were never able to elect an option which would not risk a change in their financial status, and very seldom could elect an option which did not involve uncertainty. In contrast, Mosteller and Nogee's subjects almost always had one option whose outcome was certain, and that outcome was neither to win nor to lose money. Mosteller and Nogee used a statistical method for determining indifference points while we used the method of approximation outlined.

Experimentally, the following comparisons seem the most important. We tested our subjects one at a time, and collected all the data relevant to the measurement of utility in one session, whereas Mosteller and Nogee tested subjects four and five at a time, and took a period of weeks to accumulate the data relevant to the determination of a single utility curve. As they point out (9, p. 386), there is reason to think the subjects in a given group influenced one another; in this respect our procedure seems superior. There is no *a priori* reason to prefer our single-session technique of measurement; it was at least partially forced on us by the method of approximation which allowed for no changes at all in choices between options. The single-session technique did, however, allow us to test the stability of preferences over time. Finally, we attempted to neutralize some of the effects of runs of luck, experience, success, or failure on certain offers or types of offers or with certain chance events, and changes in the size of stake by postponing the pay-off until after all choices (in a given session) were made. This procedure was suggested by Mosteller

200

and Nogee (9, p. 400), but they did not use it. Their data give some evidence that changes in the size of stake influenced choices; however, they are not sure that postponing the pay-off may not introduce a larger distortion. Our experience indicated that post-ponement did not seriously impair interest or the sense of reality of the decisions; on the other hand, our pilot studies showed that changes in stake and the other factors involved in playing off each decision immediately were sufficiently disturbing to make sub-jects change their choices, and this was incompatible with success-ful measurement by our method.

It would be interesting to compare utility curves derived by the methods used in the present experiment with utility curves for the same subjects derived by Mosteller and Nogee's method. Since no subjects have been measured by both methods, any comparisons of results are apt to be inconclusive.

A first glance at Mosteller and Nogee's utility data (see particu-larly 9, Table 9, p. 386), may seem to reveal some general dis-crepancies with our findings; for example they show every subject except one as conservative with respect to wins in the neighbor-hood of 4 ¢–5 ¢, and only three are extravagant with respect to wins in the area of 6 ¢–8 ¢. But one should bear in mind, in com-paring subjective utility curves, that whether any given point is above or below the linear-in-money utility curve depends entirely on the arbitrary choice of the two points common to the sub-jective and the linear-in-money curves. Normalizing the curves on the same two points thus has the effect of obscuring the fact that it is not points or slopes which can most meaningfully be com-pared from one subjective utility curve to another, but rather ratios between slopes at different points on the curve. Keep-ing to this basis of comparison, we find the following: over the lowest range of offers (−5 ¢ to about 4 ¢), every Mosteller and Nogee subject but one was conservative. (Over the most nearly comparable set of offers, those involving c, a, b, none of our subjects was extravagant, and nine were clearly conserva-tive.)

Comparing the slope between −5 ¢ and about 4 ¢ with the slope between 4 ¢ and the next equally spaced amount above (on the utility scale), we find that thirteen of Mosteller and Nogee's subjects were extravagant. (Over this same range, very nearly the range of a, b, and d, ten of our subjects were extravagant, none clearly conservative.)

Further comparisons are harder to make. However, most of Mosteller and Nogee's subjects like ours, show a downward turn in the utility curve between the smallest positive gains and the gains in the area of 20 ¢–25 ¢.

It seems to us that considering the very different methods used to arrive at the utility curves, the degree of similarity in these results is fairly striking. Figures 8 and 9 superimpose utility curves of typical subjects in the two experiments.

C. Subjective probability. – The results reported here on the measurement of subjective probability were included chiefly to illustrate the method and cannot be considered of much importance in themselves. However, the following comparison with previous results is suggestive. For five subjects, the subjective probability of the event *E* was found to lie within certain bounds; for four of the five subjects the upper bound was below the objective probability of 0·25. The average of the midpoints of these five intervals is 0·206. Preston and Baratta, using an extremely different method which assumed that utility is linear in money, calculated the subjective probability associated with the same objective probability to be 0·195. On the other hand, Mosteller and Nogee seem to have found that events with an objective probability of 0·25 have a subjective probability no lower than 0·25.

It should be remarked that the measurement of subjective probability as conceived in the present book in no way assumes that different events with the same objective probability will have the same subjective probability, even for a given subject.

D. Criticisms. – Many of the shortcomings or limitations of the method used in the present experiment seem to center around two points. The first is the demand imposed by the axioms that the basic alternatives be equally spaced in utility. The result of this condition is that a utility scale cannot in general be determined for a set of alternatives which are chosen in advance; rather a set of alternatives must be found with the required characteristics. In practice finding such a set of alternatives is apt to be practicable only where there is available a large number of potential alternatives which can be assumed to be ranked in small preference steps. The assumption is reasonable for amounts of money. However, it is not easy to see how the present method could be applied to alternatives of some other kinds.

Even when the alternatives are amounts of money, the need to find a set of alternatives with given (relative) utilities results in disadvantages. Obviously the alternatives must be found in some fixed sequence, since the determination of one alternative depends upon the determination of others. The experimenter therefore does not know what offers he is going to make to a subject in advance; the offers which will determine the bounds for d, for example, depend upon the prior discovery of the bounds for c.

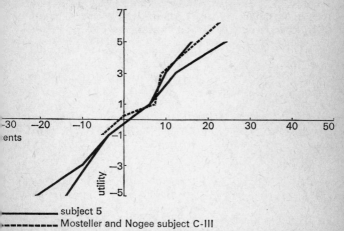

———— subject 5

- - - - - - - - Mosteller and Nogee subject C-III

Figure 8   Utility curves for subject 5 (Table 2) and Mosteller and Nogee subject C–III. The data for the utility curve for Mosteller and Nogee subject C–III was taken from Mosteller and Nogee, 'An experimental measurement of utility', J. polit. Econ., vol. 59 (1951), Table 9, and was normalized by the following transformation:

$$\phi(x) = \frac{6}{5}x + \frac{1}{5}.$$

The experimenter is forced to perform calculations throughout the experiment, thus giving the subject the (correct) impression that his choices influence the offers he will subsequently receive. In determining any particular bound, a series of closely related offers are made (three of the four amounts of money being held constant), and the subject is apt to realize that the experimenter is looking for the point at which he will switch from one option to the other. In the pilot studies elaborate methods were tried to mask the system, but none was found which was entirely effective without being too costly in time. In the end, masking was employed only where it was compatible with efficiency. It should finally be pointed out that the procedure followed in the present experiment ruled out the possibility of making the same set of offers to different subjects. It remains an open question, then, whether differences in the shapes of utility curves may not have been due, in part, to the fact that different subjects received different offers. In theory it would be possible to give each subject the same randomized series of offers by including every possible combination of basic alternatives within a given money range. In practice the number of such combinations (even eliminating 'unlikely' offers) would be far too large to test.

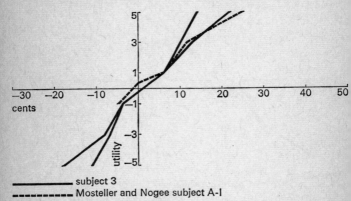

—————————— subject 3
– – – – – – – – Mosteller and Nogee subject A-I

Figure 9   Utility curves for subject 3 (Table 2) and Mosteller and Nogee subject A–I. The data for the utility curve for Mosteller and Nogee subject A–1 was taken from Mosteller and Nogee, 'An experimental measurement of utility', J. polit. Econ., vol. 59 (1951), Table 9, and was normalized by the following transformation

$$\phi(x) = \frac{4}{3}x + \frac{1}{3}.$$

A method which, while retaining the merits of the present approach, allowed the utility measurement of alternatives chosen in advance would have clear advantages: it would apply to alternatives other than amounts of money; the same offers could be made to all subjects; the offers could be given in a random sequence; the experimenter would be relieved of the necessity of performing calculations during the experiment; and (equally important) the experimenter would not know, at the time the decisions were made, what decisions a subject should make to verify the theory.

The second point on which difficulties hinge is the interpretation of indifference in terms of the method of approximation.

This method assumes that during a single experimental session a subject who chooses one option over another will never change his choice (unless the two options happen to be precisely indifferent). In the present experiment it was possible to justify the assumption by such devices as postponing the pay-off. But in general the assumption seems unrealistically strong; it can be expected to break down when one tries to apply the theory to situations in which fewer variables can be controlled. In this respect the statistical interpretation of indifference used by Mosteller and Nogee is definitely superior to our method of approximation. Unfortunately, however, it is hard to get an exact idea of what would constitute confirmation that interval measurement has been achieved using a statistical interpretation of indifference.

E. Relations to learning and motivation theory. – The general theory of decision underlying the experimental work described in the present chapter is neither an alternative to nor dependent on any particular theory of learning or motivation. The theory of decision attempts to predict accurately how subjects will respond to situations offering them well-defined alternatives. On the basis of the theory it is natural to construe decisions as determined (in the simplest cases of risky decision) by the degree of belief in various outcomes, and the relative appeal of the outcomes. But how these psychological factors are to be analyzed apart from their hypothetical role in the decision making process is a question to be answered only by appeal to a wider psychological framework.

The potential contribution of decision theory to work in learning and motivation is two-fold. First, it can hope to provide a tool for the closer investigation of many problems in those fields. The utility function of an individual represents a measure of the relative decision-determining strength of various stimuli for that individual; therefore, it is reasonable to utilize this measure in experiments where it is relevant to have a behavioristic and quantified test of the relative subjective value of specific rewards and punishments.

The measuring techniques developed in the present experiment will be useful largely to the extent that they can be shown to be applicable in a variety of circumstances. It should also be remarked that the theory of decision used as the basis of the experiments is primarily *static* in character: it deals with preferences and beliefs which are sufficiently fixed to be of approximately the same relative strength through the period of the test. The moment it is attempted to make it dynamic, the theory of decision presumably must draw on concepts from motivation and learning theory.

The second way in which the development of decision theory can hope to contribute to the progress of research in other branches of psychology is by providing a closely worked field of fact upon which broader or related theories may draw. Decision theory purports to give a detailed description of how individuals behave when faced with alternatives. Obviously the facts described, if true, invite explanation in terms of more general theories. Two sorts of questions naturally present themselves: (a) Can an explanation within the framework of particular learning theories be given for the fact that most people act as if they were attempting to maximize expected utility? (b) What factors account for individual differences in utility curves? Considering the interest of these questions, it is surprising that little has yet been done to relate decision theory to well-known psychological theories of motivation and learning.

F. Summary. – In the light of the results reported here, it seems possible to draw the following conclusions:

1. The theory presented provides a practicable approach to the problem of simultaneously and independently measuring utility and subjective probability in situations involving risk, at least for alternatives consisting of losing or winning small sums of money.

2. Under controlled conditions, some people (15 out of 19 subjects in the present experiment) make choices among risky alternatives as if they were attempting to maximize expected utility even when they do not make choices in accord with actuarial values.

3. For such people it is possible to construct a utility curve unique up to a linear transformation. The curves of the subjects tested showed certain interesting common features; so far as it was possible to compare, the results seemed well in accord with Mosteller and Nogee's findings.

4. Of the 15 subjects whose utility curves were determined, 12 had curves which were not linear in money.

5. Some evidence was obtained for the secular stability of subjects' utility curves. On remeasurement, 7 out of 8 subjects gave responses which were substantially consistent with the original results.

6. For a single chance event with an objective probability of $\frac{1}{4}$, it was shown how the method leads to the measurement of subjective probability. For 5 out of 7 subjects, it was possible to calculate the subjective probability, and for 4 out of these 5, the subjective probability was less than $\frac{1}{4}$.

References

1. COOMBS, C. H., RAIFFA, H., and THRALL, R. M., 'Some views on mathematical models and measurement theory', *Psychol. Rev.*, vol. 61 (1954), pp. 134–44.
2. DAVIDSON, D., MCKINSEY, J. C. C., and SUPPES, P., 'Outlines of a formal theory of value, I.', Stanford value theory report, Report No. 1, February 1954. (Published in somewhat revised form in *Philosophy of Science*, vol. 22 (1955), pp. 140–60.)
3. DAVIDSON, D., and SUPPES, P., 'A finitistic axiomatization of subjective probability and utility', *Econometrica*, vol. 24 (1956), pp. 264–75.
4. EDWARDS, W., 'Probability preferences among bets with differing expected values', *Amer. J. Psychol.*, vol. 67 (1954), pp. 56–67.
5. EDWARDS, W., 'The reliability of probability preferences', *Amer. J. Psychol.*, vol. 67 (1954), pp. 68–95.
6. EDWARDS, W., 'The theory of decision making', *Psychol. Bull.*, vol. 51 (1954), pp. 380–417.
7. FRIEDMAN, M., and SAVAGE, L. J., 'The utility analysis of choices involving risk', *J. polit. Econ.*, vol. 56 (1948), pp. 279–304.
8. GLAZE, J. A., 'The association value of nonsense syllables', *J. genet. Psychol.*, vol. 35 (1928), pp. 255–67.
9. MOSTELLER, F., and NOGEE, P., 'An experimental measurement of utility', *J. polit. Econ.*, vol. 59 (1951), pp. 371–404.
10. PRESTON, M., and BARATTA, P., 'An experimental study of the auction-value of an uncertain outcome', *Amer. J. Psychol.*, vol. 61 (1948), pp. 183–93.
11. RAMSEY, F. P., *The foundations of mathematics and other logical essays*, Kegan Paul, 1931.
12. SAVAGE, L. J., *Foundations of statistics*, Wiley, 1954.
13. VON NEUMANN, J., and MORGENSTERN, O., *Theory of games and economic behavior*, Princeton University Press, 2nd edn, 1947.

7 A. Tversky

Additivity, Utility and Subjective Probability

A. Tversky, 'Additivity, utility and subjective probability', *J. math. Psychol.*, vol. 4 (1967), no. 2, pp. 175–202.

Abstract

The additive conjoint measurement model is applied to the study of decision making under certainty and risk. A data matrix is called additive if it is possible to rescale its cell entries such that their order is preserved and that every rescaled entry can be expressed as a sum of its row and column components. It is shown that the SEU model, according to which individuals attempt to maximize their subjectively expected utility, is equivalent to additivity for a specified class of risky choices.

In the experimental study eleven prisoners bid for both risky and riskless offers. Additivity was confirmed by the data supporting the independence between utility and subjective probability. Two alternative variants of the SE U model were used to derive subjective probability and utility functions for each subject. In order to account for the data, one needs either (i) a positive utility for gambling or (ii) subjective probability functions where complementary events do not sum to unity. Neither variant is compatible with classical utility theory but both were successful in predicting an independent set of data. Relationships to existing data and implications for future research are discussed.

1. Theory

Underlying most decision theories are two fundamental notions: the maximization principle and the decomposition hypothesis. The former asserts that people choose the alternative they consider best according to some criterion of worth; the latter states that the worth of an alternative can be decomposed into basic independent components.

In order to develop a theory of choice from these general principles, specific assumptions about the maximized function and the composition rule are made. In general, the maximized expression is a real-valued function termed utility which is assumed to reflect the observed choices and to preserve the hypothesized structure of the preference space.

208

Decisions under certainty

In the context of riskless choice, people are assumed to rank the alternatives according to their utilities, where the utility of a commodity bundle or a multiattribute alternative equals the sum of the utilities of its components. Despite well-known counter-examples of interacting commodities such as left and right shoes, this additive model prevailed in the economic theory of consumer behavior and has generated extensive theoretical work (Samuelson, 1953, Luce and Suppes, 1965).

In contrast to the theoretical and practical interest in the additive composition model, very little experimental work has been done to test it directly, although it has been assumed to hold in many models of scaling and data analysis. The earlier literature has been critically reviewed by Edwards (1954). Since then, Gulliksen (1955) has tested additivity among several other laws of utility combination, in a pair-comparisons study of food preferences. Thurstone and Jones (1957) scaled preferences for articles such as a table lamp or a brief case by having subjects choose between singles and/or pairs of items. The scale values were determined by setting the sum of the scale values of the single articles equal to the scale value of the pairs of articles. This additive assumption yielded a fairly close fit.

Adams and Fagot (1959) reported a study in which subjects were instructed to choose among job applicants varying in intelligence and ability to handle people; each attribute had four levels. Only 6 out of the 24 subjects satisfied the additive model. All the violations, however, were due to intransitivity of the pair-comparisons.

No attempt has been made to specify the psychological conditions under which additivity holds or fails to hold. Moreover, all choices in the above studies were hypothetical, i.e., no payoff was dependent on the subjects' choices. Finally, no appropriate statistics were developed to describe, test, or evaluate deviations from additivity.

Decisions under risk

Most models of risky choice are based on maximization of some form of expectation. Although this principle dates back to Bernoulli, it was not until it was reformulated by von Neumann and Morgenstern that it attracted psychologists' attention. Savage (1954) constructed the subjective expected utility (SEU) model, according to which people act (or should act) to maximize their subjective expected utility which equals the sum of the utilities of the outcomes weighted by their subjective probability of occurrence. Formally, let G be a gamble with outcomes o_1, ..., o_n obtained contingent upon events $e_1, \ldots, e_n$; and let G' be a gamble with outcomes $o'_1, \ldots, o'_n$ obtained contingent upon events $e'_1, \ldots, e'_n$. Then there exists a real-valued utility function, u, defined on outcomes, and a subjective probability function, s, defined on events, such that G' is not preferred to G if and only if

$$(1.1) \qquad \sum_{i=1}^{n} u(o_i)s(e_i) \geqq \sum_{i=1}^{n} u(o'_i)s(e'_i).$$

The subjective expected value (SEV) and the expected utility (EU) models are defined by replacing subjective probabilities or utilities respectively by objective probabilities or monetary values. Thus, the models differ in whether probability and/or value are regarded as objective or subjective.

Unlike the riskless case the above theory has stimulated rather extensive experimental work aimed not only at testing the models but also at determining the form of the utility and subjective probability functions. For a review of this literature see Edwards (1954, 1961, 1962) and Luce and Suppes (1965).

To bypass the serious difficulties involved in simultaneous measurement of utility and subjective probability for each subject, researchers have derived and tested some empirical consequences of the SEU model. The most recent attempts of this kind were by Becker, DeGroot and Marschak (1964) and by Coombs, Bezembinder and Goode (1967). However, any test of the model based on only some of its implications is incomplete because the model may be incorrect even when the tested implications are verified. Consequently, such implications may lead to the rejection of the model, but they cannot lead to its acceptance. Testing a model by using a necessary and sufficient condition for its existence avoids this problem and permits evaluation of the goodness of fit of the model.

The present study is concerned with a simple class of gambles of the form (a, p) in which one wins a positive amount a if an event p occurs and zero if p does not occur. Let D be a data matrix whose $D(a, p)$ entry is a measure of the worth of the gamble, (a, p) such as the subject's minimal selling price or the proportion of times he prefers it to a standard gamble. In order to study the relationships between such data matrices and the SEU model the following definition is introduced.

(1.2) A data matrix $D = A \times P$ is said to be *additive* if there exist real-valued functions f, g, and ϕ defined on A, P, and D respectively such that:

(i) $\phi(a, p) = f(a) + g(p)$
(ii) $\phi(a, p) \geqq \phi(b, q)$ if and only if $D(a, p) \geqq D(b, q)$ for all a, b in A and p, q in P.

If, in addition, one can choose ϕ such that $\phi(a, p) = D(a, p)$ for all (a, p) in D, then D is called *strictly additive*.

Clearly, any strictly additive matrix is additive but not conversely. An additive representation of D is simply any numerical assignment satisfying conditions (i) and (ii). Thus a data matrix is said to be additive if it is possible to rescale its rows, columns, and cell entries such that the rank order of the cell entries is preserved, and every rescaled entry equals the sum of its row and column components. Luce and Tukey (1964) refer to this measurement model as simultaneous conjoint measurement to emphasize the fact that the dependent and the independent variables are measured simultaneously. The relationships between additivity and the SEU model for the type of gambles considered are given by the following elementary result.

(1.3) Theorem. For gambles of the form (a, p) the SEU model is satisfied if and only if D is additive.

Proof. First assume D is additive. Hence there exist functions f, g, and ϕ such that:

$$D(a, p) \geqq D(b, q)$$

if and only if

$$\phi(a, p) = f(a) + g(p) \geqq f(b) + g(q) = \phi(b, q)$$

Let $u(a) = e^{f(a)}$ and $s(p) = e^{g(p)}$
Hence:

$$D(a, p) \geqq D(b, q)$$

if and only if

$$u(a)s(p) \geqq u(b)s(q)$$

which satisfies the SEU model provided the utility of zero is set equal to zero.

Conversely, assume the SEU model is satisfied and set $u(0) = 0$; hence there exist utility and subjective probability functions such that:

$$D(a, p) \geqq D(b, q)$$

211

if and only if

$$u(a)s(p) \geqq u(b)s(q)$$

Let $f(a) = \log u(a)$ and $g(p) = \log s(p)$

Hence:

$$D(a, p) \geqq D(b, q)$$

if and only if

$$f(a) + g(p) = \phi(a, p) \geqq \phi(b, q) = f(b) + g(q)$$

which completes the proof of (1.3).

The SEV and EU models are satisfied if and only if D has an additive representation subject to the constraint that u or s correspond to monetary values or objective probabilities respectively.

The fundamental assumption of all psychological expectation models, which is independent of any particular measurement method, is that utility and subjective probability contribute independently to the overall 'worth' of a gamble. That is, judgments of desirability of outcomes are independent of judgments of likelihoods of events. More specifically, utility and subjective probability are compensatory but non-interacting. Studies and discussions of this hypothesis can be found in Irwin (1953), Edwards (1962), and Slovic (1966). Thus, if the additivity of a data matrix can be tested, theorem (1.3) provides a measurement-free test of expectation models which does not depend on the measurement of utility or subjective probability.

It should be pointed out that since the status quo is the zero point on the utility scale, $u(a)$ should be interpreted as a utility for *a more* dollars rather than the utility of a dollars. For a discussion of this interpretation and some related problems see Krantz and Tversky (1965).

The conditions under which additive representations exist have been studied extensively in recent years. Axiomizations which yield additive (or closely related) representations have been established by Suppes and Winet (1955), Pfanzagl (1959), Debreu (1959, 1960) and more recently by Luce and Tukey (1964) and by Krantz (1964). Necessary and sufficient conditions for additivity, for finite data matrices, have been established by Scott (1964) and by Tversky (1964). In order to state the latter result certain constructions are introduced.

Let $D = A \times P$ be a data matrix with a, b, c in A and p, q, r in P. Each cell is represented by an ordered pair of the form (a, p) called a data element. The set of all data elements D is enriched by introducing formal sums of data elements where addition is defined component-wise. For example,

$$(a, p) + (b, q) + (c, r) = (a + b + c, p + q + r).$$

Let Δ denote the set of all such formal sums, denoted by lower case Greek letters. Thus, Δ is the free abelian semigroup generated by D.

Two binary relations on Δ are defined by:

(1.4) Let $\alpha = (a_1, p_1) + (a_2, p_2) + \ldots + (a_n, p_n)$
and $\alpha' = (a'_1, p'_1) + (a'_2, p'_2) + \ldots + (a'_n, p'_n)$

      (i) $\alpha =_1 \alpha'$ whenever $D(a_i, p_i) = D(a'_i, p'_i)$ $i = 1, 2, \ldots, n$
     (ii) $\alpha >_1 \alpha'$ whenever $D(a_i, p_i) \geqq D(a'_i, p'_i)$ $i = 1, 2, \ldots, n$
and $D(a_i, p_i) > D(a'_i, p'_i)$ for at least one i.

$\alpha \geqq_1 \alpha'$ is defined as either $\alpha >_1 \alpha'$ or $\alpha =_1 \alpha'$. Hence, $\geqq_1$ may be regarded as the additive closure of $\geqq$. But since different sets of data elements may have the same formal sum, the latter do not determine their summands uniquely. Consequently, one may obtain both $\alpha \geqq_1 \alpha'$ and $\alpha' >_1 \alpha$ for some α and α' in Δ. The following asymmetry axiom is introduced in order to exclude this possibility.

(1.5) Asymmetry axiom. There are no α, α' in Δ such that $\alpha \geqq_1 \alpha'$ and $\alpha' >_1 \alpha$.

The asymmetry axiom states, in effect, that the order of the formal sums is invariant with respect to different combinations. That is, if by applying **(1.4)** one obtains $\alpha \geqq_1 \alpha'$, it is not possible to find a combination of data elements which yields $\alpha' >_1 \alpha$. Put differently, the axiom requires that for all α, α' in Δ, one and only one of the following holds:

    $\alpha >_1 \alpha'$, $\alpha =_1 \alpha'$, $\alpha' >_1 \alpha$, or α and α' are incomparable.

Alternatively, **(1.5)** may be formulated as an irreflexivity condition stating that there is no α in Δ such that $\alpha >_1 \alpha$. The equivalence of the above three forms is easily established and their essence is to assure that the additive closure of the observed order is a proper order relation. It has been shown (Tversky, 1964) that a data matrix of the type considered is additive if and only if it satisfies the asymmetry axiom **(1.5)**. Furthermore, the above result can be generalized to infinite matrices and to partially-ordered data. See Tversky (1967) for a detailed discussion of this result in the context of a general theory of conjoint measurement. For some related developments, see Fishburn (1967).

In the investigation of decision making and measurement theory, some consequences of the asymmetry axiom have been explored. In a paper entitled 'Testing expectation theories without measuring utility or subjective probability', Coombs, Bezembinder and Goode (1967) derived the following triple cancellation condition from the SEU model. Let $D = A \times P$ be a data matrix with outcomes a, b, c in A and events p, q, r in P. The SEU model implies that:

(1.6) If
$$D(a, q) \geqq D(b, p),$$
$$D(d, p) \geqq D(c, q)$$
$$D(b, r) \geqq D(a, s)$$

then:
$$D(d, r) \geqq D(c, s).$$

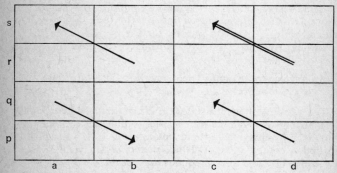

Figure 1   A graphical illustration of triple cancellation (1.6).

This condition is illustrated in Figure 1, where arrows indicate preference. The conclusion of the argument is denoted by a double arrow. Triple cancellation is an immediate consequence of the asymmetry axiom (1.5). For suppose (1.6) does not hold, hence $D(c, s) > D(d, r)$ and by applying definition (1.4) we obtain:

$$\alpha = (a, q) + (d, p) + (b, r) + (c, s)$$
$$= (a + b + c + d, p + q + r + s)$$
$$>_1 (b, p) + (c, q) + (a, s) + (d, r)$$
$$= (a + b + c + d, p + q + r + s) = \alpha$$

or $\alpha >_1 \alpha$. But since $\alpha =_1 \alpha$ for all α, by part (i) of (1.4), the asymmetry axiom is violated which completes the derivation of (1.6). Two other testable consequences of additivity are double cancellation and monotonicity (or independence) which were investigated by Adams and Fagot (1959), Debreu (1959), and Luce and Tukey (1964). A data matrix is said to satisfy *double cancellation* whenever

(1.7) $D(a, q) \geqslant D(b, p)$ and $D(b, r) \geqslant D(c, q)$ imply $D(a, r) \geqslant D(c, p)$.

A data matrix is called *monotone* (or independent) whenever

(1.8) $D(a, p) \geqslant D(a, q)$ if and only if $D(b, p) \geqslant D(b, q)$ and $D(a, p) \geqslant D(b, p)$ if and only if $D(a, q) \geqslant D(b, q)$.

To derive monotonicity from triple cancellation, assume $D(a, p) \geqslant D(a, q)$, but since $D(a, p) = D(a, p)$ and $D(b, p) = D(b, p)$ we obtain, by (1.6), $D(b, p) \geqslant D(b, q)$ as required. A symmetric argument applied to the second component completes the proof. The relationships between the various models and conditions are summarized by the following theorem. That implication does not hold unless indicated in the theorem can be shown by simple counterexamples.

(1.9) **Theorem**

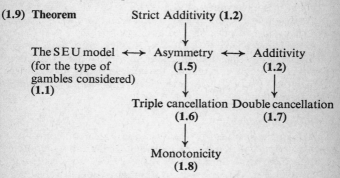

Although for the type of gambles considered, additivity is both necessary and sufficient for the SEU model, it does not determine utilities and subjective probabilities uniquely. The set of all additive representations of a given finite data matrix is the set of all solutions of the corresponding system of linear inequalities. Thus, each additive solution may be regarded as a point in some n-space, where the set of all solutions forms a polyhedral convex cone, denoted $C(D)$. The resultant scale may be viewed as a multi-dimensional, ordered metric scale. In order to obtain a (unique) numerical assignment, additional constraints are imposed.

A solution ϕ' is said to be a *least-squares* solution if it is closest to the data point D in the Euclidian distance sense. Formally, ϕ', is a least-squares solution if it minimizes

$$(1.10) \qquad \delta(\phi, D) = \sum_a \sum_p (\phi(a, p) - D(a, p))^2$$

where the summation ranges over all a in A and p in P.

The least-squares solution is an additive representation of the data which distorts them minimally in the least-squares sense. If the data are strictly additive then D must be in $C(D)$ and the data coincide with their least-squares solution. To establish the uniqueness of the least-squares solution, assume ϕ' is not unique; hence there exists a solution $\phi'' \neq \phi'$ such that:

(i) $\delta(\phi', D) = \delta(\phi'', D)$ and
(ii) there is no solution ϕ such that $\delta(\phi, D) < \delta(\phi', D)$.

Otherwise, ϕ' is either unique or not a least-squares solution. Since ϕ' and ϕ'' are equidistant from D, by (i), they lie on the boundary of a hypersphere whose center is D. Let ϕ be any point on the open line segment (ϕ', ϕ''). Since the solution space, $C(D)$, is convex, ϕ must also be in $C(D)$; but, since ϕ is clearly inside the hypersphere, $\delta(\phi', D) > \delta(\phi, D)$ contrary to (ii) above, which establishes the uniqueness of the least-squares solution. Note that although ϕ' is unique, the corresponding scales for the two factors (f and g) are determined only up to a common additive constant.

The utility of gambling

Related to the problem of measuring utility of outcomes in a risky situation is the puzzling problem of measuring the utility of gambling. Royden, Suppes and Walsh (1959) constructed the only available model for experimental measurement of the utility of gambling based on the assumption that people maximize the sum of the expected monetary value and the utility of gambling for the particular lottery. Although the model allows for individual parameters, its predictive power did not exceed that of the simple expected value model. The classical formulation of von Neumann and Morgenstern does not allow a specific utility for gambling.

The additive model offers a new approach to this problem.

Let $D(a, p)$ be the subject's minimal selling price of the gamble (a, p) in which he wins a positive amount of money a with probability p. If the subject's prices are compatible with the SEU model, then, by (1.3), there exist functions ϕ, f and g defined on prices, outcomes and events such that:

$$\phi(D(a, p)) = f(a) + g(p)$$

where ϕ preserves the order of the cell entries. Both ϕ and f, however, are defined on the same domain, i.e., money. Hence we have two utility functions for money, one for selling prices (ϕ) and one for risky outcomes (f). The normalized difference between them, denoted $\omega(a)$, is proposed as a measure of the utility of gambling:

$$(1.11) \qquad \omega(a) = \frac{f(a) - \phi(a)}{f(a) + \phi(a)}.$$

This measure is obtained by comparing the utility of a sure-thing, e.g., a price, to the utility of a risky outcome. In the classical formulation of the SEU model these functions are identical, that is, $\phi(a) = f(a)$ for all a, and hence $\omega(a) = 0$.

An alternative measure, denoted $\theta(a)$, is based on the difference between utilities derived from risky and riskless choices. Let $f(a)$ be the utility of a derived via the additive model from risky choices, and let $h(a)$ be the utility of a derived via the additive model from riskless choices. Define:

$$(1.12) \qquad \theta(a) = \frac{f(a) - h(a)}{f(a) + h(a)}.$$

Since the former measure (ω) requires interpolation between utilities whereas the latter measure (θ) can be obtained directly, the latter is used in the present study.

The additive model allows the utility for gambling to be positive, zero, or negative. Thus it permits study of problems concerned with the utility for gambling as well as the utility for different types of risk, which cannot be studied within the classical framework. In general, θ may assume different values for different values of a. Whenever θ is fairly uniform over the range considered, the average $\theta(a)$, denoted θ, may be regarded as an index of the utility of gambling. Note that both measures of the utility of gambling are independent of subjective probability. They are based on the fact that it is possible to obtain two different scales of value from the additive model. One cannot obtain a

217

similar measure based on subjective probability since it is not possible to obtain two different scales of subjective probability under two utility levels without violating additivity.

In the following experimental study, the additive model is employed to test some of the basic assumptions of utility theory and to construct utility and subjective probability scales from choices under certainty and risk.

2. Method

Subjects

Eleven male inmates from the State Prison of Southern Michigan in Jackson, Michigan, whose ages ranged from 23 to 50 served as subjects in the experiment. They were selected on the basis of their cooperativeness from volunteers who had I.Q.s above 100 and who had participated in an earlier gambling experiment. In the previous experiment, the subjects spent approximately 20

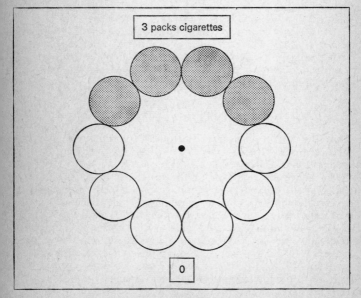

Figure 2   A typical option slide from Set I.

hours choosing between two-outcome gambles using the display described below. Prisoners were chosen as subjects since non-monetary commodities such as cigarettes and candy are used as currency in the prison and thus are effective payoffs. Also, the

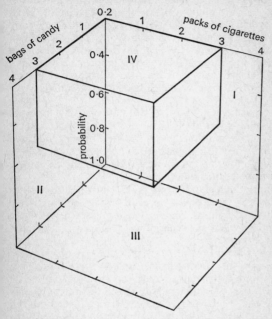

Figure 3   A geometrical representation of the experimental design.

expected payoff for a two-hour session provided a strong incentive for the inmates because it constituted a significant amount relative to their usual income.

Design and procedure

Subjects were presented with 75 options which were composed of four distinct sets. Sets I and II consisted of risky options, referred to as gambles, in which one could win a certain amount of cigarettes (Set I) or candy (Set II) with probability p, or win nothing with probability $1-p$. Set I contained all 16 combinations of (1, 2, 3, 4) packs of cigarettes with probabilities (0·2, 0·4, 0·6,

0·8), whereas Set II contained all 16 combinations of the above probabilities with (1, 2, 3, 4) candy bags. Set III contained riskless options composed of all 16 combinations of (1, 2, 3, 4) packs of cigarettes with (1, 2, 3, 4) bags of candy. Set IV consisted of compound gambles in which one could win a certain amount of cigarettes and a certain amount of candy with probability p, or win nothing with probability $1-p$. Set IV contained all 27 combinations of (1, 2, 3) packs of cigarettes with (1, 2, 3) bags of candy at each of (0·2, 0·4, 0·6) probability levels. A geometrical representation of the experimental design is given in Figure 3. Sets I, II and III are represented as three orthogonal planes, while Set IV forms a cube embedded in the space defined by them.

Options were presented on slides (see Figure 2) where the probability of winning was given by the proportion of black spots on a wheel of fortune, and the amount to be won was indicated at the top of the wheel. To reduce sequential effects and relieve boredom, colored landscape slides were projected and explained, alternating with the option-slides.

Subjects were run in a single group for three two-hour sessions every other day for three days. On each session subjects were presented with all 75 options. The sets were presented in a fixed order (I, II, III, IV), where the order of the options within each set was randomized.

Each option was presented for 30 seconds and the subjects were asked to write down their lowest selling price for the option. That is, the subjects were instructed to state the smallest amount of money for which they would be willing to sell their right to play each of the options. They were given no money to start with but were told that they were entitled to play or sell three options at the end of each session. They were further told that the experimenter would try to take advantage of them by letting them play the option if their price were high or by buying their right to play if their price were low.

Three options were selected in advance to be played at the end of each session. For each subject, the experimenter determined a buying price chosen randomly within one standard deviation of the expected value of the option. If the subject's selling price exceeded this predetermined value, the subject played the gamble or received the riskless option. On the other hand, if the buying price exceeded the subject's bid, the subject sold the option at the experimenter's buying price. It was pointed out to the subjects that under these conditions they could do no better than write down their 'true' lowest selling price, or their in-difference point. For a discussion of this point, see Becker, DeGroot and Marschak (1964, p. 228).

The gambling device was a wheel of fortune with a rotating spinner which stopped on one out of ten spots (see Figure 2). The gambles were played by having each subject spin the spinner and win the amount indicated if the spinner stopped on a black spot, and nothing otherwise.

The total winnings per session ranged from \$0–\$2.40, with an expected value of approximately \$1. Because of prison regula-tions, money had to be deposited in the subjects' accounts. Cigarettes and candies, however, were distributed at the end of each session. Since a pack of cigarettes and a bag of candy have the same price (30 ¢) at the prison store, Sets I and II were matched in expected value. In general, the study was designed to maximize the number of different options having the same ex-pected value in order to provide the most rigorous test of the theory.

3. Results

A gross depiction of the data is presented in Figures 4, 5, 6 and 7 where the average selling prices, or bids, are plotted against the monetary expected value of the gambles. The function $x = y$ is plotted as a dotted line in all figures. Inspection of the graphs reveals that the bids were above expected value in the risky Sets

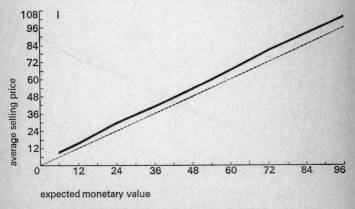

Figure 4   Average bids for Set I.

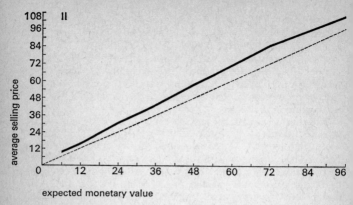

Figure 5 Average bids for Set II.

(I, II and IV) and below expected value in the riskless Set (III). The bids for cigarettes (I) and candy (II) were nearly equal, with the latter slightly higher.

The analysis is divided into three parts. First, additivity and strict additivity of the obtained bidding matrices were tested and the expectation models were compared. Next, two variants of the additive model were applied to derive subjective probability and utility scales for each subject. Finally, the derived scales were

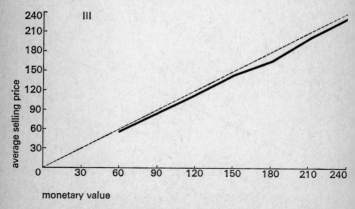

Figure 6 Average bids for Set III.

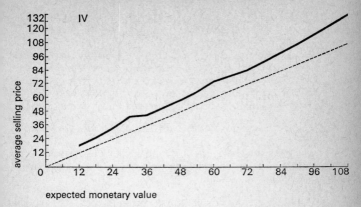

Figure 7   Average bids for Set IV.

used to predict an independent set of data (Set IV) and to compare some alternative choice models.

Additivity analysis

The test for additivity was based on the median selling prices of each of the eleven subjects, for all options from Sets I, II and III. If we let $D(a, p)$ be the median bid for the option (a, p) then the SEU model is equivalent, by (1.3), to the additivity of D. Hence, under utility theory there exist numbers $f(a)$, $f(b)$, $g(p)$ and $g(q)$ such that:

(3.1) $D(a, p) \geqq D(b, q)$ iff $f(a) + g(p) \geqq f(b) + g(q)$
for all a, b in A and p, q in P.

The above equation defines a system of linear inequalities for each data matrix of each subject. An IBM 7090 was programmed to solve the inequalities, if possible, or to find a numerical assignment which minimizes the number of inversions if no perfect solution could be found. A pair of cells (a, p), (b, q) is said to form an *inversion* with respect to a given numerical assignment whenever:

(3.2) $D(a, p) \geqq D(b, q)$ but $f(a) + g(p) < f(b) + g(q)$.

The algorithm was based on systematic eliminations of inequalities from the system (3.1) until a solvable subset, yielding the smallest number of inversions, was found. To obtain a unique numerical assignment, the least-squares solution (1.10) was approximated using a linear programming method developed in Tversky and Zivian (1966).

The other expectation models EU, SEV, and EV were tested by solving (3.1) in the manner described, subject to the constraint that $f(a)$ or $g(p)$ or both are known constants corresponding to the logarithms of value (a) and probability (p) respectively.

The riskless bidding matrices were solved under two models:

(a) The riskless utility, or the RU model, where the utilities were considered unknowns.

(b) The riskless value or the RV model, where the utilities were considered as known constants corresponding to the monetary values of cigarettes and candy.

Kendall's rank order correlation (τ) between each data matrix and its solution provided a measure of the degree of additivity. τ is the difference between the proportion of pairs of cell entries which are ordered like their additive scale values and the proportion of pairs of cell entries which are ordered differently from their additive scale values. Thus, if p denotes the proportion or the probability of an inversion, $\tau = (1 - p) - p$, and $p = 1/2(1 - \tau)$. The values of τ for each subject under the various models for Sets I, II, and III are presented in Table 1.

Table 1

Rank Order Correlation (τ) Between the Data and the Additive Solution Obtained under each Model

Models	SEU		SEV		EU		EV		RU	RV
Sets	I	II	I	II	I	II	I	II	III	III
Subjects										
1	1	1	0·949	0·916	0·916	0·916	0·812	0·776	1	1
2	1	1	0·966	0·966	0·966	0·966	0·966	0·966	1	1
3	1	0·983	0·966	0·966	0·950	0·999	0·932	0·888	0·983	0·949
4	1	0·983	0·949	0·949	0·916	0·949	0·854	0·854	1	1
5	0·950	1	0·950	0·966	0·949	0·966	0·949	0·966	1	1
6	1	1	0·966	0·983	0·966	0·949	0·966	0·940	1	0·949
7	0·950	0·983	0·950	0·966	0·950	0·966	0·932	0·966	1	0·888
8	1	1	0·966	0·966	0·966	0·966	0·966	0·966	1	1
9	0·966	1	0·950	0·966	0·966	0·966	0·949	0·966	0·966	0·880
10	1	1	0·966	0·966	0·966	0·966	0·966	0·966	1	0·897
11	1	1	0·978	0·950	0·949	0·949	0·854	0·949	1	1
Average	0·988	0·995	0·959	0·960	0·951	0·955	0·922	0·928	0·995	0·960

Out of the 33 data matrices analyzed for additivity without additional constraints (that is, under the SEU and the RU models), 25 were perfectly additive and the average probability of an inversion for all these data was less than 0·005. Naturally, this probability increases as additional constraints are imposed on the solutions by the stronger models. Although the SEV and the EU models are equally constrained, the former was slightly better than the latter.

Strict additivity

According to the theory, utilities combine additively, whereas utility and subjective probability combine multiplicatively. Hence, in order to test strict additivity (**1.2**), a logarithmic transformation was first applied to all the risky bids from Sets I and II. The transformed risky bids as well as the riskless ones (from Set III) were then submitted to a series of individual two-factor analyses of variance. This analysis provides a statistical test of the hypothesis that the two factors of each data matrix are strictly additive in the sense that there is no significant interaction between them. Unlike the previous analysis which employed only median bids, the present analysis was based on all the data. Since all main

Table 2

F-ratios for the Interaction Terms

Sets	I	II	III
Subjects			
1	0·545	0·899	0·762
2	1·231	0·979	1·087
3	0·730	0·221	0·722
4	0·180	1·245	1·592
5	1·755	3·391*	1·168
6	0·624	0·706	0·774
7	0·391	1·271	1·424
8	0·335	1·366	0·690
9	0·591	0·983	0·790
10	0·032	0·678	1·020
11	1·241	0·337	0·542

Statistical significance beyond the 0·1 level is indicated by a single star. All *F*-ratios are based on 9 and 32 degrees of freedom except for subjects 2 and 10 whose *F*-ratios are based on 9 and 16 degrees of freedom.

effects were highly significant for all subjects, only the F-ratios for the interaction terms are reported. Table 2 presents the F-ratios for all subjects and sets, where a star denotes statistical significance beyond the $p = 0.1$ level.

Out of the 33 bidding matrices, only a single one revealed a significant interaction. Hence the data show that, to the accuracy allowed by the variability of the bids, the subjects' bids for the risky options are expressable as multiplicative combinations of their probability and value components, and that the subjects' bids for the riskless options are expressable as additive combinations of their two value components.

Utility and subjective probability

Since, in general, strict additivity is preserved only by linear transformations, the strict additivity of the riskless data implies that the utility function for money is practically identical to the actual money value. (Indeed, the obtained approximate least square solution (1.10) was almost indistinguishable from the actual bids.) Strict additivity, however, imposes no constraints on the utilities for cigarettes and candy.

Although the solution is uniquely determined, the scale values of the rows and the columns are determined only up to a common additive constant. Two methods based on two different variants of the classical SEU model, called models 1 and 2, were used to determine the additive constant. According to model 1, subjective probabilities of complementary events sum to one. Model 2, on the other hand, requires the same utilities for risky and riskless choices; that is, utility is assumed to be risk-invariant and no utility for gambling is allowed. Utilities are denoted risky or riskless depending on whether they were derived from risky or riskless bids. Subjective probabilities are denoted type 1 or type 2 depending on whether they were derived from model 1 or from model 2.

The construction of the riskless utilities was based on the observation that the two commodities were equal in monetary value, and that the observed riskless bidding matrices were indeed symmetric. Consequently, the additive constant was chosen so as to equate the means of the two scales. It is important to realize that once the additive constant has been chosen for a pair of scales, the scales are uniquely determined.

The problem of identifying events in choice experiments is subtle because every event is, in a sense, unique. Since no biases associated with the color or the position of the winning spots were found, events were identified in terms of the number of winning spots on the wheel. Model 1 regards events having complementary ratios of winning to losing spots as complementary events. Since in the present study there is a unique objective probability associated with each of the experimentally identified events, subjective probability may be viewed as a function of objective probability.

The scales based on model 1 were constructed as follows: From strict additivity and (1.3) we obtain

$$D(a, p) = f(a) + g(p) = u(a)s(p)$$

Hence $\sum_p D(a, p) = u(a)[s(0 \cdot 2) + s(0 \cdot 4) + s(0 \cdot 6) + s(0 \cdot 8)]$

$$= u(a)(1 + 1)$$

and $\quad u(a) = 1/2 \sum_p D(a, p)$

since the expression inside the brackets is the sum of the subjective probabilities of two pairs of complementary events. Once the utility scale for each subject had been constructed, we solved for the subjective probabilities.

Since $D(a, p) = u(a)s(p)$,

$$\sum_a D(a, p) = \sum_a u(a)s(p) = s(p)\sum_a u(a)$$

and $\quad\quad s(p) = \dfrac{\sum\limits_a D(a, p)}{\sum\limits_a u(a)}.$

The subjective probabilities for model 2 were derived from the same equation, except that the riskless utilities replaced the risky ones in the denominator of the above equation. Note that according to model 2 the subjective probabilities of two complementary events need not sum to unity.

Both risky and riskless utilities for each subject, together with his average utility for gambling (1.12), are presented in Figures 8 (for cigarettes) and 9 (for candy). The derived utilities may be described as follows:

(a) The utility functions for cigarettes and candy were nearly identical for both risky and riskless bids.
(b) The riskless utilities were very similar for all subjects: linear, and slightly below the $x = y$ line.

227

(c) The risky utilities exceeded the $x = y$ line almost everywhere, yielding a positive index of utility for gambling for 10 out of 11 subjects.

(d) The product–moment correlation between the two indices of utility for gambling obtained from Sets I and II was 0·95, indicating invariance of the index with respect to commodity.

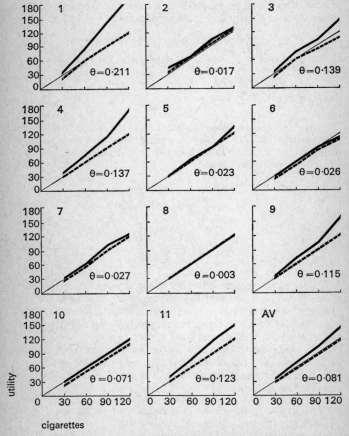

cigarettes

Figure 8 Risky (solid line) and riskless (dashed line) utility functions and θ's for cigarettes for each subject.

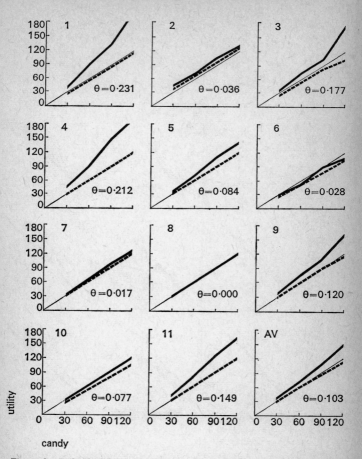

Figure 9   Risky (solid line) and riskless (dashed line) utility functions and θ's for candy for each subject.

The subjective probabilities derived from Sets I and II were nearly identical for both models. Hence, the average subjective probabilities for each subject under the two models are presented in Figure 10. The value of *s* at the lower right of each graph is the average sum of the subjective probabilities of two complementary

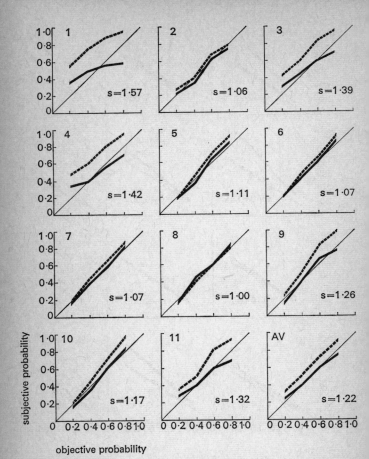

Figure 10 Average type 1 (solid line) and type 2 (dashed line) subjective probability functions and s's for each subject.

events under model 2. The derived subjective probabilities may be described as follows:

(a) Under model 1, most subjects overestimated the low probability (0·2) and underestimated the high probability (0·8). The subjective probabilities of the rest of the subjects coincided with the objective probabilities.

(b) Subjective probabilities derived from model 2 exceeded the objective probabilities everywhere for all but one subject.

(c) The two subjective probability scales appeared to be constant multiples of each other.

Independent predictions

Models 1 and 2, along with the classical SEU and the simple EV models, were compared in predicting the median bids of Set IV for each subject. This set contains gambles of the form $(p; a, b)$ in which one can win a packs of cigarettes and b bags of candy with probability p, or win nothing with probability $1-p$. The expected utility of such gambles is, therefore, $s(p)[u(a) + u(b)]$. The predictions from model 1 were obtained by multiplying the sum of the risky utilities by a type 1 subjective probability. The predictions from model 2 were obtained by multiplying the sum of the riskless utilities by a type 2 subjective probability. The predictions from the classical SEU model were obtained by multiplying the sum of the riskless utilities by a type 1 subjective probability. The expected values were computed directly. Although the models differ in the number of free parameters, no

Table 3

Average Absolute Deviation (in Cents) for Set IV under Each of Four Models

Models	Model 2		Model 1		SEU		EV
Subjects							
1	5·97		8·42	**	35·87		40·55
2	1·73		2·52		2·06	**	8·31
3	4·06		6·21	**	22·37		20·71
4	4·82		4·64	**	23·27		27·35
5	7·00		6·37	*	12·52		11·93
6	3·80		1·20		2·20	*	5·70
7	1·10		1·15	*	2·93		0·80
8	0·07		0·40		0·07		0·30
9	2·00	*	3·70	**	15·06		15·30
10	1·10		1·20	**	7·69	**	0·40
11	3·90		4·20	**	21·29		25·50
Average	3·23		3·64	**	13·21		14·26

Statistical significance beyond the 0·05 and the 0·005 levels are indicated by one and two stars respectively.

Table 4
Observed and Predicted Average Bids for Set IV

CANDY	Observed			Model 2			Model 1			SEU			EV			PROBABILITY
	1	2	3	1	2	3	1	2	3	1	2	3	1	2	3	
3	86·8	110·4	130·5	86·0	106·8	128·1	84·0	104·4	127·0	70·2	87·2	106·1	72	90	108	0·6
2	65·8	86·7	107·4	62·8	83·6	104·9	62·8	84·0	105·8	52·5	70·2	88·4	54	72	90	0·6
1	41·0	65·3	85·5	40·9	61·6	83·0	40·2	62·8	84·7	33·6	52·5	70·8	36	54	72	0·6
3	60·3	78·2	95·9	57·8	71·8	86·1	57·5	71·5	87·0	47·2	58·6	71·3	48	60	72	0·4
2	44·4	59·2	71·4	42·2	56·2	70·5	43·0	57·5	72·5	35·3	47·2	59·4	36	48	60	0·4
1	28·4	43·4	59·6	27·5	41·4	55·8	27·5	43·0	58·0	22·6	35·3	47·6	24	36	48	0·4
3	33·0	44·9	50·7	33·8	42·0	50·4	34·5	42·9	52·2	27·6	34·3	41·8	48	60	72	0·2
2	26·4	37·1	42·7	24·7	32·9	41·3	25·8	34·5	43·5	20·6	27·6	34·8	36	48	60	0·2
1	17·1	24·9	35·6	16·1	24·2	32·6	16·5	25·8	34·8	13·2	20·6	27·8	24	36	48	0·2

CIGARETTES

parameters were estimated from the predicted data. The average absolute deviations (in cents) for each subject under each one of the models are given in Table 3.

The hypothesis that there is no significant difference between models (in their average absolute deviations) was tested for the following three pairs of models: (i) 2 *versus* 1. (ii) 1 *versus* SEU. (iii) SEU *versus* EV. The variances of the absolute deviations (from all 27 data points) were computed under each model and three two-tailed *t*-tests for each subject were performed. The results are summarized in Table 3 where a single star between a pair of models indicates that the difference between them was significant beyond the 0·05 level and a pair of stars indicates that the difference was significant beyond the 0·005 level. Despite the usual difficulties in interpreting the results of multiple *t*-tests, the overall picture may be described as follows:

(a) The behavior of 3 subjects (7, 8, and 10) was in almost perfect agreement with the EV model. Consequently,the pr ediction of their data could hardly be improved by any of the other models.

(b) The SEU model was better than the EV model for 6 out of the remaining 8 subjects, although the difference was statistically significant for only 2 subjects.

(c) Model 2 was better than model 1 for 8 subjects, although only for one was the difference statistically significant.

(d) The major finding of the present analysis was the large difference between model 1 and the SEU model which was statistically significant for 8 out of the 11 subjects.

(e) Both model 1 and model 2 provided a very good fit to the data. The average deviations (over all subjects) for the models were 3·2 ¢ and 3·6 ¢, as compared with values of 13·2 ¢ and 14·3 ¢ for the SEU and the EV models respectively.

For a more detailed view of the data, the median bids were averaged over all subjects and the observed averages, along with the predicted averages under all four models, are presented in Table 4.

4. Discussion

In this section the empirical findings of the study are discussed in relation to previous work and some critical comments are offered.

The additivity analysis of the bidding matrices supported the SEU model. Out of the 22 matrices analyzed under the SEU model, 16 were perfectly additive and the overall proportion of inversions was less than 0·005. Strict additivity was also confirmed by the data as only one out of the 33 data matrices revealed a significant interaction. Hence, the subjects' bids can be expressed as simple additive (or multiplicative) combinations of the options' components. Furthermore, since strict additivity is preserved only by linear transformations, it implies the linearity of the utility for money.

Strict additivity was not directly tested in the past. The majority of the experimentally-derived utility functions, however, were not incompatible with the linearity hypothesis. See Edwards (1955) and Tversky (in press) for examples.

In studies that found interaction between utility and subjective probability, (Irwin [1953], Slovic [1966]) the latter was directly estimated by the subject rather than inferred from his choices. Moreover, payoffs were independent of the subject's estimates. It remains to be seen whether a systematic interaction effect can be demonstrated in studies where payoffs are contingent upon the subjective probabilities.

In the absence of additional constraints on the data, additivity exhausts the empirical content of the SEU model. However, once the riskless utilities are introduced and assumptions concerning complementary events are made, the invariance of the utilities and the complementarity of the subjective probabilities can be tested. Two variants of SEU model were employed to derive the scales. Model 1 is essentially equivalent to Davidson, Suppes and Siegel's (1957) 'Weak finitistic rational choice structure' in which the subjective probabilities of two complementary events sum to one. Since their axiomatization is limited to choices between risky options, utilities need not be risk-invariant.

Model 2 is practically identical to Edwards' (1962) 'weighted SEU model', in which utilities are risk-invariant, but subjective probabilities of complementary events need not sum to one. An implication of this reasoning is that the total amount of subjective probability depends on the events from which it is composed, e.g., the total amount of pie depends on the way it is cut. Using both models, two subjective probability and utility functions were obtained for each subject. These are unique up to an identity rather than a linear transformation.

Subjective probability type 1 coincided with objective probability for some of the subjects; others overestimated the low probability and underestimated the high one. The latter effect was found in numerous studies, some of which are summarized in

Luce and Suppes (1965). Subjective probability type 2 exceeded objective probability everywhere for all but one subject. Similar functions were obtained by Edwards (1955). It is interesting to note that the two most commonly found subjective probability functions correspond to those derived from models 1 and 2.

The risky and the riskless utilities differed markedly with the former exceeding the latter everywhere for all but one subject. The existence of discrepancies between the scales derived from the two models show that the data may be accounted for by two alternative models. If subjective probabilities of complementary events add to unity, then the risky utility function exceeds the riskless one. This is inadmissible under classical utility theory. Alternatively, if utility is risk-invariant, then the subjective probabilities of complementary events do not sum to unity which is incompatible with any expectation model.

The basic finding of overbidding for risky offers and underbidding for riskless ones may be explained by either: (i) a positive utility for gambling, or by (ii) a general overestimation of the objective probabilities. Thus, the data are explicable by either one of two incompatible additive models, each of which contradicts the classical SEU model. This conclusion does not depend on any particular numerical solution because if utility is risk-invariant, subjective probabilities have to exceed objective probabilities everywhere and hence they cannot sum to one. Conversely, if subjective probabilities sum to one, risky utilities have to exceed riskless utilities everywhere and hence utility cannot be risk-invariant.

The SEU model encompasses three fundamental assumptions:

(a) The independence principle: utility and subjective probability contribute independently to overall worth of a gamble.
(b) The invariance assumption: utility or subjective value are risk-invariant and no utility for gambling is allowed.
(c) The complementarity notion: subjective probabilities of complementary events add to unity.

Additivity was employed to test assumption (a). Assumptions (b) and (c) were tested indirectly by comparing models 1 and 2. The data showed that although assumption (a) was confirmed, the acceptance of (b) led to the rejection of (c) and the acceptance of (c) led to the rejection of (b). Hence the failure to satisfy simultaneously the complementarity and the invariance principles led us to reject the classical SEU model in spite of the fact that the independence principle was satisfied. This conclusion emphasizes the need for comparisons between risky and riskless offers in order to test the above assumptions.

One way to interpret the utility for gambling within the classical framework is to redefine the consequences so that winning a certain amount in a gamble is regarded as a different consequence from receiving the same amount as a sure-thing. In spite of its apparent plausibility, this approach does not yield testable predictions because consequences cannot be identified independently of gambles. Furthermore, according to this approach utility has to be defined not on monetary outcomes but on abstract consequences which depend on subjective probabilities as well. This renders the experimental identification of consequences practically unfeasible and the SEU model virtually invulnerable. Thus, although it is possible to argue that the experimental identification, rather than the SEU model, is in error, the fruitfulness of such an approach is questionable.

The discrepancy between the bids for the risky and the riskless offers may be explained in terms of the availability of the offers. The riskless offers were readily available for the subjects at the prison store and consequently their selling prices were essentially linearly related to monetary value. The risky offers, however, were not easily available and consequently had relatively higher selling prices. The availability argument can be used to explain the obtained utilities or to provide an alternative explanation which is independent of utility theory.

Both models 1 and 2 predicted the data of Set IV quite well. Model 2 tended to surpass model 1 in accuracy, indicating that the data could be fit better when the utility rather than subjective probability was constrained. This finding is reminiscent of the slight superiority of the SEV model over the EU model. These results agree with Edwards' (1955) finding that the SEV model predicted choices between two-outcome bets significantly better than the EU model. Thus, in spite of the formal symmetry between the models, the data seem to be better accounted for by subjective probabilities and objective values than by objective probabilities and subjective values.

After more than 15 years of experimental investigation of decisions under risk, the evidence on the descriptive validity of the SEU model is still inconclusive. In view of the extreme generality of the model on the one hand and the experimental limitations on the other, it seems that the basic question is not whether the model can be accepted or rejected as a whole. Instead, the problem is to discover which of the assumptions of the model hold or fail to hold under various experimental conditions. The present study showed that the SEU model was satisfied by each set separately but was violated when the risky and the riskless options were combined. Thus, although utilities and subjective probabilities were additive and subjective probabilities were commodity-invariant, utilities were not risk-invariant. Hence, the subjects' general preference structure could not be described by classical utility theory, although each separate data matrix is consistent with it. The usefulness of utility theory for the psychology of choice, however, depends not only on the accuracy of its predictions but also on its potential value as a general framework for the study of individual choice behavior.

References

ADAMS, E., and FAGOT, R., 'A model of riskless choice', *Behav. Sci.*, vol. 4 (1959), pp. 1–10.

BECKER, G. M., DEGROOT, M. H., and MARSCHAK, J., 'Measuring utility by a single response sequential method', *Behav. Sci.*, vol. 9 (1964), pp. 226–33.

COOMBS, C. H., BEZEMBINDER, T. G. G., and GOODE, F. M., 'Testing expectation theories without measuring utility or subjective probability', *J. math. Psychol.*, vol. 4 (1967), pp. 72–103.

DAVIDSON, D., SUPPES, P., and SIEGEL, S., *Decision making*, Stanford University Press, 1957.

DEBREU, G., 'Cardinal utility for even-chance mixture of pairs of sure prospects', *Rev. of econ. Studies*, vol. 26 (1959), pp. 174–77.

DEBREU, G., 'Topological methods in cardinal utility theory', in K. J. Arrow, S. Karlin, and P. Suppes (eds.), *Mathematical methods in the social sciences*, Stanford University Press, 1960, pp. 16–26.

EDWARDS, W., 'The theory of decision making', *Psychol. Bull.*, vol. 51 (1954), pp. 380–417.

EDWARDS, W., 'The prediction of decisions among bets', *J. exp. Psychol.*, vol. 50 (1955), pp. 201–14.

EDWARDS, W., 'Behavioral decision theory', *Annual Rev. Psychol.*, vol. 12 (1961), pp. 473–98.

EDWARDS, W., 'Subjective probabilities inferred from decisions', *Psychol. Rev.*, vol. 69 (1962), pp. 109–35.

FISHBURN, P. C., 'Conjoint measurement in utility theory with incomplete product sets', *J. math. Psychol.*, vol. 4 (1967), pp. 104–19.

GULLIKSEN, H., 'Measurement of subjective values', *Research Bulletin*, Educational Testing Service, 1955.

IRWIN, F. W., 'Stated expectations as functions of probability and desirability of outcomes', *J. Pers.*, vol. 21 (1953), pp. 329–35.

KRANTZ, D. H., 'Conjoint measurement: the Luce–Tukey axiomatization and some extensions', *J. math. Psychol.*, vol. 1 (1964), pp. 1–27.

KRANTZ, D. H., and TVERSKY, A., 'A critique of the applicability of cardinal utility theory', *Technical report M M P P* 65–4, Michigan Mathematical Psychology Program, 1965.

ADDITIVITY, UTILITY AND SUBJECTIVE PROBABILITY

LUCE, R. D., and SUPPES, P., 'Preference, utility, and subjective probability', in R. D. Luce, R. R. Bush, and E. Galanter (eds.), *Handbook of mathematical psychology*, III, Wiley, 1965, pp. 249–441.

LUCE, R. D., and TUKEY, J. W., 'Simultaneous conjoint measurement: a new type of fundamental measurement', *J. math. Psychol.*, vol. 1 (1964), pp. 1–27.

PFANZAGL, J., 'A general theory of measurement with applications to utility', *Naval Res. logistics Quart.*, vol. 6 (1959), pp. 283–94.

ROYDEN, H. L., SUPPES, P., and WALSH, K., 'A model for the experimental measurement of the utility of gambling', *Behav. Sci.*, vol. 4 (1959), pp. 11–18.

SAMUELSON, P. A., *Foundations of economic analysis*, Harvard University Press, 1953.

SAVAGE, L. J., *The foundation of statistics*, Wiley, 1954.

SCOTT, D., 'Measurement models and linear inequalities', *J. math. Psychol.*, vol. 1 (1964), pp. 233–48.

SLOVIC, P., 'Value as a determiner of subjective probability', *IEEE Transactions on Human Factors in Electronics*, H F E-7 (1966), pp. 22–8.

SUPPES, P., and WINET, M., 'An axiomatization of utility based on the notion of utility differences', *Mgmt Sci.*, vol. 1 (1955), pp. 259–70.

THURSTONE, L. L., and JONES, L. V., 'The rational origin for measuring subjective values', *J. Amer. statist. Assoc.*, vol. 52 (1957), pp. 458–71.

TVERSKY, A., 'Additive choice structures', Doctoral dissertation, University of Michigan, 1964.

TVERSKY, A., 'A general theory of polynomial conjoint measurement', *J. math. Psychol.*, vol. 4 (1967), pp. 1–20.

TVERSKY, A., 'Utility theory and additivity analysis of risky choices', *J. exper. Psychol.*, in press.

TVERSKY, A., and ZIVIAN, A., 'A computer program for additivity analysis', *Behav. Sci.*, vol. 11 (1966), pp. 78–9.

VON NEUMANN, J., and MORGENSTERN, O., *Theory of games and economic behavior*, Princeton University Press, 1944.

8   L. Phillips and W. Edwards

Conservatism in a Simple Probability Inference Task

L. Phillips and W. Edwards, 'Conservatism in a simple probability inference task', *J. exper. Psychol.*, vol. 72 (1966), part 3, pp. 346–54.

Three experiments investigated the effects on posterior probability estimates of (1) prior probabilities, amount of data, and diagnostic impact of the data; (2) payoffs; and (3) response modes. In all the experiments the Ss usually behaved conservatively, i.e., the difference between their prior and posterior probability estimates was less than that prescribed by Bayes's theorem. Conservatism was unaffected by prior probabilities, decreased slightly as the amount of data increased, and decreased as the diagnostic value of each datum decreased. More learning occurred under payoff than under nonpayoff conditions and between-S variance was less under payoff conditions. Estimates were most nearly Bayesian under the (formally inappropriate) linear payoff, but considerable overestimation resulted; the log payoff condition yielded less conservatism than the quadratic payoff. Estimates were most nearly Bayesian when Ss estimated odds on a logarithmic scale.

In several recent studies of the ability of human Ss to make inferences in probabilities, Ss behaved conservatively. In one experiment (Phillips, Edwards and Hays, 1965) Ss were presented with four hypotheses, only one of which could be true. A sequence of data was shown and Ss were required, after each datum, to estimate how probable they thought each hypothesis was. Other than the data itself, only two kinds of information were given to the Ss: the probabilities assigned to the hypotheses before observing the data, and the probability that each single datum would occur given that a particular hypothesis were true. These two quantities, prior probabilities, $P(H)$, and likelihoods, $P(D \mid H)$, when combined using Bayes's theorem, yield a set of posterior probabilities that describe the opinions, in the light of the data, of an ideal person (Edwards, Lindman and Savage, 1963). The amount of probability revision is indicated by the difference between posterior and prior probabilities. Revision was consistently smaller for Ss in this experiment than the amount prescribed by Bayes's theorem. This reluctance of Ss to extract from the data as much certainty as is theoretically implied by Bayes's theorem has been called the conservatism effect (Edwards and Phillips, 1964).

Several factors influence conservatism. Peterson, Schneider and Miller (1965) found greater conservatism when Ss were presented with large samples than when they were given successive small samples. In another experiment (Peterson and Miller, 1965), the amount of conservatism was found to depend on the prior probabilities of the hypotheses and on the theoretical diagnostic impact of a single datum, i.e., on the likelihood ratio. In general, conservatism was greater the further the likelihood ratio was from one, and when prior probabilities were equal rather than extreme. Finally, Phillips, *et al.*, found Ss to be more conservative for ambiguous sequences of data than for sequences whose Bayesian posterior probabilities quickly approached $1 \cdot 0$ and 0.

The following experiments explored several other factors that affect conservatism. Experiment I examined the effects of prior probabilities, amount of data, and the diagnostic impact of the data. In Experiment II payoffs were imposed on the task, and in Experiment III the effects of different response modes were examined.

Experiment I

The purpose of this experiment was to determine the effect of prior probabilities, amount of data, and diagnostic impact of the data on Ss' posterior probability estimates.

Method

Subjects. – Five volunteers, University of Michigan undergraduate men, served as Ss. They were paid $1.25 per hour.

Procedure and design. – The Ss were told to imagine ten bags, each of them containing 100 poker chips, with red chips predominating in r of the 10 bags, and blue chips predominating in the remaining $10-r$ bags. They were shown a bag and told that E had chosen it from the 10 bags, where each of the 10 bags was equally likely to have been chosen. The Ss were asked to make estimates of the probabilities that a predominantly red or a predominantly blue bag was the chosen bag. If these estimates differed from $r/10$ and $(10-r)/10$ E explained that since no other information was available, $r/10$ and $(10-r)/10$ were the best estimates of the prior probabilities, and their estimates should be changed to these values. This procedure ensured that all Ss started with the same prior probabilities.

The Ss were told that the predominantly red bags contained the percentage p of red chips and percentage q of blue chips, while the predominantly blue bags contained the inverse percentages, p blue chips and q red chips. The values of p and q were either 70%–30% or 60%–40%. Twenty chips were then shown one at a time; Ss were told that the sequence of chips was the result of random draws, with replacement, from the chosen bag. After each new chip was shown, Ss revised their previous intuitive estimates of the probabilities that each type of bag had been chosen. Estimates were made by distributing 100 metal washers over two pegs, the height of each stack representing the probability of the corresponding hypothesis. This process of selecting one bag at random from 10 and then drawing 20 chips from the bag was repeated 24 times; thus, every S made 20 pairs of estimates for each of 24 sequences. The sequences of 20 draws were actually planned prior to the experiment so that the same sequences could be shown to all Ss.

Half of the 24 sequences came from 70%–30% bookbags, the other half from 60%–40% bookbags. Of the 12 sequences in each half, two started with prior probabilities of 0·3 and 0·7, two started with 0·4 and 0·6, four started with 0·5 and 0·5, two with 0·6 and 0·4, and two with 0·7 and 0·3. The predominant color of the chosen bag was counterbalanced within each set of 12 sequences.

Data analysis. – Theoretical probabilities for each sequence can be calculated from Bayes's theorem:

$$P(H_R \mid D) = k \, P(D \mid H_R) \, P(H_R) \qquad (1)$$
$$P(H_B \mid D) = k \, P(D \mid H_B) \, P(H_B) \qquad (2)$$

The hypotheses being considered, that a predominantly red or predominantly blue bag was chosen, are represented by H_R and H_B. The prior probabilities of these hypotheses are represented by $P(H_R)$ and $P(H_B)$, while $P(H_R \mid D)$ and $P(H_B \mid D)$ represent the posterior probabilities, the probabilities of the hypotheses after observing the data D. $P(D \mid H_R)$ and $P(D \mid H_B)$ represent the likelihoods of the data, or the conditional probabilities of the data given the truth of the particular hypothesis. The normalizing constant k ensures that

$$P(H_R \mid D) + P(H_B \mid D) = 1.$$

A form of Bayes's theorem that is more convenient for data analysis can be obtained by dividing (1) by (2) whenever H_R is the correct hypothesis, and (2) by (1) whenever H_B is correct. This gives,

$$\Omega_1 = L\,\Omega_0 \tag{3}$$

The posterior odds in favor of the correct hypothesis is given by Ω_1, while Ω_0 represents the prior odds in favor of the correct hypothesis. L represents the likelihood ratio of the data.

The chips drawn from the chosen bag are best described by a binomial process, in which a success will be defined as the drawing of a chip with the same color as the predominant chips in the chosen bag, and a failure as the drawing of a chip of the other color. If the probability of a success is represented by p, and the probability of a failure is $q = 1 - p$, then the likelihood ratio of the data is given by

$$L = \left(\frac{p}{q}\right)^{s-f} \tag{4}$$

where s represents the number of successes in the sample, and f the number of failures. Thus, the diagnostic value of the data, as reflected by the size of the likelihood ratio, is a function of the proportion of red and blue chips in the bags, and of the numerical difference between the red and blue chips in the sample. (Note: Equation 4 is appropriate only if the hypotheses are equidistant from 0·5, as is the case in this experiment.)

Likelihood ratios inferred from Ss' estimates were also computed by first converting their estimates to posterior odds and then dividing these posterior odds by the corresponding prior odds given at the start of the sequence. Since log L varies linearly with $s - f$, for given values of p and q, the logarithms of the inferred likelihood ratios were examined for this linear relationship. Further, Ss' performance was compared to Bayesian performance by computing the ratio of the inferred log likelihood ratio to log L. This ratio will be termed the 'accuracy ratio' (after Peterson, et al., 1965). An accuracy ratio of less than 1 indicates that an S's revision of his subjective probabilities is less than the amount calculated from Bayes's theorem.

Results

Plots of inferred log likelihood ratios (averaged across Ss and sequences) as a function of $s - f$ showed no systematic effects from prior probabilities. Accuracy ratios based on the mean inferred log likelihood ratios are shown in Figure 1. (The accuracy ratio is not defined for $s - f = 0$. Consequently, the plots from $s - f = -1$ to $s - f = 1$ are connected with dotted lines.)

For all values of $s - f$ and for both bag compositions, accuracy ratios are less than 1. Further, performance is less Bayesian for sequences using 70–30 bags than for sequences using 60–40 bags. If inferred log likelihood ratios varied linearly with $s - f$, the curves in Figure 1 would be horizontal. Since they are not, this simple model of Ss' behavior, suggested by Bayes's theorem, is

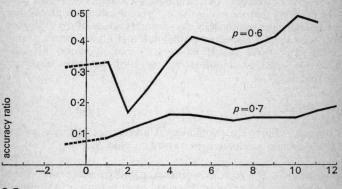

Figure 1   The effect of bag composition on accuracy ratio.

not adequate. The positive slopes of the curves indicate that probability revisions become more nearly like Bayesian revisions as the data become more diagnostic. However, the extent of this nonconstancy of the accuracy ratio is fairly small; a model implying that accuracy ratios are constant would be a tolerable first approximation.

Discussion

Despite the simplicity of this task, Ss' probability revisions still show considerable conservatism. Apparently, the conservatism effect in the Phillips, *et al.*, experiment is not entirely caused by the complexity of that task. The finding that conservatism is largely unaffected by prior probabilities would seem to conflict with the results obtained by Peterson, *et al*. However, within our experiment's restricted range of prior probabilities and Bayesian likelihood ratios, our results agree with theirs.

Experiment II

A possible reason for conservatism is that Ss were not motivated adequately; there was nothing to prevent them from waiting for more information before making probability estimates more nearly like Bayesian probabilities. In other words, Ss' subjective probabilities may have been more extreme than their estimated probabilities. Experiment II imposed a payoff scheme on Ss' probability estimates. Two of the payoff schemes examined have the property that the subjectively expected value of a probability estimate is a monotonically decreasing function of the difference between the S's estimated probability and his subjective probability. For these payoff schemes, S can maximize his subjectively expected winnings by reporting his true subjective probability.

Method

Subjects. – Forty-eight volunteers, University of Michigan undergraduate and graduate men, served as paid Ss.

Procedure. – The basic experimental paradigm was the bookbag-and-poker-chips situation described in Experiment I. However, only bag compositions of 70%–30% were used, all sequences started with prior probabilities of 0·5–0·5, and each S was presented with 20 sequences. After each sequence of 20 draws, S was told which hypothesis was correct. He then spun a spinner which randomly selected one of his 20 pairs of estimates; the estimate for the correct hypothesis determined the amount of his payoff in points. Payoffs were accumulated over the 20 sequences, and the total points were converted linearly to money. The resulting bonus was added to the basic pay rate, $1.00 per hour. The maximum bonus possible was $2.00; Ss earned between $1.29 and $1.92 in bonuses.

Design. – The Ss were assigned randomly to four groups, twelve Ss per group. The control group received no payoff but they were told which hypothesis was correct after each sequence. The first experimental group received payoffs that were logarithmically related to the probability estimates and a second group received payoffs that had a quadratic relationship to the estimated probabilities. Letting p equal the probability estimated for the correct hypothesis, and $v(p)$ equal the payoff for the probability p, then, for the log payoff group,

$$v(p) = 10,000 + 5,000 \log_{10} p,$$

and for the quadratic payoff group,

$$v(p) = 10,000 - 10,000 (1 - p)^2.$$

(The $-\infty$ payoff encountered in the log scheme when $p = 0$ was handled by telling Ss they would lose all their earnings in the experiment up to that point. As a result, most Ss never estimated probabilities more extreme than 0·01 and 0·99, and no S in the log payoff condition ever estimated a probability of 0 on the correct hypothesis.) For these payoffs, the optimal strategy is for subjects to estimate their subjective probabilities rather than any other probabilities. This strategy is optimal in the sense that it maximizes subjectively expected value (SEV). Specifically, letting ψ equal the S's subjective probability for the correct hypothesis, the SEV function, as given by

$$\text{SEV} = \psi \, v(p) + (1 - \psi) \, v(1 - p),$$

has its maximum at the point where $p = \psi$. Further discussion of this class of payoffs can be found in Toda (1963), and van Naerssen (1962).

A third group received linear payoffs where $v(p) = 10,000 \, p$. For this scheme the optimal strategy is to estimate $1·0$ for the more probable hypothesis.

The sequences were selected prior to the experiment so that the same sequences could be presented to all Ss. Actually, the 20 sequences were 10 different sequences replicated once; the order in which the sequences were presented in the replication was the same as in the original presentation. These 10 sequences were divided into two blocks of 5 and were presented randomly within each block. A different random order was shown to each S. The order of presenting the blocks was counterbalanced within each group of Ss.

The 10 sequences were generated by a repeated Bernoulli process but were constrained to have the proper error characteristics. This means that if a perfect Bayesian S had to select the correct hypothesis after n draws, he would be wrong the expected number of times for each block of 5 sequences. This procedure prevents wildly unrepresentative samples from occurring.

Apparatus. – The *S*s were shown a vertical row of twenty push-buttons mounted on an upright panel. A green light bulb was located just to the left of each button, and a red light bulb was located on the right. Pressing a button would cause either the green or the red bulb to light. Thus, pressing each successive button revealed to *S*s the result of each draw in the sequence. The pattern of red and green lights was changed for each sequence by changing prewired plugs inserted into the machine.

Each *S* estimated probabilities by distributing 100 white discs, each $\frac{1}{4}$ in. thick, in two troughs, the height of the discs in each trough indicating the probabilities of the two hypotheses. Probabilities could be read directly from scales located along the outer edges of the troughs. The payoff schedule was displayed as a column of 101 numbers in the space between the troughs. Thus, *S* could look to the outer scale to read the probability corresponding to the highest chip in the stack, and to the inner scale for the payoff he would receive if that hypothesis were correct. Bag compositions were shown on a separate display.

Results. – The *S*s in the experimental groups sometimes estimated the probability of the correct hypothesis to be $1 \cdot 0$. Since this estimate leads to an accuracy ratio of infinity, a different dependent variable was used in this experiment: absolute deviations, in probability, of *S*s' estimates from Bayes's theorem. This variable will be referred to subsequently simply as '*S*s' deviations'. The difference between each *S*'s estimate and the corresponding Bayesian probability was computed and averaged across *S*s within each group, and within each block of 5 sequences. Figure 2 shows the mean absolute deviations, times 100, of the control group plotted as a function of the number of draws. Nearly all of these deviations were conservative.

A small amount of learning can be seen to have occurred from the first to the fourth block; *S*s' estimates tended to become more Bayesian later in the experiment. The percentage decrease, from Block 1 to Block 4, of *S*s' deviations was computed for each group and plotted, as a function of the number of draws, in Figure 3. After the eighth draw, all experimental groups showed more learning than the control group. There was no evidence that learning had reached an asymptote by the fourth block.

The effects of payoffs on *S*s' deviations were compared for the three experimental groups by computing percent-improvement scores on the mean absolute deviations. Letting M_c be the mean absolute deviation of the control group for a given block and for

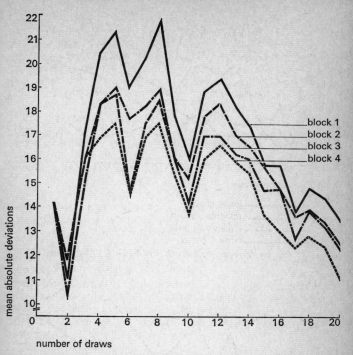

Figure 2 *The effects of practice in the task on the mean absolute deviations of S's estimates from Bayes's theorem.*

a given value of $s - f$, and M_e the same quantity for one of the experimental groups, the improvement score is given by

$$\text{Percent-improvement} = \frac{M_c - M_e}{M_c} \times 100.$$

Improvement scores are shown in Figure 4 for the fourth block of sequences.

Similar results were obtained for the other three blocks. These curves show that payoffs have different effects, the linear payoff producing the most nearly Bayesian performance. The Ss in the quadratic group made estimates that were generally more conservative than those of the control group up to the thirteenth draw. Less than one-third of the estimates made by Ss in the

247

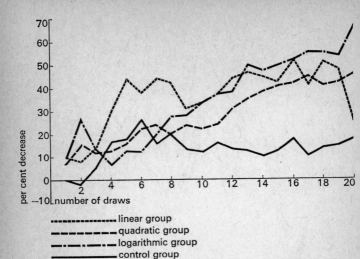

Figure 3 Percent decrease, from Block 1 to Block 4, of Ss' absolute deviations.

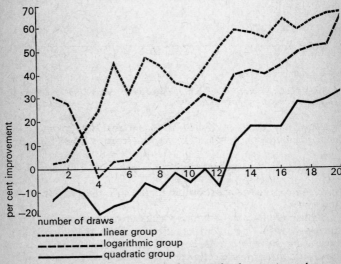

Figure 4 Percent improvement of performance for the experimental groups as compared to the control group.

248

control, quadratic, and logarithmic groups were more extreme than the Bayesian probabilities, while over two-thirds of the estimates made by the linear group were more extreme.

The between-subject variance of Ss' deviations was greater for the control group than for any of the experimental groups. The between-subject variance averaged over the 20 draws was 0·0122 for the control group, 0·0071 for the quadratic group, 0·0046 for the linear group, and 0·0039 for the log group. The greatest differences between the control group and experimental group variances occurred after the sixth draw.

Discussion. – Payoffs help to decrease the amount of conservatism shown in Ss' probability estimates, but they still do not eliminate conservatism. The extreme estimates frequently made by Ss in the linear payoff group reflect the extent to which Ss are influenced in the direction of the optimal strategy of estimating 1·0 for the more probable hypothesis.

Although the optimal strategy for both quadratic and logarithmic payoff groups was to estimate true subjective probabilities, Ss' estimates were different, those of the quadratic group differing little from those of the control group, while the logarithmic group showed less conservatism than the control group. One possible explanation for this theoretically unexpected discrepancy is to be found in the slope of the SEV functions. The SEV function for the quadratic payoff is more peaked at the value of ψ than is the SEV function for the logarithmic payoff. Thus, in the logarithmic case Ss can report a probability value slightly higher than their subjective probability at only a slight cost in SEV. This strategy applied in the case of quadratic payoffs would result in a greater loss in SEV than in the logarithmic case. In other words, it appears that Ss are not maximizing SEV, but are trying to effect some reasonable trade-off between the amount they would win if Bag G were correct and the amount they would win if Bag R were correct. It is not reasonable to attribute the difference between these two groups to nonlinear utility functions, for most Ss in the logarithmic group won only a few pennies more, on the average, than Ss in the quadratic group.

The smaller between-subject variances of the experimental groups were probably due not only to the motivating property of the payoff schemes, but also to their instructional value (Edwards, 1961). If Ss are initially vague about the value of their subjective probability at a given draw, they are aided in discovering these values by observing the payoffs they actually were given as compared to those they could have obtained had they made a different estimate. Instructional value of payoffs is supported by the greater amount of learning shown by the payoff groups than by the control group.

These results suggest that payoffs should be used in probability estimation studies when small between-subject variances are desirable. Further, logarithmic payoffs are more effective than no payoffs, quadratic payoffs, or linear payoffs in producing estimates more nearly like probabilities calculated from Bayes's theorem, without incurring excessive overestimation.

Experiment III

All Ss in the previous experiments responded by distributing 100 washers or chips between the two hypotheses. If this mode of response was incompatible with the Ss' population stereotypes, the difficulty in making a response may have caused some amount of conservatism. The purpose of this experiment was to examine the effects of other response modes on conservatism.

Method

Subjects. – Forty-eight volunteers, University of Michigan undergraduate men, served as Ss. They were paid $1.25 per hour.

Procedure. – The experiment followed the bookbag-and-poker-chip paradigm. All sequences started with equal prior probabilities, and fifteen sequences of twenty draws each were shown. To minimize learning effects, S was not told which hypothesis was correct at any time. No payoffs were used.

Apparatus. – The same data-display device described in the previous experiment was used. Three response devices, one discrete and two continuous, were used. One group of Ss estimated probabilities on the two-trough device described in Experiment II. Another group of Ss estimated odds by setting a sliding pointer on a scale of odds spaced logarithmically. Probabilities were estimated by another group of Ss by setting a sliding pointer on a scale of probabilities, where the spacing of the probabilities was determined by converting the probabilities to odds and scaling the odds logarithmically. The continuous probability scale extended from 0·50 to 0·9999, while the odds scale ran from 1:1 to 10,000:1. Both scales were $27\frac{1}{4}$ in. long, and the pointer moved horizontally. Bag compositions were shown on separate displays.

Design. – The *S*s were assigned randomly to four groups, twelve *S*s per group. In the first group *S*s estimated probabilities on the discrete device. In the second group, *S*s gave verbal statements of the posterior odds after each draw. The *S*s in the third group estimated posterior odds on the continuous device, while *S*s in the fourth group estimated probabilities on the continuous scale of probabilities. These four groups will be referred to as the probability, verbal odds, log odds, and log probability groups.

Odds were always in the direction of $x:1$, so *S*s in the third group had to state which bag they thought was the chosen bag, before they estimated how much it was more likely to be that bag than the other. The *S*s using the log probability scale had to state which bag was most probable before estimating how probable it was. The *S*s were told that the length of the scale was arbitrary; they were free to use only a small portion of it, or they could, if they wanted to, make verbal estimates to extend the scale. Most of the responses of *S*s fell within the limits of the scale.

Five of the 15 sequences were generated from 85%–15% bags, five from 70%–30% bags, and five from 55%–45% bags; thus, the composition of each bag identifies a block of sequences. These blocks were shown to *S*s in completely counterbalanced order, and sequences within a block were shown in a different random order for each *S*.

Results. – Estimates made by *S*s in the two odds groups were converted to probabilities and the mean absolute deviations of all *S*s' estimates from Bayes's theorem were computed within each group and block. Figure 5 shows these deviations as a function of $s - f$. Conservatism is again evident, but it is least for the verbal odds and log odds groups. The method of responding makes very little difference when a single chip has little diagnostic value, i.e., when the bag composition is close to 50%–50%.

The decrease of *S*s' deviations as $s - f$ increases suggests that *S*s' estimates are becoming more Bayesian as evidence piles up. This, however, is an artifact caused by the boundedness of probabilities. Odds data do not have this property, so accuracy ratios better reflect the degree to which *S*s are Bayesian. Accuracy ratios are shown in Figure 6 for the log odds group. For the more diagnostic data, the degree of Bayesianness shown by *S*s is a constant. The same results were obtained from the verbal odds groups, but for the probability groups the accuracy ratios increase as a function of $s - f$. However, accuracy ratios computed from

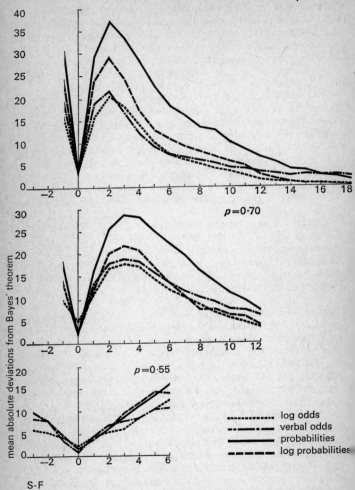

Figure 5 The effect of bag composition on the mean absolute deviations of Ss' estimates from Bayes's theorem.

likelihood ratio is defined in Equation 4, and Ω_0 represents the prior odds stated at the beginning of the experiment. The fitted parameter c is a function of p, as can be seen in Figure 6. This model holds only for values of p that are greater than about 0.6 (see Figures 1 and 6); when p is less than 0.6, c becomes a function of both p and $s - f$. However, this model with c a function of p only describes median performance for each group very well.

These experiments show that payoffs and response modes affect the amount of conservatism found to some extent. But the amount of conservatism found is large relative to the effects of these procedural variables. The failure of Ss to extract from the data all the certainty that is theoretically available is consistent and orderly, and may reflect a general limitation on human ability to process information.

References

EDWARDS, W., 'Costs and payoffs are instructions', *Psychol. Rev.*, vol. 68 (1961), pp. 275–84.

EDWARDS, W., LINDMAN, H., and SAVAGE, L. J., 'Bayesian statistical inference for psychological research', *Psychol. Rev.*, vol. 70 (1963), pp. 193–242.

EDWARDS, W., and PHILLIPS, L. D., 'Emerging technologies for making decisions', in G. L. Bryan and M. W. Shelly (eds.), *Human judgments and optimality*, Wiley, 1964, pp. 360–401.

PETERSON, C. R., and MILLER, A. J., 'Sensitivity of subjective probability revision', *J. exp. Psychol.*, vol. 70 (1965), pp. 117–21.

PETERSON, C. R., SCHNEIDER, R. J., and MILLER, A. J., 'Sample size and the revision of subjective probabilities', *J. exp. Psychol.*, vol. 69 (1965), pp. 522–7.

PHILLIPS, L. D., EDWARDS, W., and HAYS, W. L., 'Conservatism in complex probability inference', *IEEE Trans. on hum. Fact. in Electronics*, (1965) in press.

TODA, M., 'Measurement of subjective probability distribution', Division of Mathematical Psychology, Institute of Research, State College, Pennsylvania, Report no. 3, 1963.

VAN NAERSSEN, R. F., 'A scale for the measurement of subjective probability', *Acta Psychol.*, vol. 20 (1962), no. 2, pp. 159–66.

Part Three RISKLESS CHOICE

The traditional theory of riskless choice starts by assuming that there is some index of preferability, called utility. Given a choice among objects or acts, the one with the highest utility will be chosen. About the only property this simple-minded idea has is transitivity.

The theory of riskless choice starts to be interesting as soon as you look behind the utility function and ask what makes it the way it is. In any interesting riskless choice situation, the objects or acts among which you are choosing are multi-dimensional, and the same act is not best on all dimensions. Among the girls you might marry, the one with the best disposition is unlikely to be the most beautiful, and neither of those two have the wealthiest family. (You may feel that an example involving marriage is quite out of place in a discussion of riskless choice. In fact, the idea that any choice may be considered riskless is perhaps unrealistic. Still, the problem of multidimensionality, which is the essence of the topic of riskless choice, arises in risky choices also, and is more complicated there.)

One idea so completely dominates the literature on riskless choice that it has no competitors. It is the additive composition notion. It asserts that the utility of a multi-dimensional alternative, such as a commodity bundle or a job offer, equals the sum of the utilities of its components. The essence of this model is that the various components of a multidimensional object contribute independently to its overall worth or utility. This notion is closely related to the lack of interaction in the analysis of variance. One essential difference, however, is that in the analysis of variance the actual response measures (the dependent variable) are assumed unique, whereas in the additive utility model one searches for a rescaling of the dependent variable that would render it additive. Hence, the lack of significant interactions, in the analysis of variance sense, is sufficient but not necessary for independence in the additive utility sense.

Why does the additive utility model dominate the literature on riskless choices? The reasons are numerous. For one thing, it is conceptually a very simple model. This makes it attractive both to the decision maker who is faced with a complex choice and to the psychologist who is trying to explain that choice. In addition, no alternative tractable formulations that describe non-independent structures have been constructed. Furthermore, many non-independent structures can be approximated very closely by independent ones.

All in all, we use additive models not because the world is additive, but rather because we can say more interesting things about those segments of it that are.

Shepard's paper, first in this section, is a wise discussion of the topic of combining values of attributes, oriented to a large extent toward problems of application. It provides a sort of overview of issues in the field, along with a small experiment showing that people find combination of conflicting attributes difficult even in rather simple choice situations.

Adams and Fagot's paper is among the first to have used the additive utility model in the psychological literature (it appeared much earlier in economics). It presents a simple development of the model, confined to the case in which each act or object has only two attributes, along with a discussion of its empirical consequences. It also presents a minor experiment applying the model to hypothetical choices. A more recent experimental application of this model is contained in Tversky's paper in the preceding section.

Yntema and Torgerson's paper is the only one in this group that explicitly considers the problem of interactions. Their paper has an explicit practical motivation: they want to work out methods by which value judgments could be communicated to a computer in form general enough so that the computer could thereafter make decisions more or less identical with those that a man would have made. The problem is realistic, and the techniques that Yntema and Torgerson propose are entirely practical. (Incidentally, the concept that is usually called 'utility', Yntema and Torgerson call 'worth'.)

9 R. N. Shepard

On Subjectively Optimum Selections among Multi-attribute Alternatives[1]

R. N. Shepard, 'On subjectively optimum selections among multi-attribute alternatives', in Shelley, M. W., and Bryan, G. L., *Human judgements and optimality*, Wiley, 1964, pp. 257–81.

Many practical decision problems require that a choice be made among alternatives, each of which consists of a number of subjectively disparate attributes. But, after a choice of this kind has been made, the decision maker sometimes comes to the realization that his particular choice was not the best one even by his own subjective standards. One source of the subjective non-optimality of such decisions seems to be man's demonstrable inability to take proper account, simultaneously, of the various component attributes of the alternatives; that is, although he will probably experience little difficulty in evaluating the alternatives with respect to any one of these subjective attributes, a considerable number of experiments reviewed here indicate that his ability to arrive at an over-all evaluation by weighing and combining or 'trading off' all of these separate attributes at the same time is likely to be less impressive.

Some recent proposals are examined according to which a closer approach to subjective optimality might be achieved by analyzing such decision problems into two distinct parts. The first part, which would require a set of elementary comparisons with respect to the underlying subjective attributes, would necessarily be performed by man; but the second part, which would consist of the purely logical or combinatorial process of putting these elementary judgments together to arrive at an over-all decision, might better be entrusted to the digital computer.

An illustrative experiment is then used to lead into the consideration of a remaining problem; namely, that the relative weights to be assigned to the component attributes are not always determinate and may, in fact, depend on the adoption of one of several incompatible but equally tenable systems of

1. This chapter is based on a talk presented at the symposium on 'Use of judgments in making optimal decisions' held at the annual meeting of the American Association for the Advancement of Science in Philadelphia, 26 December, 1962.

subjective goals. That these weights depend on the adopted goals (or 'state of mind') suggests a specific hypothesis of the cause of the subjective nonoptimality of some human decisions: there may be a tendency to achieve a spurious resolution of a conflictual decision problem by temporarily accepting a special state of mind (or unrealistic goal) that – although it will prove untenable in the long run – at least has the advantage of entailing a system of weights that clearly favors one alternative over its competitors and permits the decision to be consummated.

The Notion of 'Subjective' Optimality

As the title of this chapter is intended to suggest, I believe that the definition of optimality – in order to be useful – should include explicit acknowledgement of certain subjective elements. Of course, the choices actually made by organisms are objective; but, clearly, actual choices are not in general optimum choices. (Indeed, if they were, there would be no motivation for studying the problem of optimality, as such, in the first place.) An attempt to retain objectivity without equating optimum behavior to actual behavior could perhaps be developed from evolutionary considerations. Such an approach would hinge on the observation that the rules that govern the decisions made by actual organisms have been selected precisely on the basis of their long-range contribution to survival and propagation. This is not to say that these rules are optimum for this purpose. For one thing, rules beyond a certain level of complexity have not yet been tried. Nevertheless, this suggests the possibility of defining optimum rules to be those that *do* maximize survival in this sense. Unfortunately, such hypothetically optimum rules must depend on the structure of the environment, which, when viewed through man's limited analytical apparatus, appears inexhaustibly complex (and nonstationary as well). In short, there seems to be no hope of discovering rules that are strictly optimum in the real world according to any such 'objective' definition.

In order to arrive at a serviceable definition of 'optimality', we must abandon the search for a completely objective basis, I think, and return to the observation that presumably led to the problem of optimality in the first place. I mean the observation that we sometimes reach the retrospective realization that our earlier decision was not in fact optimum – even by our own standards. This suggests a 'subjective' definition that might run something like this: the optimum choice (out of a given set of alternatives) is the one that leads to the highest subjective evaluation of its ensuing consequences.[2] Roughly, the notion here is that limitations on our analytical powers often prevent us from foreseeing the consequences of our actions – even when the relevant information is fully available. Yet, when those consequences finally materialize, we may have little difficulty in judging whether they are good or bad.

Actually, of course, the consequences of any particular decision are never fully realized but ramify indefinitely into the future. Still, there are often certain recognizable points beyond which a subsequent change or reversal of the evaluation of a prior decision, though never impossible, becomes much less probable. In games these focal points are called *subgoals*. They have the property that the evaluation of any move leading to a given subgoal will generally be highly correlated with the evaluation of the subgoal itself. The positive evaluation of that subgoal, in turn, depends on the extent to which the achievement of that subgoal has been found to lead to a final win (which, of course, is really just another subgoal in the life of the player). Outside the artificially truncated game there is only a system of differentially weighted subjective subgoals that, although roughly hierarchical in structure, seem to defy all attempts at reduction to one ultimate goal (like the final 'win' of the conventional game). Instead, the attempt at such a reduction leads inevitably into an increasingly obscure and shifting set of more or less irreducible subgoals. Evolutional considerations indicate that the achievement of any one of these subgoals contributes to survival, but only on the average, not necessarily in any one instance. Indeed, because of the relative independence of the physiological sources of many of these more fundamental subgoals, they can even come into conflict with one another.

This state of affairs may seem to provide an unsatisfactory basis for the study of optimal decisions. However, in the absence of an alternative basis, I think the possibility should be considered that the specification of subgoals and the evaluation of their outcomes – although necessarily subjective – can be made explicit enough to support scientific investigation. The particular aim of the present discussion is to examine certain techniques that may be capable of helping man to achieve his subjectively given subgoals and to reduce the occurrence of subsequent

2. Koopmans examines the choice between alternatives with respect to their preserving the flexibility of future preferences, which is another way of examining the consequences of a decision. [In Shelley, M. W., and Bryan, G. L., *Human judgements and optimality*, Wiley, 1964, chap. 12.]

judgments that the wrong choice was made in some earlier decision. This general problem evidently divides rather naturally into two distinct subproblems. First, I propose to consider those situations in which the failure to achieve a subgoal is attributable to limitations on man's powers of rational calculation and not to the existence of a conflict between subgoals. Later we shall return to the more difficult problem posed by the occurrence of such conflicts. The notion that the alternatives among which an individual must select at any choice point are usually composed of subjectively disparate attributes will assume a position of increasing significance.

The Use of the Computer as an Aid to the Solution of 'Objective' Decision Problems

Sometimes the subjective value of a given subgoal far outweighs the subjective value of all potentially competing subgoals, and there is, in effect, no problem of incompatibility or conflict among goals. Even so, the problem of using the available information to achieve the closest possible approach to the given goal can be of enormous – sometimes prohibitive – complexity. In such cases we are motivated to look for external aids to our innate but limited computational machinery.

In some phases of its operation, of course, this built-in machinery is extremely difficult to improve on. For example, man's ability to distinguish among people's faces or to segment and interpret sequences of speech sounds transcends anything that can presently be accomplished by machine. To extract the appropriate invariants under the wide class of transformations and plastic deformations that occur in the proximal energy pattern, the numerous individual components of this pattern must be subjected to what is itself a complex decision process (Sebestyen, 1962). The goal of this decision process is the analysis of the multidimensional sensory influx into a manageable set of discrete environmental properties and objects. This process of perceptual analysis is then followed by an analogous but reverse process of motor synthesis in which responses, initiated as unitary wholes, are elaborated into complex coordinated behavior sequences (Lashley, 1951).

Together, these two phases of perceptual reduction and motor elaboration probably account for the bulk of the information processing performed by higher organisms. Once the organism has identified an object as something that is food for it or as something whose food it is, say, little further calculation is required in order to decide which behavior sequence to initiate – pursuit or flight. The sophisticated computations are those required for the stimulus analysis that precedes – and the response development that follows – that decision. The efficiency with which the built-in sensory and motor mechanisms perform these computations is attributable, presumably, to the enormous length of the trial-and-error period over which these mechanisms have been evolving.

On the other hand, with the comparatively recent development of technological society, it is no longer sufficient simply to classify stimuli according to the more or less immediate consequences that they portend for a few alternative responses (such as pursuit or flight). A larger number of alternatives must now be distinguished, and the important consequences of any one alternative are becoming more remote and difficult to calculate. As a result, our evolutional background has poorly prepared us for the increasing load of logical and combinatorial manipulation that must intervene between the interpretation of a given situation and the initiation of final action with respect to it. Because of the limitations of our innate capacities, we have had to depend more and more upon external adjuncts to memory and manipulation – pencil and paper, for example. Indeed, investigations into the effects of extreme sensory isolation have indicated that the total withdrawal of such external supports is typically followed by the collapse of all orderly processes of calculation and thought (Bexton, Heron and Scott, 1954; Freedman, Grunebaum and Greenblatt, 1961). Even under ordinary circumstances, the minimal deductive requirements of the syllogism lead many people into uncertainty and error (Woodworth and Schlosberg, 1954, pp. 845–8).

It is in this phase of the decision process, then, that man is outperformed by the artificial machinery of the digital computer, with its peculiar facility for rapid storage, retrieval, and re-arrangement or recombination according to strict deterministic rules. It is true that the computer's powers of abstracting important invariants from the raw environment are poor in comparison with ours; but, once we have performed these abstractions for it, it far exceeds us in its ability to sustain protracted sequences of logical and numerical operations on these abstractions. Thus a division of labor is emerging in which different phases of the decision process are apportioned between man and the machine to take maximum advantage of the unique capabilities of each.

Contrast, for example, the roles played by men and computers in the kind of optimization problem that might occur in a business enterprise. It is, first of all, the men (namely certain top executives) who must supply an explicit prescription of the ultimate goal of the enterprise. As a convenient oversimplification, let us assume that they define it to be the one that returns maximum profits over some specified period. It is also the men (in this case, staff specialists) who must abstract from the vast complexity of the real situation a manageable set of explicit aspects or features relevant to the problem of approaching the prescribed goal. Once the real situation thus has been reduced to an explicit model, the computer will often be much more effective at carrying out the extensive formal manipulations (of linear programming, say) that are then necessary to solve the maximization problem for that abstract model.

In examples of this kind it is clear that the final course of action taken on the basis of such formal optimization techniques will not generally be strictly optimum in the real world. For the formal optimization is attained only with respect to the abstract model – not with respect to the world itself. That the results can nevertheless be of great practical value attests to the uniquely human ability to capture the most essential features of the real world in the abstract model. In practice, then, formal optimization always involves subjective judgment. There is, first, the subjective judgment as to what is to be taken as the goal; and there is, second, the subjective judgment as to what is to be taken as an appropriate model.

That all optimization procedures must rest in part on certain subjective evaluations has often been obscured in the use of formal models by the absence of any explicit representation of these subjective elements within the formal models themselves. This has encouraged a somewhat fictitious distinction between those decision problems that can be dealt with by objective formal methods and those decision problems that are presumed to be wholly and incurably subjective (like those of deciding which house to buy, which job to accept, or which person to hire). Although we are more or less aware of a number of subjective factors that are relevant to these kinds of decisions, there has not seemed to be any satisfactory way of quantifying these factors or of stating exactly how they should interact or 'trade off' with one another. In effect, then, it has been our conceit that the subtle weighing and combining of factors required for such subjective decisions can be accomplished only by the mysterious intuitive deliberations of human intelligence – not by the inflexible automatisms of artificial machinery. There is reason to question this prejudice, however, and to reopen the question whether some intermediate kinds of decision problems may not exist that would benefit from a more formal treatment of their admittedly subjective factors.

Some Limitations on Man's Ability to Combine Factors in 'Subjective' Decision Problems

At the level of the perceptual analysis of raw sensory inputs, man evinces a remarkable ability to integrate the responses of a vast number of receptive elements according to exceedingly complex nonlinear rules. Yet once the profusion and welter of this raw input has been thus reduced to a set of usefully invariant conceptual objects, properties, and attributes, there is little evidence that they can in turn be juggled and recombined with anything like this facility. On the contrary, the contention that they can belies the obvious disparity between the effortless speed and surety of most perceptual decisions and the painful hesitation and doubt characteristic of these subsequent 'higher level' decisions. A number of experimental investigations into our innate capabilities at this 'higher level' now indicate that there are good reasons for the halting and uncertain course of these decision processes.

Miller (1956), first of all, has assembled a persuasive variety of results to show that there are rather severe limitations on the number of conceptual units that can be handled at any one time. Moreover, although a small number of attributes evidently can be combined according to simple linear or additive rules (Adams and Fagot, 1959; Anderson, 1962; Gulliksen, 1956; Hoffman, 1960; Rimoldi, 1956; Spence and Guilford, 1933), nonlinear rules or complex interactions between variables seem to offer great conceptual difficulty. This emerges clearly when subjects are required to learn or remember different types of classifications of the same set of multiattribute objects. Thus Shepard, Hovland, and Jenkins (1961) found that learning was swift and accurate when the classification was based on only one attribute of the objects (say over-all size), whereas progress was slow and difficult when the classification was based on a complex interaction between several attributes (such as size, color, and shape).

It is essentially this phenomenon, too, that had previously been pointed out by Estes (1957, pp. 616–17) when he showed that, in the course of learning to respond to complex patterns of cues, subjects first reach a plateau in which their responses are controlled by the cues singly rather than in patterns. In addition, he argued that as the number of cues (or attributes) increases the non-optimum performance corresponding to this intermediate plateau will become more and more protracted. Such conclusions may seem to run counter to the results of certain experiments – like those reported by Brunswik (1956, pp. 100–10) and by Azuma and Cronbach (1961) – in which subjects exhibited a clear tendency to respond specifically to patterns or interactions between attributes. However, these particular experiments differed from those considered elsewhere in this section in that the interactions tended to be immediately appreciated perceptually; they did not have to be 'built up', so to speak, from perceptually isolated attributes (cf. Shepard, Hovland and Jenkins, 1961, p. 35).

The same basic difficulty posed by interactions between attributes in experiments on learning and memory may also underlie certain well-known phenomena that emerge when subjects are asked to rate objects or other people on each of several specified dimensions. Results presented by DeSoto (1961) and by Osgood, Suci, and Tannenbaum (1957, pp. 114–16), for example, reveal a striking inability of subjects to take account of the independent way in which the objects vary along the different dimensions. Instead, there seems to be an overweening tendency to collapse all dimensions into a single 'good *versus* bad' dimension with an attendant loss in detailed information about the configuration or pattern of attributes unique to any one object.

Of course, if our sole purpose is to arrive at a choice between two or more multiattribute alternatives, we only need to know which of the alternatives is 'best'; further specifically 'configurational' information is superfluous. In many practical decision problems, then, to collapse the various component dimensions into one over-all evaluative dimension may not in itself be amiss. The point at issue, however, is whether people perform this dimensional compression in any optimum way. An examination of the pertinent experimental literature suggests that they do not.

Meehl (1954), in particular, has methodically reviewed a considerable number of studies in which predictions from a given set of predictor variables to a given criterion variable were independently attempted in two ways; intuitively, by the deliberations of trained specialists and mechanically by routine actuarial procedures (typically, by computing a simple linear combination of the predictor variables). The predictions were attempted in real-life settings and the criterion variables were of considerable practical interest; namely, such things as future grade point scores for college students or future length of hospitalization for mental patients. The predictor variables ranged from essentially objective measures (such as prior high school grade averages) to completely subjective measures (such as prior clinical ratings of 'oral eroticism'). But, whatever the input variables, predictive success was generally greater when these variables were combined mechanically than when they were combined by intuitive deliberation. This was true even though the specialists who did the deliberating were not confined, like the formal equations, to linear rules of combination.

Further evidence of this kind has more recently been secured by Yntema and Torgerson (1961) and, following them, by Pollack (1962) under the somewhat more artificial but more tightly controlled conditions possible in the laboratory. Subjects were required to learn, for each stimulus, a certain arbitrarily assigned value called its 'worth'. In one experiment reported by Yntema and Torgerson, for example, the stimuli were 180 ellipses varying in size, shape, and color. The experimenters assigned 'worth' in such a way that it always increased monotonically with the three component factors of 'size, thinness, and brownness', but not in a simple linear or additive way. Even after considerable training, the subjects failed to take proper account of the resulting interaction between the three factors; although their responses did come to reflect, rather accurately, the linear contributions (or 'main effects') of the three separate factors. This finding is somewhat reminiscent of the results, mentioned earlier, by Estes. Perhaps the most interesting of the Yntema–Torgerson results – and one that has subsequently been verified in two different experiments by Pollack (1962) – is this: even when the underlying factors combine according to a nonlinear rule, a machine using a purely linear rule of combination can yield estimates of 'true' worth that surpass in accuracy those of trained subjects who are not constrained in this way.

There is a temptation to argue that these comparisons, as well as those reviewed earlier by Meehl, give the machine an unfair advantage by focusing on cases in which the number of component attributes or predictor variables is quite small. Possibly, the intuitive method is suited rather to cases in which the number of factors that must be combined in some complex or subtle manner is very large. Actually, though, the available evidence provides little encouragement for this contention. It certainly runs counter

265

to the general arguments advanced by Miller (1956) and by Estes (1957, pp. 616–17). A number of experiments more specifically directed at this question have shown that any increase in the number of variable attributes of the stimuli generally produces a marked rise both in errors (Archer, Bourne and Brown, 1955) and in decision time (Hayes, 1962). Moreover, a closer examination of the results we have already discussed reveals a systematic bias in the subjects' judgments, even in those experiments, that is quite contrary to this contention. Although it is true that the number of factors is already restricted, there seems to be a consistent tendency for the subjects to restrict it still further by relying too heavily on one or two of these factors while, in effect, ignoring the significant contributions of the remaining factors. Among the studies surveyed by Meehl, the one by Sarbin (1942) makes particular mention of this phenomenon. It also emerges clearly in Pollack's more recent study. Other results presented, for example, by Smedslund (1955), by Bruner, Goodnow, and Austin (1956, pp. 200–1), by Shepard, Hovland, and Jenkins (1961), and by Shepard (1963b) indicate that this could be described as an attentional phenomenon: in making an evaluative judgment a subject can take account of only a very limited number of factors at any one time.

Curiously, subjects often seem to lack insight into the extent to which they have restricted themselves in this way. This shows up in the experiments reported by Hoffman (1960, pp. 126–7) and by Pollack (1962). In both cases subjects were asked not only to make an over-all evaluation of each stimulus but also to judge the extent to which each attribute of the stimuli was subjectively weighted, on the average, in making these evaluations. The degree of 'insight' of a subject could then be assessed by comparing his announced subjective weights with the weights that were in reality controlling his over-all evaluations (as determined by multiple regression procedures, for example). The results suggest that although the weights actually controlling the subjects' responses are usually concentrated on only one or two attributes the subjective weights reported by the subjects tended to be more evenly distributed over the whole set of attributes. Indeed, there is some indication in Pollack's findings that the announced subjective weights tended to err in the opposite direction of ascribing too much importance to the less important variables. Possibly our feeling that we can take account of a host of different factors comes about because, although we remember that at some time or other we have attended to each of the different factors, we fail to notice that it is seldom more than one or two that we consider at any one time.

In any case, the confidence that we have tended to invest in our rational ability to weigh and combine many subjective factors appears to have been somewhat misplaced. It is only recently, as a result of the application of more sophisticated psychological techniques to the measurement and control of these subjective factors, that the fact has come fully to light. The one encouraging aspect of this otherwise disheartening revelation is the possibility that by a more intimate cooperation between man and machine we may yet achieve something approaching a rational decision procedure – even, perhaps, for 'subjective' problems.

Toward the Explicit Use of Subjective Judgments in Computer-aided Decisions

As a first step, I suggest we abandon any hard and fast distinction between 'objective' decision problems, which are often best submitted to the formal optimization procedures of the computer, and 'subjective' decision problems, which allegedly yield only to the intuitive deliberations of the human mind. Neither are the so-called objective problems free from subjective elements, nor are the *avowedly* subjective problems entirely inaccessible to mechanized procedures. Clearly, though, a successful division of labor between the man and the computer will have to be based on a careful examination of the different capabilities of these two instruments as well as of the particular requirements of the decision problem at hand.

As one illustration, consider the employment problem: to find an optimum assignment of N candidates to K vacant positions. This has been handled typically as a purely subjective problem because, even if optimality were strictly defined in terms of the maximization of some explicit variable (such as corporate profits), there would still be no formal or objective procedure for determining how much any proposed assignment would contribute to that variable. However, as Aumann and Kruskal (1958) and Smith (1956) have observed, such a problem can readily be decomposed into two distinct subproblems. The first subproblem is to arrive at a set of elementary judgments of the form 'candidate A would be "better" than candidate B in position X'. The second subproblem is then to discover the 'best' over-all assignment implied by these elementary judgments. Aumann and Kruskal argue, quite reasonably I think, that although the first subproblem may be more successfully handled by man, the

267

combinatorial complexity inherent in the second subproblem makes it more suitable for the digital computer. They then proceed to show, in detail, how a technique of this kind may be applied to an analogous assignment problem of considerable practical interest in naval operations; specifically, the problem of determining the optimum allocation of available units of electronic equipment to existing ships (Aumann and Kruskal, 1959).

The feasibility of the method in this case stems from the fact that the total set of pairwise preferences among all possible alternatives (e.g., assignments) is so highly redundant that the entire set of these preference relations can generally be reconstructed from a relatively small subset by purely mechanical operations, such as repeated application of the rules of transitivity and additivity set forth by Aumann (1964). Indeed, because of this extreme overdetermination apparently qualitative constraints (like inequalities of the form '$A > B$ with respect to X') can, when provided in sufficient number, determine a measure of over-all 'goodness' on an essentially quantitative scale. In addition to the mathematical argument presented by Aumann and Kruskal (1959), this general fact of numerical analysis has been utilized independently in diverse scaling methods developed independently by Abelson and Tukey (1959), Davidson, Suppes and Siegel (1957, chapter 3), Shepard (1962a, b, 1963a), and others. The purpose of all of these methods is to extract the maximum amount of metric information from a given collection of judgments, each of which, taken by itself, is of a qualitative or nonmetric character. I am hopeful that these methods may go some way toward providing at least a partial solution to the problem that earlier methods for scaling subjective factors have been susceptible to various kinds of systematic errors and biases. Possibly such distortions are not a necessary affliction of all subjective judgments but have entered primarily when judgments have been sought that in a psychological sense were too complex or unnatural. The potential value of these new methods, then, is that they permit us to reduce this psychological complexity to the minimum level by shifting to the computer the entire logical-combinatorial burden of putting the primitive judgments together in an optimum manner. The psychologist's part of this task is to determine which of the subsets of preference relations that form a sufficient basis for reconstructing the whole preference structure is most amenable to subjective judgment.

The idea of assigning to man only that part of the decision

process that cannot be done better by machine is presented in quite another connection by Edwards and Phillips (1964). Their concern is with certain practical decision problems for which the optimal procedure calls for extensive application of Bayes's rule. The experimental findings reviewed by them indicate that as soon as the situation becomes at all complicated the unaided decisions of human subjects exhibit systematic departures from this optimum procedure. Presumably, therefore, the numerical calculations prescribed by Bayes's rule should be turned over to the computer. At the same time, of course, there are quantities necessary for the application of Bayes's rule that may be wholly unavailable except through human judgment. These quantities include the conditional probabilities of various outcomes, given the alternative hypotheses about the state of the world (as well, possibly, as the 'prior' probabilities associated with these hypotheses).

It is an essential feature, too, of many of the kinds of situations considered by Meehl (1954), Yntema and Torgerson (1961), and Pollack (1962) that practical decisions must be made on the basis of factors, some of which are unavoidably subjective. Yntema and Torgerson make some valuable suggestions, particularly with respect to the handling of decisions requiring 'common sense' in real-time systems, in which the sheer load of information processing is likely to swamp the system unless delegated as fully as possible to the computer. What distinguishes many of these situations is the fact, emphasized by Yntema and Torgerson, that the over-all value or 'worth' of any alternative is a monotonic function of the separate attributes of that alternative. Thus the over-all value of a house, say, increases with any improvement in price, location, quality of construction, etc. I would argue here that we do not need to insist that worth be monotonically related to all subjective attributes. For example, the contribution of the location of a house to its total worth need not be monotonically related to its distance, say, from place of employment. The most favorable distance from work might have some intermediate value. All that is really required is that the *desirability* of the location (not the location itself) contributes monotonically to total worth.

What we actually seek, then, is a decomposition of over-all worth into separate part-worths; here, for example, the part-worth attributable to location, the part-worth attributable to quality of construction, and so on. The advantage to be derived from this decomposition is that the part-worths, if properly chosen, lend themselves much more readily to subjective evaluation than does the over-all 'whole' worth. Typically, we find it relatively easy to judge which of two houses is better with respect to some one attribute such as location or quality of construction. The difficulty comes when we try to take account of all such attributes simultaneously and thus make an absolute judgment of over-all worth. Presumably the decomposition should be carried until the subjectively most unitary or natural attributes are encountered. Possibly, for example, the part-worth attributed to location should be further analyzed into two part-worths: one attributable to desirability of neighborhood *per se* and another attributable to distance from work.

Whatever the degree of reduction, in cases of this kind there will inevitably be components that cannot be reduced entirely to physically measurable quantities and so will have to be evaluated subjectively. Nevertheless, the results already reviewed indicate that the recombination of these various components for the purposes of reaching an over-all decision will often be more effectively accomplished mechanically rather than intuitively. The mechanization of this phase of the decision process is greatly simplified by the monotonicity condition, since, as Yntema and Torgerson (1961) and Pollack (1962) have shown, a simple linear combination of the separate factors typically works very well under that condition. Of course, if there should happen to be an unusually severe interaction or nonadditivity of effects of the contributing factors, a simple linear combination may fail to reflect the complexity of the true situation (Aumann, 1964). Still, in cases of this kind it may be possible to restore the necessary degree of additivity by applying appropriate nonlinear transformations to the component subjective scales. Luce and Tukey (1964) have recently made a significant advance in this direction by providing an axiomatic foundation for what they call 'simultaneous conjoint measurement'. They give, in effect, a constructive algorithm that yields, at the same time, the appropriate non-linear transformations of scale and the resulting additive measure of over-all worth (or 'utility').

Note, however, that the general problem of combining separate factors to arrive at an over-all decision really consists of two distinct subproblems: the subproblem of specifying an appropriate form for the rules of combination and the subproblem of assigning appropriate weights to the component factors. The important contributions of Yntema and Torgerson as well as of Luce and Tukey, I think, are their demonstrations that under the stated 'monotonicity condition' the subproblem concerning the form of the rules of combination is by no means so difficult as it appears at first. However, the second subproblem, concerning the assignment of appropriate weights, seems to present some relatively more difficult aspects.

An Experiment Illustrating the Problem of Weights in Choosing among Multi-attribute Alternatives

When one alternative is obviously better than another with respect to all subjectively important attributes, there is, of course, no problem of deciding between them. Unfortunately, decision problems often are not of this form. Frequently, when one alternative is better with respect to some attributes, the other alternative is better with respect to other attributes, and so there is the possibility of a conflict. For example, one of two equally expensive houses may have the nicer location, whereas the other may be the more solidly constructed. In such cases one attribute must be balanced off against another, and the final resolution of the conflict will obviously depend on the relative weight assigned to each factor.[3]

We shall discuss here an experiment that, although not specifically concerned with the problem of optimum choice, may help to illustrate the kind of difficulty that is presented when the weights are not subjectively determinate. Each stimulus in this experiment consisted simply of a circle (or 'rim') and one radial line (or 'spoke'). These stimuli therefore had just two variable attributes; namely, the diameter of the circular rim and the inclination of the radial spoke. The task of the subjects, basically, was to indicate the stimulus in a presented series that was most similar to a given standard stimulus (which was always $\frac{3}{4}$ in. in diameter with a 45° spoke). The critical feature of this experiment is that the subjects were instructed to take account of differences both in size and in inclination and arrive at their choices on the basis of over-all resemblance.

A large number of different kinds of series were included in the

3. In a presently unpublished report that came to my attention too late to be covered adequately here Yntema and Klem describe an interesting experiment that follows up the earlier work of Yntema and Torgerson (1961) – but with particular consideration of the effect of conflicts of this kind between the separate dimensions of the alternatives. In this experiment they had experienced aircraft pilots make judgments regarding the relative dangerousness of landing under conditions that differed along the three dimensions of 'ceiling', 'visibility', and 'fuel reserve' (Yntema and Klem, 1962).

original experiment, but for present purposes we need consider only two kinds of series – these I call the 'one-dimensional series' and the 'two-dimensional series'. (For a more complete description of the original experiment, see the report by Shepard,

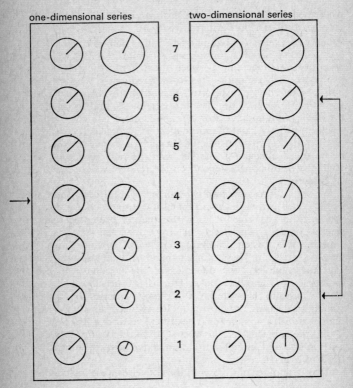

one-dimensional series   two-dimensional series

Figure 1

1964.) In the one-dimensional series the stimuli varied either in size or in inclination, but never in both respects within the same series. In the two-dimensional series, however, the two kinds of variations always went together according to a perfect linear correlation. Abbreviated versions of the two kinds of series are presented in Figure 1.

The left-hand stimulus in each pair is always the same standard stimulus. The right-hand stimuli, however, vary in a regular progression from the bottom to the top of the series. Note that, in the one-dimensional series, the right-hand stimuli vary only in size. Since there is no way of reducing the fixed difference in inclination between the standard and the variable stimulus in this series, most subjects naturally pick (as most similar to the left-hand standard) the variable stimulus that matches the standard in size (namely, number 4, as indicated by the small arrow to the left of the series). For such a series, the relative importance ascribed to each of the two attributes has no influence on the

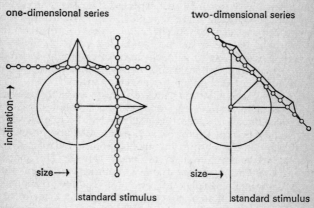

one-dimensional series

two-dimensional series

inclination ———→

size ———→

standard stimulus

size ———→

standard stimulus

Figure 2

choice. Consider, however, the two-dimensional series shown on the right. Here the appropriate choice is critically dependent on the relative weight given to inclination as opposed to size. If differences in angle seem much more salient than differences in size, the subject can minimize the over-all disparity by choosing the pair of stimuli that match with respect to angle (number 6); but if differences in size are seen as overriding differences in angle, the subject can minimize the over-all difference by selecting the pair that matches with respect to size (number 2). For any more even distribution of weights the appropriate choice may fall anywhere between these two perfect matches (as indicated by the bracket at the right of the series).

Each of 60 subjects made such choices for each of four one-dimensional and each of four two-dimensional series. Each series contained 15 variable stimuli (rather than just seven as shown in Figure 1). The results are presented in Figure 2. Each stimulus is represented there by the position of a point (designated by a small circle); the abscissa and ordinate of any such point correspond, respectively, to the size and inclination for that stimulus. Thus each variable series is represented in the figure by a rectilinear array of 15 points passing near the point for the fixed standard stimulus. The rectilinear array is oriented either horizontally or vertically, for the one-dimensional series, or at 45°, for the two-dimensional series. The actual distributions of choices made by the 60 subjects are constructed directly on these rectilinear arrays as base lines. As expected, the one-dimensional series led to compact, sharply peaked, unimodal distributions that are almost identical in shape regardless of whether the variation was in size or in inclination. By contrast, the two-dimensional series led to a much flatter distribution with two widely separated modal peaks (one corresponding to a match in size, the other corresponding to a match in angle).

Apparently, stimuli of this kind are almost invariably analyzed into perceptually distinct and incomparable attributes (such as size and inclination). Once this analysis has been performed, moreover, the manner in which the disparate attributes should be recombined for the purpose of making some kind of over-all judgment about the stimuli is not really defined. This incomparability was further demonstrated in another experiment with these same stimuli. Briefly, subjects were required to match a variable difference in angle to a given difference in angle or to a given difference in size. The obtained distributions of settings had almost identical medians under the two conditions, but the variance of the distribution for the cross-dimensional task was nearly 19 times that for the intradimensional task. Again, subjects do not appear to have any fixed common rule for comparing subjective units of size with subjective units of inclination. Indeed, the bimodality of the distribution for the two-dimensional series in Figure 2 suggests that subjects are capable of switching between orderings of the alternatives in which one of the two dimensions completely dominates the other. It is interesting that such orderings are like the 'lexicographic orderings' which cannot in general be represented by a numerical utility function (e.g., see Aumann, 1964; or Debreu, 1954).

Even when the weights associated with the separate variables do not assume such extremely disparate values, the fact that these weights can shift at all makes the particular form taken by the psychological rules for combining or 'trading off' these variables rather difficult to pin down. This may partly explain the fact that although economists concerned with the prediction of consumer behavior have placed great theoretical emphasis on what they variously call equal-preference contours, constant-utility curves, or indifference maps actual empirical determinations of the curves are notably lacking (see Edwards, 1954, pp. 384–7). The same instability may tend, also, to interfere with the construction of cardinal utility scales by the method of 'simultaneous conjoint measurement' recently proposed by Luce and Tukey (1964). Psychologists have, of course, made a variety of attempts to determine the rules by which response tendencies arising from separate sources combine (e.g., Binder and Feldman, 1960; Birch, 1957; Eninger, 1952; Guilford, 1931; Gulliksen, 1956; Hull, 1943, pp. 209–24; Miller, 1939; Powloski, 1953; Schoeffler, 1954; Warren, 1953). But since the experimental results are usually averaged over trials and/or subjects, their interpretation is seriously complicated by the possibility that the psychological weights associated with the component factors may shift from one subject or trial to the next. Since the results are likely to be insufficiently reliable without some averaging, it may be necessary to classify subjects (or subject-trial combinations) according to the underlying state of attention as inferred on the basis of just part of the data and, then, to test for the rules of combination under each such state on the basis of the remaining data (Shepard, 1964).

Finally, the experiments described suggest that psychologically meaningful comparisons between highly analyzable stimuli can probably be made only when those stimuli differ from each other along the same direction in their underlying spatial representation. This implies that, psychologically, this spatial representation is really determined only up to an affine transformation. More detailed analyses (not given here) indicate further that the appropriate geometry probably is not the variety with which we are familiar from Euclidean space but rather one of the weaker varieties such as that associated with the more general 'Minkowski spaces' (Shepard, 1964). I think, therefore, that there is a real question whether the kinds of 'frozen' Euclidean representations obtained by standard multidimensional scaling procedures (like those described by Gulliksen, 1964, and Tucker, 1964) will prove completely adequate for such highly analyzable stimuli.

The Connection between the Problem of Weights and Conflicts among Goals

The fact that subjects do not always employ an optimum weighting of attributes was noticeable in some of the experiments already reviewed, particularly those by Pollack (1962), Sarbin (1942), and Smedslund (1955). However, the full extent of this difficulty may have been somewhat obscured in those studies because a large number of judgments were made on stimuli for which a criterion variable or 'true worth' was defined. This raises the possibility that as a result of accumulating experience the optimum or 'true' weights may gradually have been learned by the subjects – at least to some extent.

Many practical decision situations differ in that previously experienced situations may not have been sufficiently numerous or similar to the present situation to support a statistical estimation of weights (e.g., by multiple-regression methods, as in some of the studies reviewed by Meehl (1954), or by Bayesian methods, as in the application considered by Edwards and Phillips, 1964). What is worse, the criterion variable to be optimized is often not even defined. Instead, there are only vaguely defined subgoals that may be more or less achieved at various subsequent times. Generally, the different attributes of a multiattribute alternative will be differentially associated with these various subgoals, and so the way in which the weights are apportioned to these attributes will strongly depend on the subjective weights of the subgoals themselves.

A recent report by Harlow, Miller, and Newcomb (1962) describes the kind of difficulty that is likely to beset practical decision problems of this kind. They were concerned with the judgment of creative talent in young psychologists on the basis of an examination of their doctoral dissertations. They noted that in many instances there was considerable disparity between the evaluations made by different judges. They go on to make the following statement: 'The judges tended to show high agreement when judging which of two dissertations was best if these dissertations were concerned with similar problems in the same area of study. However, less agreement was noted when the two dissertations being compared involved different types of studies in different areas.' This seems to me to be a pervasive kind of phenomenon. Frequently, a person who is asked to make a choice between two things will say, 'I find it hard to make up my mind – they seem so different.' To modify the hypothetical example given by Restle (1961, p. 62), a person might easily decide between a gift of $1000 and a gift of $1001, but the choice between $1000 and, say, a free vacation in Hawaii might prove more difficult (even though the difference in 'true worth' in the second case is unlikely to be as small as one dollar).

It is probably this difficulty that accounts for the widespread practice of dividing up any field into special categories for the purposes of a contest. In art, for example, a prize will be awarded for the 'best' still life, the 'best' portrait, the 'best' sculpture, and so on. And, surely, it *is* much easier to compare two still-life paintings than to compare a painting with, say, an abstract sculpture. Similarly, Harlow, Miller, and Newcomb simplified their problem by dividing the field of psychology into three separate subareas and ended up by awarding one prize for the outstanding contribution within each of these three subareas.

Presumably, the reason for the great difficulty in comparing widely different things is that such unrelated subgoals are involved. Consider the case of ranking three dissertations when two of them make theoretical contributions in the area of animal learning, whereas the third makes an experimental contribution to some aspect of social psychology. Typically, a ranking will be much easier to settle on for the two dissertations directed toward similar subgoals than to place the third dissertation with respect to them. For the relative placement of the third will obviously depend in a critical way on the relative importance ascribed in general to contributions to social psychology as opposed to animal behavior as well as on the weight given to theoretical *versus* experimental contributions; that is, the judgment of specific contributions will correlate appreciably with the evaluations of the general subgoals underlying them. As these underlying evaluations change, the relative ranking of the studies of different types may also change drastically, but, since the evaluations of the two studies of the same type will tend to go up and down together, their relative positions will remain more nearly unchanged.

In the last analysis, then, the uncertain and shifting character of over-all evaluative judgments is probably an unavoidable consequence of the inherent instability or indeterminacy of the system of weights associated with the underlying subgoals. Two scientists who agree about the relative merits of two contributions in the same field may disagree sharply about contributions in two different fields simply because they cannot agree about the relative values of the fields themselves. Moreover, since there is no possibility of tracing all subgoals back to one universally accepted final goal, there is no way, really, to settle such a dispute about the proper weights to be attached to the subgoals. This does not mean that the weights are entirely arbitrary. This would be true only if all subgoals were mutually independent. In reality, of course, some are quite closely tied together, whereas others are essentially incompatible. As a consequence, only a few of the possible assignments of signed weights will be at all tenable.

These considerations play a prominent role in several psychological theories, notably Heider's (1958) theory of 'cognitive balance' and Festinger's (1957) theory of 'dissonance resolution'. There have even been some interesting mathematical formulations of these ideas (for example, by Cartwright and Harary, 1956; Abelson and Rosenberg, 1958). Notice, though, that the notion that quite different configurations of weights may be relatively harmonious and therefore stable is consistent with the possibility that the pattern of weights may differ – not only from one individual to another, as pointed out by Gulliksen (1964) and by Tucker (1964) – but also from one occasion to another within the same individual. Thus a given individual can adopt different attitudes, frames of mind, or points of view, and each such state may have its own associated system of weights. The intraindividual switches from one such state to another, then, would be closely akin (if not identical) to the fluctuations of attention discussed before.

Now consider an individual who is faced with a decision problem of the typical kind in which no alternative is better than every other in all respects. The subjective ranking of the alternative with respect to over-all value will then depend on his current 'state of mind', since that is what determines the relevant set of subjective weights. But, at the moment when a decision is required the fact that each alternative has both advantages and disadvantages poses an impediment to the attainment of the most immediate subgoal; namely, escape from the unpleasant state of conflict induced by the decision problem itself. I suggest, therefore, that one device that people use to resolve the conflict and to consummate the decision is to 'try out' various frames of mind until they find one whose associated subjective weights give one alternative the clearest advantage over its competitors. This principle of human decision making differs from that propounded by Festinger (1957) in one important respect: Festinger argues that the change of attitudinal state occurs subsequent to the actual decision and serves to reconcile the individual with a choice already made; I am proposing that the change of state precedes the decision and serves to render the decision possible. The presently available experimental data on this crucial point is, in my opinion, inconclusive.

In any case, if there are such things as optimum weights, they presumably are independent of the particular set of alternatives that we happen to be considering at a particular moment. Thus the kind of alterations of weights we have described must be a matter of cognitive expedience and not a part of some optimum rational strategy. Surely any optimal decision procedure should entail transitivity of preferential choices; but it has long been recognized that just such fluctuations of weights as we have been considering in the case of multiattribute alternatives can easily lead to violations of transitivity (e.g., see Flament, 1958; May, 1954; Morrison, 1962; Quandt, 1956). Salesmen are probably among the principal beneficiaries of this human weakness. As a colleague of mine remarked: how many sets of encyclopedias have been sold by encouraging, in the prospective buyer, an unusual state of mind in which he temporarily convinces himself that, yes, he is going to become a scholar and astonish his acquaintances with his range of knowledge? Only after months of failing to consult the newly acquired encyclopedia does he realize the extent to which his decision problem was spuriously resolved by temporarily embracing an impractical or, indeed, untenable view of himself.

Just how the processes underlying such subjectively non-optimum decisions can be improved is not at all clear to me. In some situations a kind of mechanical averaging process might help to remove the inordinate influence of transitory states of mind. In fact, as I believe has already been suggested, for example, by Savage (1954), Anscombe (1964), and Radner (1964), the problem of finding the optimum over-all strategy could probably be regarded as one of finding the over-all strategy that is the most internally consistent; that, is, because of the instability of the subjective weights associated with the conflicting subgoals, not all pairwise choices between alternatives are consistent with one another (e.g., transitive). In this case the best we could do, presumably, would be to discover that simple ordering of all alternatives that does the least subjective violence to the whole set of weighted subgoals.

Precisely what kind of averaging process will maximize consistency is probably difficult to specify in general. Possibly there are situations in which the course of action dictated by either of two different states of mind will be more satisfactory than any kind of average of the two. Certainly there are anomalous circumstances in which an apparently reasonable averaging of transitive orderings leads to intransitivity (May, 1954). Morrison (1962 and in personal communications) has called my attention to the importance of distinguishing between two contrasting decision procedures in this connection. In one procedure differences between the contending alternatives are first estimated with respect to each distinguishable *attribute* separately; and then these estimated differences are combined in some way to arrive at an over-all decision. In the other procedure estimates of the several attributes are first combined for each *alternative* separately; and then the final choice is made on the basis of a comparison among the resulting combined values for the different alternatives. Morrison points out that the second procedure (in which the combination of attributes *precedes* the comparison of alternatives) avoids the susceptibility to intransitivity inherent in the first procedure (in which the combination of attributes *follows* the comparison of alternatives). In any case, a more detailed knowledge of the underlying psychological processes actually used in human decision making would probably be helpful in any attempt to achieve a closer approach to subjective optimality. For this purpose the most prominent theories of choice behavior (like that of Luce, 1959) seem to me to be incomplete because they treat the underlying choice tendencies as static and independent of the particular set of alternatives being considered at any one time.

References

ABELSON, R. P., and ROSENBERG, M. J. (1958). Symbolic psychologic: A model of attitudinal cognition. *Behavioral Sci.*, **3**, 1–13.

ABELSON, R. P., and TUKEY, J. W. (1959). Efficient conversion of nonmetric information into metric information. *Proc. Amer. Statist. Assoc. Meetings, Social Statistics Section*, 226–230.

ADAMS, E. W., and FAGOT, R. (1959). A model of riskless choice. *Behavioral Sci.*, **4**, 1–10.

ANDERSON, N. H. (1962). Application of an additive model to impression formation. *Science*, **138**, 817–818.

ANSCOMBE, F. J. (1964). Some remarks on Bayesian statistics. In Shelley, M. W., and Bryan, G. L. *Human judgements and optimality*, New York: Wiley, chap. 10.

ARCHER, E. J., BOURNE, L. E., and BROWN, F. G. (1955). Concept identification as a function of irrelevant information and instructions. *J. exp. Psychol.*, **49**, 153–164.

AUMANN, R. J. (1964). Subjective programming. In Shelley, M. W., and Bryan, G. L. *Human judgements and optimality*. New York: Wiley, chap. 12.

AUMANN, R. J., and KRUSKAL, J. B. (1958). The coefficients in an allocation problem. *Naval Res. Logistics Quart.*, **5**, 111–123.

AUMANN, R. J., and KRUSKAL, J. B. (1959). Assigning quantitative values to qualitative factors in the naval electronics problem. *Naval Res. Logistics Quart.*, **6**, 1–16.

AZUMA, H., and CRONBACH, L. J. (1961). Performance on a concept-attainment task with scaled cues. Mimeographed manuscript, Univer. Illinois, March.

BEXTON, W. H., HERON, W., and SCOTT, T. H. (1954). Effects of decreased variation in the sensory environment. *Canad. J. Psychol.*, **8**, 70–76.

BINDER, A., and FELDMAN, S. E. (1960). The effect of experimentally controlled experience upon recognition responses. *Psychol. Monographs*, **74** (9), 43 pp.

BIRCH, D. (1957). A model for response tendency combination. *Psychometrika*, **22**, 373–380.

BRUNER, J. S., GOODNOW, J. J., and AUSTIN, G. A. (1956). *A study of thinking*. New York: Wiley.

BRUNSWIK, E. (1956). *Perception and the representative design of psychological experiments*. Berkeley, Calif.: Univer. California Press.

CARTWRIGHT, D., and HARARY, F. (1956). Structural balance: A generalization of Heider's theory. *Psychol. Rev.*, **63**, 277–293.

DAVIDSON, D., SUPPES, P., and SIEGEL, S. (1957). *Decision making: an experimental approach*. Stanford, Calif.: Stanford Univer. Press.

DEBREU, G. (1954). Representation of a preference ordering by a numerical function. In R. M. Thrall, C. H. Coombs, and R. L. Davis (Eds.), *Decision processes*. New York: Wiley, pp. 159–165.

DESOTO, C. B. (1961). The predilection for single orderings. *J. Abnorm. soc. Psychol.*, **62**, 16–23.

EDWARDS, W. (1954). The theory of decision making. *Psychol. Bull.*, **51**, 380–417.

EDWARDS, W., and PHILLIPS, L. D. (1964). Man as a transducer for probabilities in Bayesian command and control systems. In Shelley, M. W., and Bryan, G. L. *Human judgements and optimality*. New York: Wiley, chap. 18.

ENINGER, M. U. (1952). Habit summation in a selective learning problem. *J. comp. physiol. Psychol.*, **45**, 604–608.

ESTES, W. K. (1957). Of models and men. *Amer. Psychologist*, **12**, 609–617.

FESTINGER, L. (1957). *A theory of cognitive dissonance*. Stanford, Calif.: Stanford Univer. Press.

FLAMENT, C. (1958). Analyse pluridimensionnelle des structures hiérarchiques intransitives. *Bull. Cent. Etud. Rech. Psychotech.*, **7**, 171–179.

FREEDMAN, S. J., GRUNEBAUM, H. U., and GREENBLATT, M. (1961). Perceptual and cognitive changes in sensory deprivation. In Solomon et al. (Eds.). *Sensory deprivation*. Cambridge, Mass.: Harvard Univer. Press, pp. 58–71.

GUILFORD, J. P. (1931). The prediction of affective values. *Amer. J. Psychol.*, **43**, 469–478.

GULLIKSEN, H. (1956). Measurement of subjective values. *Psychometrika*, **21**, 229–244.

GULLIKSEN, H. (1964). Optimality and individual differences. In Shelley. M. W., and Bryan, G. L. *Human judgements and optimality*. New York: Wiley, chap. 5.

HARLOW, H. F., MILLER, J. G., and NEWCOMB, T. M. (1962). Identifying creative talent in psychology. *Amer. Psychologist*, **17**, 679–683.

HAYES, J. R. (1962). Human data processing limits in decision making. Electronics System Division Report ESD-TDR-62–48, July.

HEIDER, F. (1958). *The psychology of interpersonal relations*. New York: Wiley.

HOFFMAN, P. J. (1960). The paramorphic representation of clinical judgment. *Psychol. Bull.*, **57**, 116–131.

HULL, C. L. (1943). *Principles of behavior*. New York: Appleton-Century-Crofts.

LASHLEY, K. S. (1951). The problem of serial order in behavior. In L. A. Jeffress (Ed.), *Cerebral mechanisms in behavior*. New York: Wiley, pp. 112–146.

LUCE, R. D. (1959). *Individual choice behavior*. New York: Wiley.

LUCE, R. D., and TUKEY, J. W. (1964). Simultaneous conjoint measurement: A new type of fundamental measurement. *J. Math. Psychol.*, **1**, 1–27.

MAY, K. O. (1954). Intransitivity, utility, and the aggregation of preference patterns. *Econometrica*, **22**, 1–13.

MEEHL, P. E. (1954). *Clinical versus statistical prediction*. Minneapolis, Minn.: Univer. Minnesota Press.

MILLER, G. A. (1956). The magical number seven, plus or minus two. *Psychol. Rev.*, **63**, 81–97.

MILLER, J. (1939). The rate of conditioning of human subjects to single and multiple conditioned stimuli. *J. gen. Psychol.*, **20**, 399–408.

MORRISON, H. W. (1962). Intransitivity of paired comparison choices. Doctoral dissertation. Univer. Michigan.

OSGOOD, C. S., SUCI, G. J., and TANNENBAUM, P. H. (1957). *The measurement of meaning*. Urbana, Ill.: Univer. Illinois Press.

POLLACK, I. (1962). Action selection and the Yntema–Torgerson 'Worth' function. Paper read at the 1962 meetings of the Eastern Psychological Association, April 27.

POWLOSKI, R. F. (1953). The effects of combining hunger and thirst motives in a discrimination habit. *J. comp. Physiol. Psychol.*, **46**, 435–437.

QUANDT, R. E. (1956). A probabilistic theory of consumer behavior, *Quart. J. Econ.*, **70**, 507–536.

RADNER, R. (1964). Mathematical specification of goals for decision problems. In Shelley, M. W., and Bryan, G. L. *Human judgements and optimality*. New York: Wiley, chap. 11.

RESTLE, F. (1961). *Psychology of judgment and choice*. New York: Wiley.

RIMOLDI, H. J. A. (1956). Prediction of scale values for combined stimuli. *Brit. J. statist. Psychol.*, **9**, 29–40.

SARBIN, T. R. (1942). A contribution to the study of actuarial and individual methods of prediction. *Amer. J. Sociol.*, **48**, 593–602.

SAVAGE, L. J. (1954). *The foundations of statistics*. New York: Wiley.

SCHOEFFLER, M. S. (1954). Probability of response to compounds of discriminated stimuli. *J. exp. Psychol.*, **48**, 323–329.

SEBESTYEN, G. S. (1962). *Decision-making processes in pattern recognition*. New York: Macmillan.

SHEPARD, R. N. (1962). The analysis of proximities: multidimensional scaling with an unknown distance function: *Psychometrika*, **27**, 125–140. (a). *Psychometrika*, **27**, 219–246. (b).

SHEPARD, R. N. (1963a). Analysis of proximities as a technique for the study of information processing in man. *Human Factors*, **5**, 33–48.

SHEPARD, R. N. (1963b). Comments on Professor Underwood's paper: Stimulus selection in verbal learning. In C. N. Cofer and B. S. Musgrave (Eds.), *Verbal behavior and learning: problems and processes.* New York: McGraw-Hill, pp. 48–70.

SHEPARD, R. N. (1964). Attention and the metric structure of the stimulus space. *J. Math. Psychology*, **1**, 54–87.

SHEPARD, R. N., HOVLAND, C. I., and JENKINS, H. M. (1961). Learning and memorization of classifications. *Psychol. Monogr.*, **75** (13, Whole No. 517).

SMEDSLUND, J. (1955). *Multiple-probability learning.* Oslo: Akademisk Forlag.

SMITH, J. W. (1956). A plan to allocate and procure electronics sets by the use of linear programming techniques and analytical methods of assigning values to qualitive factors. *Naval Res. Logistics Quart.*, **3**, 151–162.

SPENCE, W., and GUILFORD, J. P. (1933). The affective value of combinations of odors. *Amer. J. Psychol.*, **45**, 495–501.

TUCKER, L. R. (1964). Systematic differences between individuals in perceptual judgments. In Shelley, M. W., and Bryan, G. L. *Human judgements and optimality.* New York: Wiley, chap. 6.

WARREN, J. M. (1953). The additivity of cues in visual pattern discrimination by monkeys. *J. comp. physiol. Psychol.*, **46**, 484–486.

WOODWORTH, R. S., and SCHLOSBERG, H. (1954). *Experimental psychology.* (Rev. ed.). New York: Holt.

YNTEMA, D. B., and TORGERSON, W. S. (1961). Man-computer cooperation in decisions requiring common sense. *IRE Trans. Human Factors Electron.*, *HFE-2*, 20–26.

YNTEMA, D. B., and KLEM, L. (1962). Telling a computer how to evaluate alternatives as one would evaluate them himself. Paper presented at First Congress on the Information System Sciences, Hot Springs, Va., November 18–21. (Preprint.)

10 E. W. Adams and R. Fagot

A Model of Riskless Choice

E. W. Adams and R. Fagot, 'A model of riskless choice', *Behav. Sci.*, vol. 4 (1959), pp. 1–10.

Current researches on how we arrive at decisions concentrate on utility functions. This article deals with individuals' choices among pairs of alternatives involving only two components, in situations where no risks are incurred. For instance, Alice's father announces he will buy her a Ford coupé for graduation. She is permitted to select between blue and yellow, and to decide whether or not it is to be convertible. A model for choices of this type is detailed here and a test of it reported.

Introduction

The purpose of this paper is to present a model for the explanation and prediction of *individual* decision-making in situations of *riskless* choice. The model provides a method of measuring 'subjective value' or 'utility' which under some conditions leads to an ordered metric scale, and under still more restrictive conditions to an interval scale of utility (cardinal utility function). An experiment has been carried out to test the model in a simple situation of riskless choice, and some results of this experiment are summarized.

The model is concerned with subjects' choices in pair-wise comparisons between alternatives which involve just two '*components*'.[1] Such alternatives might be, for example, political candidates who are described as varying in two characteristics, liberality and foreign policy. In such a case liberality would be one component and foreign policy would be a second component, and a political candidate would be characterized by a specified degree of liberality, and a specified foreign policy. In a typical experiment to which the model would apply, constructed hypothetical alternatives – such as political candidates in the above example – would be presented pair-wise to the subjects, and they would be required to state a preference for one of the alternatives of each presented pair.

This model deals with a certain class of such two-component choice situations. This class can be characterized intuitively as one

1. We shall discuss briefly the multi-dimensional case on page 292, but otherwise this paper will be devoted to the two-component case.

in which the individual behaves as though he assigns subjective values to each of the components *independently*, and then adds the values together to get the value of the composite alternative. He then chooses that alternative of every presented pair which has the higher value, or utility. When an individual evaluates a composite alternative by adding the separate utilities of each component, he will be said to have an *additive utility function*.

This 'additive' hypothesis of the combination of utilities is not new. The assumption was common, for example, in the classical economic theory of consumers' behavior, in which it was often assumed that the utility of a 'commodity bundle' was the sum of the utilities of the separate items composing the bundle (see, for example, Samuelson [15]). Irving Fisher (9) has made an analogous assumption the basis of a method for obtaining a measure of marginal utility which could be used in theories of welfare economics. Additivity hypotheses also underlie certain modern theories of the scaling of multi-dimensional stimuli. Factor analysis is concerned with the problem of isolating factors or dimensions in stimuli to which the subject responds as though he has an additive weighting function. Ward Edwards (5) has assumed a kind of additivity in a limited form in his 'N-bets' method of determining a measure of utility of certain choices involving risk independent of subjective probability. Coombs and Kao (4) have made a very general study of alternative models for the explanation of the preference-behavior of subjects confronted with alternatives with two or more components. Finally, Gulliksen (10) tested several possible laws of utility combination, including an additive one, for a special class of two-component alternatives (what we shall call '*commutative*' alternatives); see page 293 to determine which of them gives the 'best fit' for utilities previously determined by the method of paired-comparisons for groups of subjects.

One of the objects of this paper will be to make a more detailed logical analysis of the additivity hypothesis and its consequences than has heretofore been made. Except in the case of Gulliksen's study cited above, in which an independently determined utility function was tested for additivity, theories of additive utility functions serve both to define 'utility' and to predict preferences, and it is important to separate out in such theory the parts of it which are merely 'conventional', because they are consequences of definitions, and the non-logical, empirical consequences. The very fact that the assumptions of the theory are utilized in determining the utility values which are used in making predictions and testing the theory may cause some doubt as to what constitutes a valid test of the theory, and this can only be resolved by a careful analysis to determine just what the empirical consequences of the theory are. Once we have specified exactly what observable consequences follow from a set of observed preferences on the assumption that the theory holds, then we are in a position to make a valid test of the theory.

The description of the model and the analysis of its implications will cover the following points: the formal model; some of its more important directly observable consequences; certain extensions of the model; the problem of the uniqueness of the utility values determined from the model; and finally some applications of the model, including the analysis of an experiment conducted to test the model.

Formal Structure of the Additive Utility Model

Let K be a set of *alternatives*, any two of which a subject can compare in order of preference. A subject's *strict preference relation* among the members of K is denoted P, and his *indifference relation* is denoted I. For reasons of formal simplicity, it is customary to base the theory of preference on the *preference-or-indifference* relation, which we denote by R, rather than immediately on the preference and indifference relations, and we shall follow this approach. The relations P and I are defined in terms of R in the usual way (see, for example, Arrow [2, pp. 13–15]).

The alternatives in the model are describable in terms of two *components*. Formally, the alternatives are ordered pairs (x_1, x_2) where x_1 is an object of some kind, and x_2 is an object of another kind. Thus x_1 may be a 'liberality' rating, and x_2 may be a 'foreign policy' rating, and (x_1, x_2) will characterize a person with that liberality and foreign policy rating. Abstractly, the first components x_1 will be members of some set K_1 (in the above example, a set of liberality ratings), and the second components x_2 will be members of another set K_2. The set of alternatives (x_1, x_2) will be a subset of the cartesian product $K_1 \times K_2$, which is the set of all ordered pairs (x_1, x_2) where x_1 is a member of K_1 and x_2 is a member of K_2. We shall assume that the set of alternatives is actually equal to the set $K_1 \times K_2$. Thus we require that if (x_1, x_2) and (y_1, y_2) are two alternatives, then (x_1, y_2) and (y_1, x_2) are also alternatives. Note that this requirement clearly indicates that the set of alternatives will in general include alternatives which are only 'conceivable', but not necessarily actually available as possible courses of action. We assume that an individual is able to evaluate these unavailable alternatives even though he may not be able to choose them for practical reasons.

The fundamental assumption of utility theory is that utility magnitudes determine preferences; i.e., a *utility function U* is assumed to represent the strengths of the subject's preferences for the alternatives in *K*. The present model assumes the existence of a special kind of utility function, called an *additive utility function*. Intuitively, this *additive hypothesis* states that the utility of an ordered pair (x_1, x_2) is equal to the utility of x_1 added to the utility of x_2. A formal definition of an additive utility function is given below.

Definition 1. – Let *U* be a real-valued function defined over $K_1 \times K_2$; then *U* is an *additive utility function* if it satisfies the following conditions:

(a) For all x_1, y_1 in K_1 and x_2, y_2 in K_2, $(x_1, x_2)R(y_1, y_2)$ if and only if $U(x_1, x_2) \geqslant U(y_1, y_2)$.

(b) There exist functions U_1 and U_2 defined over K_1 and K_2 respectively, such that for all x_1 in K_1 and x_2 in K_2, $U(x_1, x_2) = U_1(x_1) + U_2(x_2)$.

The basic assumption of the model may now be stated:

Additive Hypothesis. – There exists an additive utility function for the set $K_1 \times K_2$ and the preference-or-indifference relation *R*.

It will be noted that in condition (a) *U* is defined only for alternatives as a whole, and hence in condition (b) it is necessary to introduce two new utility functions U_1 and U_2 representing the utility values of the first and second components of the alternatives, respectively. The interpretation of U, U_1 and U_2 are clear: these are any functions satisfying Definition 1. Testing the additive hypothesis simply tests whether or not there *exist* functions U, U_1 and U_2 which satisfy the fundamental hypothesis.

In a second possible interpretation of the utility functions U, U_1 and U_2, the utility values of the alternatives and their components may be those determined in a different theory of utility. For example, the theory of decision-making under risk furnishes a method of measuring the utilities of certain types of alternatives, and U, U_1 and U_2 can be assumed to be the functions determined by this theory. With this interpretation of the utility functions the additive hypothesis is much stronger in predictive consequences than if this hypothesis is simultaneously used to determine the utility values with which predictions are to be made, as in the first interpretation considered. This point will be considered in more detail on page 297.

Of course, it is not immediately evident what conditions must be satisfied by any preference field in order that it satisfy the additive hypothesis, and therefore in the following section we shall specify some of the consequences about the structure of the preference field which follow from the additive hypothesis.

Some Empirical Consequences of the Additive Hypothesis

In this section we shall present some of the empirical consequences of the assumption of additivity. An 'empirical' or 'observable' consequence is any consequence implied by the additive hypothesis about the relations P, I and R themselves. One important feature of such consequences is the fact that they can be tested directly by observation without first computing the utility values of the alternatives.

Another reason for giving the empirical consequences of the additive hypothesis is that in many instances in which the model is not perfectly satisfied by a subject, it is of interest to attempt to discover which of the consequences he does satisfy and which he does not; i.e., to discover precisely in what way additivity fails to hold. Unfortunately, there is no simple set of consequences which completely exhausts the empirical significance of the additive hypothesis, even for finite sets if K_1 and K_2 can be of any finite size. Therefore in this section we shall give only some of the more important observable consequences of additivity. The proofs of these 'theorems' which follow from the additive 'axiom' are mathematically trivial, and hence shall be omitted. The *Empirical Consequences* will be formulated in terms of the relation R, but in each case the modifications obtained by replacing R with the relations P and I follow directly.

Empirical Consequences 1. – R is a weak ordering of $K = K_1 \times K_2$; i.e., R satisfies the conditions:

(*a*) For all x and y in K, either xRy or yRx.
(*b*) For all x, y and z in K, if xRy and yRz, then xRz.

The fact that R is a weak ordering yields consequences for the relations P, I and R (for example, that the relations P and I are transitive), which are more or less 'corollaries' of Consequence 1. All of these consequences are well known, and we shall not restate them here.

Consequence 2, which follows, is perhaps the most important of the empirical consequences peculiar to the model.

Empirical Consequence 2. (The Independence Condition.) – For all x_1 and y_1 in K_1 and x_2 and y_2 in K_2:

(*a*) If $(x_1, x_2)R(x_1, y_2)$ then $(y_1, x_2)R(y_1, y_2)$.
(*b*) If $(x_1, y_2)R(y_1, y_2)$ then $(x_1, x_2)R(y_1, x_2)$.

The Independence Condition states essentially that each of the sets K_1 and K_2 can be ordered in preference independently of the others; i.e., it is possible to assign a preference ordering to the individual components, derived from the ordering of the total alternatives. Thus we infer that x_1 is preferred to y_1 if $(x_1, x_2)P(y_1, x_2)$. Consequence 2 guarantees that the order of preference between x_1 and y_1 obtained by comparing (x_1, x_2) with (y_1, x_2) will not be changed if x_2 is replaced by any other element y_2 of K_2. Below we give a formal definition of the preference orderings within the individual sets K_1 and K_2 for systems satisfying the Independence Condition.

Definition 2. – For all x_1, y_1 in K_1 and x_2, y_2 in K_2, $x_1R_1y_1$ if and only if $(x_1, x_2)R(y_1, x_2)$, and $x_2R_2y_2$ if and only if $(x_1, x_2)R(x_1, y_2)$.

If Consequences 1 and 2 are satisfied, then the relations R_1 and R_2 establish weak orderings over the sets K_1 and K_2 respectively, analogous to the weak ordering R over $K_1 \times K_2$.

It should be noted in connection with the definition of R_1 and R_2 that these preference relations on the components are derived from comparisons of composite alternatives and not from direct comparisons of single components. It is at least logically possible that, say, $x_1P_1y_1$ might be inferred from comparisons of two-component alternatives according to Definition 1, but that if asked directly the subject might say that he preferred y_1 to x_1 in a choice between these components taken individually.

Psychologists sometimes tacitly make this assumption of independence. Gulliksen (11, p. 125), for example, in deriving a least squares solution for paired comparisons with incomplete data, suggests that in experiments in which composite alternatives are used, it would be desirable to exclude such comparisons as (*a* and *b*) with (*a* and *c*), where *a*, *b* and *c* are objects of some kind. Such an omission assumes the independence condition, but allows for no test of this assumption. It is obvious that there will be many situations in which one would not expect the independence condition to hold, such as for *competing* and *complementary* objects (see, for example, Edwards [6, pp. 382–389]). Therefore, in applying this model, one must look for situations in which the components are independent.

One important corollary of Consequences 1 and 2 is that if one alternative *dominates* another, in the sense that the first alternative is 'at least as good' as the other on both components, then the first alternative must be preferred-or-indifferent to the second. If an alternative (x_1, x_2) dominates another alternative (y_1, y_2), we write $(x_1, x_2)D(y_1, y_2)$. A formal definition of dominance is given below.

Definition 3. – For all x_1, y_1 in K_1 and x_2, y_2 in K_2, if $x_iR_iy_i$ for $i = 1, 2$, then (x_1, x_2) *dominates* (y_1, y_2); i.e., $(x_1, x_2)D(y_1, y_2)$.

The relation D is transitive, and in fact, D is a *quasi-ordering* of $K_1 \times K_2$ (see, for example, Arrow [2, p. 35]). D would be a weak ordering of $K_1 \times K_2$ if it were the case that for all x_1, y_1 in K_1 and x_2, y_2 in K_2, either $(x_1, x_2)D(y_1, y_2)$ or $(y_1, y_2)D(x_2, y_2)$. However, for certain pairs of alternatives, the relation of dominance does not hold, and these pairs are particularly important in that a choice between two such alternatives involves an element of *conflict*. For example, a comparison between (x_1, x_2) and (y_1, y_2) involves conflict if x_1 is preferred to y_1 but y_2 is preferred to x_2. The *strength* of a subject's preferences for x_1 over y_1 and y_2 and x_2 can be represented by the two *utility intervals* $X_1 - Y_1$ and $Y_2 - X_2$, respectively (where the capital letters denote the utilities of the components). The subject resolves this conflict, and hence makes a choice, by evaluating these two utility intervals. Thus if for some subject $X_1 - Y_1 > Y_2 - X_2$, then that subject will prefer (x_1, x_2) to (y_1, y_2). Although obviously some conflict choices may be predictable from transitivity, it will usually be the case that a residue of conflict choices is independent of Consequences 1 and 2. In other words, from a specific set of preferences, some subset of the conflict choices will be predictable from the additive hypothesis, but not from Consequences 1 and 2. This result is to be expected on theoretical grounds, since Consequences 1 and 2 are not sufficient to guarantee the existence of an additive utility function.

We present below one final Empirical Consequence (which is independent of Consequences 1 and 2) of the additive hypothesis which has implications for the conflict choices.

Empirical Consequence 3. – For all x_1, y_1 and z_1 in K_1 and x_2, y_2 and z_2 in K_2, if $(x_1, x_2)R(y_1, y_2)$ and $(y_1, z_2)R(z_1, x_2)$, then $(x_1, z_2)R(z_1, y_2)$.

The intuitive significance of Consequence 3 is not nearly so obvious as that of Consequences 1 and 2, but it becomes clearer if it is expressed in terms of the corresponding inequalities among utility values. It should be clear from the discussion above that the three preference relations in Consequence 3 may be expressed directly as the following inequalities in utility intervals:

$$(1) \qquad X_1 - Y_1 \geqslant Y_2 - X_2$$

$$(2) \qquad Y_1 - Z_1 \geqslant X_2 - Z_2$$

$$(3) \qquad X_1 - Z_1 \geqslant Y_2 - Z_2.$$

According to Consequence 3, inequality (3) is implied by (1) and (2). By simple addition of intervals this is easily seen to be the case, since $X_1 - Z_1$ is the sum of the two intervals $X_1 - Y_1$ and $Y_1 - Z_1$, and $Y_2 - Z_2$ is the sum of the two intervals $Y_2 - X_2$ and $X_2 - Z_2$. Each interval represents a difference in utility between elements *within* one of the sets K_1 and K_2. Hence we may think of the subject as comparing utility intervals, where each interval represents the difference in utility between two elements within one of the sets K_1 or K_2. Then Consequence 3 may be interpreted as requiring that such utility intervals be additive.

In empirical situations, it is usually easier to use these consequences directly rather than attempt to use the additive hypothesis in making predictions from any system of observed preferences. Thus, if we observe $(x_1, x_2)P(y_1, x_2)$, then we can use the Independence Condition to infer $(x_1, z_2)P(y_1, z_2)$. It is obvious that the other consequences can be used analogously in making predictions.

It is clear that the foregoing empirical consequences must be satisfied in any additive preference field, since they are deducible from the additive hypothesis. They are not, however, sufficient to guarantee the existence of an additive utility function. Therefore, it is not sufficient in determining whether or not a given preference system satisfies the model to determine whether it satisfies the empirical consequences given in this section, since there will be systems which satisfy these consequences but for which there is not an additive utility function. In fact, as a consequence of a result obtained by Scott and Suppes (16, pp. 16–27), it can be shown that no set of empirical consequences of the additive hypothesis of the types we have been considering in this section exhausts the empirical content of the additive hypothesis for all finite sets of alternatives. Therefore it is not possible to give such a set of necessary and sufficient conditions for the existence of an additive function for all finite systems.

Since Consequences 1–3 do not exhaust the empirical significance of the additive hypothesis (and hence do not have the 'predictive strength' of the additive hypothesis), it is possible to define a 'weaker' model which has Consequences 1–3 as 'axioms'. We may also define still weaker models in terms of the empirical consequences, such as the *Ordinal Model*, which has Consequence 1 as its only axiom, and the *Independence Model* which has Consequences 1–2 as axioms. Experimental comparisons of the alternative models can thus be made.

We might indicate at this point how one might determine if the additive model, or one of the weaker models defined above, is satisfied for a system of observed preferences. In the case of the additive model, a *decision procedure* can be given for determining unequivocally whether or not a system of observed preferences satisfies the additive hypothesis. It is clear that every choice that a subject makes can be represented by an equality or inequality among utility values. There will be one such inequality (or equality) for each preference observed, and the problem of determining whether or not the system of preferences satisfies the additive model reduces to the problem of determining whether the corresponding system of inequalities and equalities is consistent, i.e., has a solution. There is a well-known procedure for determining whether or not such a system has a solution and for constructing a solution if it has one, and we shall not repeat it here (see, for example, Kuhn [14]). In the event that such a solution does not exist, i.e., the additive model is not perfectly satisfied, we may test to determine if one of the weaker models is satisfied by directly testing the axioms (consequences).

Extensions of the Model

In this section we discuss briefly possible extensions of the present model to wider classes of decision situations. One of these is the obvious one to alternatives of more than two components, and another is to situations involving elements of risk.

If the number of components is a fixed number n, then each alternative can be represented as an ordered n-tuple $(x_1, \ldots, x_n)$. If $K_1, \ldots, K_n$ are the sets of first, second, n-th components, then the total set of alternatives is $K_1 X \ldots X K_n$. The additive hypothesis is that there exists a utility function U for the set

$K_1 X \ldots X K_n$ and functions $U_1, U_2, \ldots, U_n$ over the sets K_1, $K_2, \ldots, K_n$ such that for all x_i in K_i, $i = 1, 2, \ldots, n$.

(1) $U(x_1, \ldots, x_n) = U_1(x_1) + \ldots + U_n(x_n)$.

Although this extension follows obviously from the two-component case, the empirical consequences of the additive hypothesis for n-component systems are not so obvious and will not be discussed in this paper.

Another possible extension of the model would be to *commutative systems* in which the alternatives are arbitrary sequences of objects from some basic set K', and not sequences of fixed size. A formal characterization of commutative systems will not be given here, but the following example of such a system shows clearly the kind of situation to which this extension would apply. This example is provided by an experiment conducted by Thurstone and Jones (18) in which the basic set K' consisted of several different articles which might be received as birthday gifts, such as a pen and pencil set, a brief case, and a table lamp. An alternative was either a single article or a pair of articles, although any arbitrary sequence of articles from the basic set K' could have been included. A comparison of this example of a commutative system with the example of political candidates for a non-commutative system (see page 284) should clarify a fundamental difference between the two systems, which is the kind of alternatives admissible in each system. Thus in the commutative case an alternative could be (desk lamp, desk lamp) (i.e., *two* desk lamps), whereas in the non-commutative case such alternatives are not admissible; for example, the alternative (high liberality, high liberality) could not be a member of $K_1 \times K_2$ in the non-commutative case.

Gulliksen's study of food preferences (Gulliksen [10]) is another example of an experiment on commutative systems. It is worthwhile pointing out, however, that neither of these two studies were concerned with *individual* decision-making, as is the present model. An interesting problem would be the relationship between the individual utility functions determined by this model and the *group* utility functions determined in the two studies cited above.

The present theory may be combined with a theory of utility under risk by extending the set of alternatives to include risk combinations of the original two-component alternatives. Suppose that K is a set of two-component alternatives. If (x_1, x_2) and (y_1, y_2) are elements of K, then it is possible to form a risk 'mixture' of them, $p(x_1, x_2) + (1 - p)(y_1, y_2)$, representing the 'prospect' of getting alternative (x_1, x_2) if an event of probability p occurs and getting (y_1, y_2) if it does not occur. If we proceed to form probability mixtures of K, mixtures of these mixtures, and so on, we form a set which is the mixture space generated by K (see Hausner [12]).

Uniqueness of Additive Utility Functions

Intuitively, a preference field with an additive utility function yields an *interval scale* of utility (or *cardinal* utility function) if it is the case that the utility function is completely determined once a zero point and a unit of utility have been chosen. Mathematically, to say that a preference field has a cardinal utility function means that any two additive utility functions for this field must be related by a linear transformation. A decision procedure can be given to determine whether or not the utility function (if it exists) is in fact a cardinal utility function (see Adams and Fagot [1, pp. 44–51]).

A question arises as to the uniqueness of additive utility functions in those cases in which they are not unique up to a linear transformation (i.e., are not interval scales). There is a close connection both formally and empirically between additive utility functions and ordered metrics (see Coombs [3]). It is clear from the discussion of Consequence 3 in Section 3 that the additive model provides a partial ordering on certain utility intervals. Thus a comparison between (x_1, x_2) and (y_1, y_2) provides an ordering on the two utility intervals $U_1(x_1) - U_1(y_1)$ and $U_2(y_2) - U_2(x_2)$. But since we are able only to infer a preference ordering within the sets K_1 and K_2 separately, and not within the *union* of K_1 and K_2 (i.e., within the set which contains all the members of both K_1 and K_2) then we can only get a partial ordering on utility intervals, and not a complete ordering. However, it is easy to show that the additive model does provide a complete ordering on utility intervals for commutative systems.

Applications of the Model

In this section we shall discuss three types of situations to which the model may be applied. The first is a direct test of the additive hypothesis, or of one of the weaker alternative models. In this case one simply tests to determine whether or not subjects do in fact behave in accordance with the additive hypothesis; if not, one attempts to determine precisely which of the empirical consequences are disconfirmed. Intuitively, this case corresponds to the *measurement* problem: if the model is satisfied we have in fact constructed a scale.

The second and third situations might be thought of as the *prediction* problem: given a particular scale (a set of observations satisfying a model), what predictions can be made? In the second situation we shall consider the use of a subset of observations to predict to another subset, and the allied problem of using the scale derived from the model as an independent measure of utility to be used in conjunction with another theory. In the third situation, an independent measure of utility is obtained from some other theory, and this measure is used to make predictions between multi-component alternatives under the assumption that the additive hypothesis (or one of the weaker models) holds. This latter situation is related to the comparison of utility scales derived by different methods.

An experiment will now be described which was designed to test whether or not subjects do in fact behave in accord with the model. This experiment will not be presented in great detail, since its only purpose is to illustrate how the model may be tested. In this experiment each of 24 subjects was instructed to take the role of a personnel manager for a large corporation and choose among hypothetical applicants, two at a time, for an executive position for which a job description was supplied. The applicants were described in terms of just two characteristics, or components, which were 'intelligence' and 'ability to handle people'. On each of these components, four levels of ability were distinguished, making a total of 16 alternatives. Thus one of a subject's choices would be between an applicant of high intelligence and low ability to handle people and a second applicant with low intelligence and high ability to handle people. Each decision that a subject makes can be represented as an inequality in utility values. The additive model is perfectly satisfied for a particular subject if and only if the resulting set of inequalities has a solution. Analysis of the data showed that 6 subjects (25%) perfectly satisfied the additive model; i.e., for each of these 6 subjects, the 77 choices[2] he was required to make resulted in 77 inequalities in utility values, these inequalities being consistent. Of those subjects who did not perfectly satisfy the additive model, it was observed that *in all cases the ordinal model as well was disconfirmed.*

2. All possible paired comparisons would constitute 120 choices, but 43 *dominance* relations were omitted (see Definition 3). These could be specified in advance since there is an assumed *a priori* ordering *within* each of the sets K_1 and K_2.

In other words, the following result holds for this experiment without exception: if the ordinal model was satisfied, then the additive model was satisfied, and if the additive model was disconfirmed, then the ordinal model was disconfirmed. This result does not fit at all the notion that transitivity is a simple condition which we should expect to be satisfied, whereas additivity is a more complex requirement which we should hardly expect to be satisfied. Analysis of the kinds of errors the subjects made suggests to us that disconfirmation was due largely to occasional inattention to the task. In other words, when the subject was sufficiently attentive to be transitive, he was also additive. This suggested an analysis of the data in terms of the largest subset of inequalities consistent with the model (for each subject). This kind of analysis showed that 80% of the subjects had at most 3 such 'errors' each; i.e., for each of these subjects, at least 74 of the 77 observed choices were consistent with the additive model. Only 2 of the subjects had more than 4 such errors.[3]

One problem of great interest which may be discussed in connection with this experiment, is the relative 'predictive strengths' of alternative models. One way of obtaining a measure of the predictive strength of a model is to determine the minimum number of preferences necessary and sufficient to predict the remaining preferences by means of the axioms of the model. For example, suppose we observe the following preferences: xPy, yPz, and xPz. Then the first two preferences are sufficient to 'characterize completely the system of preferences in the ordinal model', since the third preference is a consequence derived from the axiom of transitivity. The third preference contains superfluous information, and can be utilized as a test of the tenability of the assumption of transitivity. Thus any set of observed preferences can be reduced to a minimum number of preferences from which the remaining preferences are predictable by means of the axioms of the model. The smaller the number of observations necessary to characterize the complete set of observations, in the manner described above, the greater the predictive strength of the model. The model of greater predictive strength is thus capable of predicting certain preferences which are unpredictable in the weaker model. For example, in the ordinal model $(n - 1)$ preferences – where n is the number of alternatives – are necessary and sufficient to predict the remaining $(n - 1)(n - 2)/2$ preferences. The greater predictive strength of the additive model

3. For a detailed analysis of this experiment, see Fagot (8).

can be assessed by the reduction in the minimum subset from $(n-1)$ preferences.

In the experiment above, the mean of all subjects of the number of preferences necessary to characterize the set of observations was 15 for the ordinal model, 10 for the independence model, and 7 for the additive model. No general results were obtained for comparing the alternative models, but theoretical discussions of this problem are available in Kemeny and Oppenheim (13), and Fagot (7).

As an example of a second possible application of the model, in which one subset of observations is used to predict another, consider the following extension of the above experiment. We introduce a third component, K_3, 'capacity to assume responsibility'. We now have three sets of components, K_1, K_2, K_3. These sets could be utilized to form three two-component sets of alternatives, (1) $K_1 \times K_2$, (2) $K_1 \times K_3$ and (3) $K_2 \times K_3$, and one three-component set of alternatives, (4) $K_1 \times K_2 \times K_3$, where $K_1 \times K_2$ is the set of alternatives actually used in the experiment above. We could then have each subject make pair-wise choices among the alternatives *within* each of the four sets. The choices within any two of the first three sets of alternatives could be utilized to construct a utility function, and this utility function could be used to predict the choices among the alternatives of the third set. Finally, the choices among the alternatives within each of the first three (two-component) sets could be utilized to construct a utility function, and this function could be used to predict choices among the alternatives of the fourth (three-component) set. Each of the three models, the ordinal, independence and additive, could then be compared on the prediction of these observations.

The present model can also serve a useful purpose in connection with other utility theories, particularly the theory of choices under risk. In this theory a problem usually arises in separating the two factors of utility and subjective probability in determining a subject's reaction to the alternatives involving risk. Since the theory involves two variables, utility and subjective probability, it is often not possible to obtain an independent measure of either within the framework of the theory, and it is necessary to go outside the theory or make additional assumptions in order to obtain a measure of utility independent of subjective probability. The present model could then be used to furnish a measure of utility independent of subjective probability which could be introduced into the model of decisions under risk to obtain a measure of subjective probability.

297

It has been stated previously that the basic assumption of the additivity of the components is usually used simultaneously to determine the utility values and to make further predictions. Under these conditions the predictive consequences of the model are much weaker than if the utility values were obtained outside the model by independent methods of measurement. Two such theories which could be utilized for this purpose are those of Siegel (17) and Fagot (7), provided the commutative case is used (see page 293). Such theories could be used to assign utility values to the components of the alternatives, then predictions of choices between two-component alternatives could be made under the assumption that the additive hypothesis holds.

References

1. ADAMS, E. W., and FAGOT, R. F., 'A model of riskless choice', Technical Report No. 4, Contract Nonr 225(17), Stanford University, 7 August 1956.
2. ARROW, K. J., *Social choice and individual values*, Cowles Commission Monograph, No. 12, 1951.
3. COOMBS, C. H., 'Psychological scaling without a unit of measurement', *Psychol. Rev.*, vol. 57 (1950), pp. 145–58.
4. COOMBS, C. H., and KAO, R. C., 'Non-metric factor analysis', *Engineering Research Bulletin*, No. 38, Engineering Research Institute, University of Michigan, August 1951.
5. EDWARDS, W., 'The prediction of decisions among bets', *J. exper. Psychol.*, vol. 50 (1955), pp. 201–14.
6. EDWARDS, W., 'The theory of decision making', *Psychol. Bull.*, vol. 51 (1954), pp. 380–417.
7. FAGOT, R. F., 'An ordered metric model of individual choice behavior', Technical Report No. 13, Contract Nonr 225(17), Stanford University, August 1957.
8. FAGOT, R. F., 'A theory of decision making', Ph.D. dissertation, Stanford University, 1956.
9. FISHER, I., 'A statistical method for measuring "marginal utility" and testing the justice of a progressive income tax', in *Economic essays in honor of John Bates Clark*, Macmillan, 1929.
10. GULLIKSEN, H., 'Measurement of subjective values', *Res. Bull.*, Educational Testing Service, Princeton, 10 July 1955.
11. GULLIKSEN, H., 'A least squares solution for paired comparisons with incomplete data', *Psychometrika*, vol. 21 (1956), pp. 125–34.
12. HAUSNER, M., 'Multidimensional utilities', in Thrall, R. M., Coombs, C. H., and Davis, R. L. (eds.), *Decision processes*, Wiley, 1954, pp. 169–74.
13. KEMENY, J., and OPPENHEIM, P., 'Systematic power', *Philosophy of Science*, vol. 22 (1955), pp. 27–33.
14. KUHN, H. W., 'Solvability and consistency of linear equations and inequalities', *Amer. math. Monthly*, vol. 63 (1956), pp. 217–32.

15. SAMUELSON, P. A., *Foundations of economic analysis*, Harvard University Press, 1953.
16. SCOTT, D., and SUPPES, P., 'Foundational aspects of theories of measurement', Technical Report No. 6, 1 April 1967, Contract Nonr 225(17), Stanford University.
17. SIEGEL, S., 'A method for obtaining an ordered metric scale', *Psychometrika*, vol. 21 (1956), pp. 207–16.
18. THURSTONE, L. L., and JONES, L. V., 'The rational origin for measuring subjective values' *J. Amer. Statist. Ass.*, vol. 52 (1957), pp. 458–71.

11   D. B. Yntema and W. S. Torgerson

Man–Computer Cooperation in Decisions Requiring Common Sense

D. B. Yntema and W. S. Torgerson, 'Man–computer cooperation in decisions requiring common sense', *I R E Transactions on human factors in electronics*, H F E-2 (1961), pp. 20–26.

Summary. Men and computers could cooperate more efficiently in real-time systems – and perhaps in long-range planning too – if a man could tell the computers how he wanted decisions made, and then let the machine make the decisions for him. In the next few years there will probably be considerable pressure on system designers to adopt such arrangements. The problem of enabling a man to convey his decision rules to a machine will in many cases prove less formidable than it might at first appear. Three methods are discussed. As experience with man–machine cooperation of this type accumulates, problems for research will be generated. An attempt is made to foresee what some of them will be.

High-speed digital computers can be programmed to process large amounts of information quickly and to make decisions very rapidly, but they have not yet been made to show more than the first glimmerings of intelligence. In the present state of the art, they certainly cannot be programmed to display the generalized sort of good judgment called common sense. Thus the designers of a large control system usually conclude that some of the decisions the system must make are too important or too complicated to be entrusted to a machine. Such decisions are left to a man who acts as a sort of deputy planner, filling out the design of the system when contingencies arise that could not be included in the computer program.

A perennial problem in such cases is how to combine the machine's speed and the man's flexible good sense without sacrificing too much of either. One typical solution is to have the machine assemble and present to the man the facts he will probably want in reaching a decision, allow him to call for additional information if he thinks he needs it, and require him to indicate to the computer the action on which he decides. Another is to let the machine make the decisions according to the comparatively simple rules that can be programmed into it, but require the man to monitor the situation and countermand the machine's orders if he finds them too foolish. Either way, the man must examine one by one all of the situations calling for judgment. He must digest the information presented to him, perhaps ask for and digest more information, reach his decision, and perhaps communicate it to the machine. This takes at least a few seconds, which is a long wait by computer standards. And the seconds can pile up if a number of actions must be taken in quick succession. Unless the system has been shrewdly designed, a sudden flurry of decisions may cause the man to fall behind. He may then become a bottle-neck, or be so hurried that he behaves foolishly himself.

Watching an operator struggle with a crisis like that gives one the impression that man and computer are not complementing each other efficiently. The inefficiency seems particularly obvious when, as is often the case, the man appears to be doing the same job over and over. The decisions are all slightly different, but the factors he considers in making them are the same. He is in effect using the same decision rule again and again – a rule that takes account of all the special facts and temporary considerations that are known to him but are not recognized by the machine. One feels that he and the computer could cooperate better if he could tell it what his temporary rule was. He would then be free for other tasks, and the machine would be free to make the decisions at its own speed.

That, we suggest, is precisely what will have to be done in many cases. In the next few years, real-time systems will be required to make decisions calling for even more judgment than is now needed, more speed will be required, and the number of decisions will be larger. One might say that the sheer volume of good judgment demanded per minute will increase. Either the number of men will have to increase too – which rapidly makes a system unwieldy – or some of the decisions will have to be mechanized. Until computers acquire a little common sense, mechanization implies that people will have to direct the machines by choosing the rules according to which the decisions are made.

All this may sound more dramatic than we intend. The early techniques for telling a computer how to make decisions will probably involve approximations and be subject to a certain amount of error. So the first decisions to be mechanized will usually not be the large, spectacular ones that demand the utmost delicacy of judgment. Probably the computer will at first be used to back up the operator in lesser situations where prompt action is desirable. From time to time, he will give the machine approximate instructions that will enable it to take some fairly sensible action at once, instead of just waiting idly when he falls behind or is busy with other tasks. Then too, there are always a number of routine, time-consuming problems that have no direct bearing on the output of the system, but still require a certain amount of common sense. How the system should distribute the data-processing load among its own parts is one example. Mechanizing these smaller decisions will help keep the men free for the larger ones.

So far we have been discussing real-time systems, where the emphasis is on speed. Distilling an expert's judgment into a computer may prove equally important in long-range planning. In logistics and in business it is now common to use computer programs that calculate how to maximize some quantity or other; linear programming is the prime example. As the mathematics become more sophisticated and computers become more powerful, the success of these methods will depend less and less on the number of variables and the complexity of the relations that can be considered. Planners will find themselves paying even more attention than they do now to the precise definition of the quantity to be maximized. And here expert judgment is necessary. What is the trading relation between cost in dollars and the speed with which orders can be filled? And how are both of these factors to be balanced against the nonmonetary disadvantages of more employees? One way of dealing with such questions will, we anticipate, be to get an expert to summarize his experience and good sense in rules that define with acceptable accuracy the worths of all possible plans. The form of the rules must be such as to admit of a practical algorithm for selecting the best solution from the infinity of alternatives typical in these planning situations, but otherwise the problem is not too different from that which will be faced in real-time systems. We assume that many of the psychological techniques developed for one application will be useful in the other.

Some Quasi-Mathematical Encouragement

Telling a machine how he would make decisions sounds at first like a very complicated thing to ask a man to do. There are, however, reasons for thinking that the problem will often be less formidable than it appears.

Definitions

The discussion will be quasi-mathematical; so it will be helpful to establish some notation. Making a decision will be regarded as choosing between two or more alternative courses of action, each of which has a *worth*, W. The dimensions of worth may be anything at all: W may be a probability, an amount in dollars, or an expected number of survivors. In any case, the alternative whose current worth is largest is by definition the correct course of action. It is convenient to regard W as a true, correct worth and to agree that a person's appreciation of it can be mistaken or even self-inconsistent.

We shall be concerned with situations in which the worth of an alternative depends on several of its characteristics, which we shall call *factors*. The notation is simpler if each factor appears only at a discrete set of levels; so if the characteristic is really a continuous variable, we shall suppose it to have been arbitrarily quantitized. When there are three factors, we shall write W_{ijk} for the worth of an alternative in which the first factor appears at its ith level, the second at its jth level, and the third at its kth level.

It may be well to pause here and make it clear that the sort of decision we are describing is different from the kind that has attracted most attention from psychologists and statisticians. There is an element of risk inherent in the situations that have usually been studied. The decision-maker generally cannot know with certainty what pay-off will result from the choice of any given alternative; so his problem is one of choosing the alternative that, under the given conditions, offers the most attractive mixture of pay-offs and probabilities that those pay-offs will be received. In other words, his choice is a gamble. We are considering situations in which it is more natural to say that each alternative has a definite, fixed worth. The problem is simply one of deciding which worth is largest. This sort of decision has been called a 'riskless choice'. The distinction between the two types is perhaps more one of spirit than of strict logic, and it is likely that both kinds will on occasion be made cooperatively.[1]

The rest of the notation we need will be familiar to students of the analysis of variance. If i, j, and k run over finite sets of values and W is finite for all combinations of i, j, and k, then there is a straightforward procedure for writing the function W in the form

$$W_{ijk} = M + A_i + B_j + C_k + D_{ij} + E_{jk} + F_{ik} + G_{ijk}, \quad (1)$$

1. S. S. Walters and his colleagues at the Hughes Aircraft Co. Engrg Div., Culver City, Calif., have been considering man-computer cooperation in recognition under conditions of uncertainty. The computer has in storage the conditional probabilities that various reports will be received if any given one of the events to be recognized occurs. Experts control the decision procedure by supplying the machine with estimates of the *a priori* probabilities of the various events.

where the sum of any term over all values of any one of its subscripts vanishes. The constant M is of course the grand mean of all the Ws. The term A_i is called the *main effect* of the first factor at its ith level. It is the average worth, relative to the grand mean, of all combinations of levels in which the first factor appears at Level i. Sometimes it is convenient to call A_i the average worth of the ith level of the first factor; but one must then remember that this is an average in which combinations of levels are weighted equally – *not* according to frequency of occurrence. The term D_{ij} is called the *interaction* between the first and second factors at their levels i and j. It shows how the change in worth resulting from a change in the first factor depends on the level of the second, and vice versa. And finally, G_{ijk} is called the three-factor interaction. An expression like (1) can be derived whatever number of subscripts W may have (2). There is a main-effect term for each factor, and an interaction term for every combination of the factors taken two at a time, three at a time, four at a time, and so on, up to whatever number of factors there may be.

The main-effect approximation

There are many practical situations in which a change that is usually an improvement is always an improvement. Buying a car is a good example. The prospective purchaser will almost certainly feel that when other factors are held constant the worth of any particular kind of car always increases with any improvement in price, in gasoline mileage, in availability of repairs, or in almost any other factor one can name. It seems to be quite common for worth to behave in this way. Indeed we are tempted to guess that such situations will in practice prove more common than the other kind, the kind where a given change can be either desirable or undesirable, depending on the levels of the other factors. To state the matter quite formally, there should be a great many practical situations in which the levels of the factors can be numbered in such a way that W will be a monotone-increasing function of any of its subscripts at every value of its other subscripts.

It seems to be the case that when W behaves in this way it can often be well approximated by its grand mean plus the main effects of the various factors, all interactions being ignored entirely. For example, if there are three factors, the approximation consists of the first four terms of (1) and the rest are discarded. The assertion that this simple additive expression will often prove adequate is not the sort of statement that can be proven rigorously. The best way to appreciate the power of the approximation is to consider an example. Suppose that

$$W_{ijk} = ij + jk + ik, \qquad \begin{aligned} i &= 1, 2, \ldots, 7, \\ j &= 1, 2, \ldots, 7, \\ k &= 1, 2, \ldots, 7, \end{aligned} \qquad (2)$$

and for simplicity let all 7^3 combinations of the subscripts be equally likely. The Ws then range from 3 to 147, and their root-mean-square deviation from their grand mean is about 29. At first sight there would seem to be a large amount of interaction in this function – the change in W resulting from a given change in i is only one-seventh as great when $j = k = 1$ as when $j = k = 7$ – yet describing W by its mean and main effects works quite well. In fact, the approximation accounts for 94 per cent of the variance of W. Or to put it another way, the root-mean-square deviation of the approximate from the exact value is only about 7, roughly a four-to-one reduction from the previous figure of 29. This is moderately encouraging already. The approximation begins to look good enough to be of practical value in some applications.

But there is more encouragement to come. Usually the problem is not to estimate the absolute worth of a single alternative, but to discriminate between two or more alternatives by choosing the one whose current worth is largest. Unless W is an extraordinarily irregular function, the errors created by the main-effect approximation will tend to be systematic.[2] Thus the approximation will often discriminate correctly between two alternatives even though it distorts the worths of both of them. And the mistakes that do occur are likely to be small. In the present example, if two alternatives differ in worth by more than 6 (they will 86 per cent of the time), then the probability of a wrong decision is only 0·005. If the difference in worth is more than 12, the approximation never makes a mistake. This is decision-making of high quality indeed – much higher than might be expected when one considers that the standard error of approximation is 7.

It appears, then, that just adding up the average worths of the considerations on either side will often be a surprisingly good way

2. To be a little more precise, the errors will tend to be systematic if W is a reasonably smooth function of the main effects. This requirement should not be much of a restriction in practice; it is difficult to think of a practical case where W increases with all its subscripts and yet is not a smooth function of the main effects.

to decide between two courses of action. Even when the considerations influence each other, that fact can often be ignored.

Consider an example of the sort that arises in the tactical control of forces. Let us make the improbable assumption that a computer is to be used in dispatching forces to put out forest fires. The fire-fighters are stationed at bases scattered about in the forest, and it is considered impractical to move them from one base to another to fill the gap left by a force that has gone to a fire. The computer has a record of the current amount of force at each base. When a new fire is reported the time required to get there from any given base can be calculated automatically.

The bases are then the alternatives among which a choice must be made, and the worth of each depends on the time required to get to the fire and on the way the remaining force would be distributed if that base were chosen. This looks like a formidable problem. Evaluating a distribution of forces sounds like one of those complicated tasks that can be performed by a person but cannot easily be explained to a computer.

Consider, however, the factors that determine the worth of a tentatively chosen base. If there are n bases, then there are $n + 1$ factors: one for speed, and one for the amount of force that would remain at each base, including the chosen one. More speed would always be desirable, and other things being equal, any situation would be improved by the addition of more force at any base. In other words, the worth of a tentatively chosen base increases with all of the factors. Thus the computer would probably make a fairly good decision if it were provided with the average worth of each delay in getting to a fire and the average worth of each level of force at each base. Or to be more practical, it would probably mimic the tactical commander's decisions fairly well if supplied with the average worths he would attach to various delays and to various amounts of force remaining at various bases. The grand mean of all worths can be ignored: it applies equally to all alternatives.

Factors about which the computer has no information

Suppose next that the commander were informed that part of the forest had become particularly dry. If he were making the decisions himself he would try to conserve force in that region by choosing other bases whenever he had a reasonable choice. He could make the computer behave in much the same way by telling it to weight especially heavily the worth of force at bases in the danger area. This illustrates one way of taking account of conditions known to the man but not to the machine: it will some-times be possible to express the influence of outside information by weighting the main effects of the factors considered by the computer.

To be explicit, let there again be three factors whose levels are called i, j, and k. The machine is automatically kept informed of the current value of i, j, and k for each alternative course of action. And let the index r run over the various states of the rest of the world, states that are known to the man. The decision is made by choosing the alternative with the largest value on the special function

$$W'_{ijkr} = a_r A_i + b_r B_j + c_r C_k. \tag{3}$$

A_i, B_j, and C_k are the main effects of the factors considered by the machine. They would perhaps be estimated in advance by a panel of experts, and presumably would not be changed often while the system was running. a_r, b_r, and c_r are weights that the operator would change from time to time to take account of special circumstances.

Eq. (3) can be rewritten

$$W'_{ijkr} = A_i + B_j + C_k + (a_r - 1)A_i \\ + (b_r - 1)B_j + (c_r - 1)C_k. \tag{4}$$

Observe that the last three terms have two subscripts apiece. Comparison with (1) then makes it clear that this scheme is essentially an attempt to approximate by those three terms the interactions between the outside-world factor and the factors considered by the machine. (The main effect of the outside factor does not appear. Like the grand mean, it affects all alternatives alike.) Finding numbers $(a_r - 1)$ to describe a set of interactions is, in essence, like approximating a surface by a family of straight lines parallel to one of the coordinate planes. If the world of psychological worth is like the physical world in containing many broad, sweeping functions whose curvature is nowhere very large, then such an attempt should succeed fairly often. These inter-actions, like interactions between factors considered by the machine, may not be so important as they would at first sight appear; so they may not need to be approximated accurately. Furthermore, the errors created by the approximation are still systematic; so there is a good chance of a correct decision even when the worths of both alternatives have been distorted.

In some cases the effect of outside information will be to increase the attractiveness of a particular alternative rather than to change the relative importance of the considerations that affect all alternatives. The man would then want to tell the machine to add an arbitrary amount to the worth it calculated for that alternative. Suppose that the problem were to pick an airfield at which to land a jet in bad weather, and that the computer were programmed to calculate the worth of each field by considering ceiling, visibility, and the fuel the airplane would have to spare when it got there. And suppose that the operator had heard there was a thunderstorm near one of the fields, right on the instrument approach course. He would then want the computer to choose another field if it reasonably could. To a first approximation he could tell the machine what he wanted by instructing it to subtract a certain quantity from whatever worth it might calculate for the field in question. This amounts to defining a special factor whose level at each field is known to the man – but not to the machine – and asking the man to approximate the influence of that factor by telling the machine what the main effect at each field is. Again, this is an approximation that should often work well.

Psychophysical Methods

We have pointed out that there will be considerable pressure to have people tell computers how they want decisions made, and that there is a common type of riskless choice in which some simple but approximate instructions should enable the computer to mimic a man's judgments reasonably well. We now turn to the psychological problem of estimating the quantities that appear in these approximations. It is difficult to predict just what psychophysical methods will be used. Techniques will probably proliferate rapidly as cooperative decision-making becomes common. It is possible, however, to foresee three methods that will almost surely be used in one application or another.

Individual worths

The first method is appropriate for long-range planning and other applications where accuracy is more important than a man's time. In theory it is quite straightforward: an expert simply estimates the worths of all possible combinations of all levels of all of the factors. If there are a great many combinations, it may be necessary to choose a few levels of each factor, evaluate all possible combinations of those levels, and then interpolate. But in any case, the man's task is simply to evaluate particular combinations of levels, just as an appraiser puts a value on a particular house. There is in theory no question of approximation, and no problem about whether the interactions are small enough to be ignored.

Simple as the method may be in theory, sophistication can be useful in the analysis of the results. An experiment on which the authors collaborated with W. C. Lee will serve as an illustration. The subject was to learn to evaluate 180 ellipses, each of which had been assigned an arbitrary worth. They varied in size, shape, and color – all possible combinations of six sizes, six shapes, and five colors being used. Worth was assigned in such a way that it always increased with size, thinness, and brownness and was a reasonably smooth function of those three factors. Mean and main effects accounted for about 94 per cent of the variance, just as in the example of (2). But here the main effects were curvilinear: for example, the first few steps in size had on the average much less effect on worth than the last few steps. Furthermore, the factors were not equally important: changing size from one extreme to the other had on the average more effect than changing color or shape from one extreme to the other.

The subject indicated his judgment of worth by setting a marker that could be moved over a range of about two feet. The surface over which it travelled was kept as featureless as possible, so that he would learn to make his setting by reference to the ends of the range, not by reference to minute irregularities of the surface. After he had made a setting, the experimenter moved the marker to the correct position (using a scale invisible to the subject), and then showed him the next ellipse. On each day after the first, the subject was shown all 180 ellipses in a scrambled order, he judged each and was corrected on each judgment. This procedure was continued for ten days.

On the twelfth day, he was again shown all 180 ellipses in a scrambled order, but this time the procedure was different, the essential change being that correction was no longer given. In other words, his judgment was examined by the method of individual worths. The product-moment correlation between the true worths and the judgments made on this twelfth day was computed, and its average for the six subjects was found to be 0·84. They had learned to make the judgment fairly well, though by no means perfectly.

To find out how much damage would be done by ignoring interactions, the main effects in each subject's responses on the twelfth day were computed and used to predict the worth of each ellipse. Surprisingly, the average correlation between the true worths and these predictions was 0·89, higher than before. Throwing away all information about interaction improved the estimate of worth instead of degrading it. This was particularly startling since it could be shown that the subjects had in some sense taken account of the interactions in making their responses.

The resolution of the paradox was quite simple. There was apparently random error in the subjects' responses; it was as if they had made small, unpredictable mistakes in trying to set the marker exactly where they wanted it. The computation of a main effect involved taking the mean of some thirty responses; so the random error tended to be averaged out. But computation of the interactions involved less averaging, and enough error remained to outweigh any advantage gained from trying to use them.

In practice, the true worths will of course be unknown; so it will be necessary to deduce indirectly which interactions are worth including – and which main effects, for that matter. It may be possible to have an expert make two independent judgments of the worths of some or all of the combinations. The inconsistency in his judgments can then be estimated, and calculations similar to an analysis of variance can be performed to estimate whether the error incurred by using a main-effect or interaction term is less than the variance for which the term accounts. (This is not a test of significance. A term can be highly significant and still not worth including.) Alternatively, responses from two or more judges can be analysed in a somewhat similar fashion.

The improvement achieved by averaging a number of responses suggests an intriguing possibility. Artificial, precomputed judgments may in some cases be better than those the man could make himself if he dealt with each situation as it arose.

Interpolation between the corners

The second method is less laborious than the first, but it should be fairly accurate when worth increases with each of its factors. In the first step only two levels of each factor are considered, the levels at which its main effect is algebraically largest and least. The expert is presented all possible combinations of such levels, and he estimates the individual worths just as in the last method. We call these combinations the 'corners'. In the second step he estimates what can be called the shape of the main-effect function of each factor. He is, for example, asked to make tick marks on a line, one mark for each level, the space between marks indicating the relative difference in average worth between one level and the next.

Worths are then approximated by using the shapes of the main-effect functions to interpolate between the combinations that the expert evaluated individually. For instance, if he put the mark for A_5 half-way between the mark for A_6 and the mark for A_1, then for purposes of interpolation, Level 5 is regarded as half-way between Level 6 and Level 1.

The experiment on ellipses will again serve for an illustration. The responses given on the twelfth day to the eight ellipses with extreme values of size, shape, and color can be taken as the subject's estimates of the worths of the eight corner combinations. Later he was required to mark the average worths of the various sizes, shapes, and colors on three lines on which the scale and origin were regarded as arbitrary. The interpolation could then be performed, and the resulting approximations correlated with the true worths. For the six subjects the average correlation was 0·89, which in this case is as good as the correlation obtained by the more laborious method.

Range and shape of main effects

The final method will probably be the most attractive for many applications in real-time systems. It should be quick, but it makes no attempt to preserve any information about interaction. The man estimates the shapes of the main-effect functions, just as before, and in addition he estimates the relative ranges of the main effects of the several factors. For example, he might be asked to draw a series of lines, all to the same scale and each showing the average change in worth resulting when one of the factors is changed from its lowest level to its highest. Estimating the ranges of the main effects is of particular interest because it is one way of specifying the lower-case coefficients in (3) and is, therefore, one way of taking account of facts not known to the computer.

The method was explored in a small experiment performed by L. Klem on members of the laboratory staff. Hypothetical jobs were defined in terms of salary (specified in dollars), quality of co-workers ('second rate', 'average', or 'outstanding'), and permanence (two years, ordinary, or for life). As a check on the accuracy of their estimates, the subjects were given pairs of jobs and asked to say directly which they would prefer. The subjects were people accustomed to thinking quantitatively, and the results were fairly good. However, we had the impression that even these subjects 'really knew better' than to make some of the estimates that they gave of the ranges of main effects.

Some straightforward work on the development of psycho-physical techniques should be fruitful here. Relative change in average worth is an abstract concept, and a rather slippery one. Posing the question in the right way and asking the man to in-dicate his response in the right form may help him considerably in conveying his best judgment. We suspect too that estimating average worths is a skill that can be taught by showing the subject the worth function implied by his estimates and then letting him change them until the function looks more reasonable to him.[3]

Some help on these very practical problems may come from research that is not concerned with man-machine relations at all. Hoffman (6), for example, has been investigating the way in which a clinical psychologist rates a person on a trait like sociability after examining that person's scores on a number of tests. One of the questions is whether the clinician can say how much weight he gives to each of the tests. This is somewhat like asking whether a person can estimate the range of the main effect of a factor.

A Prediction about Research

The desire to tell a computer how to make decisions should stimulate interest in basic research on how people make evalu-ative judgments. While such interest has long existed (7), it will be strengthened and will probably be refocused a little. We are rash enough to make a prediction about one direction that future experiments will take.

The key concept could be called *simplification*. Up to this point we have tacitly assumed that while approximations may be necessary in instructing a machine, a man would try to use all of the available information if he made the judgment himself. This assumption is probably too cautious. Problems calling for good judgment can be extremely complex: there can be a large number of alternatives, each with many factors; the factors can have many levels, or even be continuous; and they can interact. It seems likely that when the problem becomes complicated enough, people simplify it in one way or another. For example, the halo effect and the logical error in merit ratings (5) are indicative of a

3. Such training may prove useful in teaching a person not to weight combinations of levels according to the frequency with which they have occurred in his experience. A main effect, it should be remembered, was defined as an average in which combinations are weighted equally. At least in theory, there are circumstances where weighting combinations according to frequency of occurrence is not at all a good thing to do.

sort of simplification. We suggest, then, that future investigators will often find themselves asking whether people simplify the task of making evaluative decisions and, if so, under what conditions.

In one sort of complicated situation – namely, laboratory experiments on concept formation – it has been shown that a person may attempt to sort his way through a welter of information by adopting a 'strategy' that reduces the number of facts he must consider at one time, or avoids the 'cognitive strain' of processing information in uncongenial ways (3). It would not be surprising to find that similar procedures are used by a person faced with a complicated decision problem. One possibility is a *sequential* procedure, in which the factors are considered in order of decreasing importance. If the alternatives are far apart on the first factor, he stops and makes his decision right there. If they are close together, he looks at the next factor, and so on.[4]

He might instead ease his processing load by considering only a few of the most important factors, always ignoring the rest. An alternative would be to consider all of the factors, but with each partitioned into a very few large categories. An extreme version of the latter strategy would be to reduce each factor to a good–bad dichotomy, and select the alternative with the most factors in the good category.

Even when a person does not resort to such drastic procedures, he may still tend to simplify the task by ignoring interactions. For example, Adams and Fagot asked judges to select hypothetical job applicants defined as having different amounts of 'intelligence' and 'ability to handle people' (1). Their results suggest that the two factors did not interact very much. Whenever a judge was entirely self-consistent (not all of them were, of course), his choices could be described perfectly by a non-interactive model.

Another way of dealing with interactions was suggested by one of the subjects in our experiment on ellipses. He complained that we had stretched one end of the worth scale, the scale on which the marker moved. In a sense he was right: transforming our arbitrary scale so as to shrink the end to which he objected would have reduced the amount of interaction. Perhaps this is what people do when they learn good judgment about practical matters. Perhaps they tend to define scales of worth in such a way as to minimize interactions.

The question of simplification is related to that of making

4. This strategy is being investigated by Dr John R. Hayes, Naval Res. Lab., Washington D.C.

decisions under pressure – pressure of time, distraction, or bodily discomfort. Do the interactions drop out as pressure increases, or are fewer factors considered, or do people just break down and make more and more wild choices? If they do not break down, then applying pressure will be one way of finding out what types of simplification they are prone to use.

We would not be surprised to find that people tend to use rather simple procedures in making even the most important decisions. Any such finding will be welcomed by designers interested in duplicating those procedures in machines, but it may be a little disconcerting from another point of view. What we humans are pleased to call the exercise of good judgment may turn out to be a simpler matter than we would like to think it is.

References
1. ADAMS, E. W., and FAGOT, R., 'A model of riskless choice', *Behav. Sci.*, vol. 4 (1959), pp. 1–10.
2. BENNETT, C. A., and FRANKLIN, N. L., *Statistical analysis on chemistry and the chemical industry*, Wiley, 1954, pp. 387–8.
3. BRUNER, J. S., GOODNOW, J. J., and AUSTIN, G. A., *A study of thinking*, Wiley, 1956.
4. EDWARDS, W., 'The theory of decision making', *Psychol. Bull.*, vol. 51 (1954), pp. 380–417.
5. GUILFORD, J. P., *Psychometric methods*, McGraw-Hill, 2nd edn, 1954, pp. 278–80.
6. HOFFMAN, P. J., 'The paramorphic representation of clinical judgement', *Psychol. Bull.*, vol. 57 (1960), pp. 116–31.
7. JOHNSON, D. M., *The psychology of thought and judgement*, Harper, 1955.

Part Four   CHOICE MODELS

Behaviour varies. When faced with the same alternative courses
of action several times, people do not always make the same
choice. Such changes can in principle always be explained as
the result of learning, fatigue, adaptation, or other similar
changes in the organism. But often the variation in behaviour
is not syste natic or progressive, as any of these explanations
would lead us to expect. Instead, to an outside observer it
appears random. Students of behaviour disagree about whether
this seeming randomness reflects actual random processes at
work inside the organism, or whether it is the inevitable result
of trying to use very simple methods of prediction to predict
behaviour that has very complicated causes. This disagreement
is profound, and extends beyond decision theory and beyond
psychology; Einstein, objecting to the fundamental role that
random processes play in quantum physics, is supposed to have
said 'God is not a gambler'.

Psychological decision theorists, like other kinds of
psychological theorists, may and do attack this apparent
randomness in two different ways. One is to refine experiments
so as to observe less of it and to refine theories so as to be
able to predict more effectively the behaviour they do observe.
This attack, while indispensable, has never succeeded in
removing *all* apparently random variability from repeated
responses. To deal with what remains, psychological theorists
use extensively the concept of probability of responses. The
basic idea is that a response is a random variable, controlled
by what are called stochastic (probabilistic) processes. Some
people who use such theories think of the processes inside the
head that control behaviour as being actually probabilistic.
Others, more interested in data than in underlying processes,
simply want to predict the results of their experiments, and care

315

little if at all whether the theory they use to predict data corresponds to processes inside the head.

The most elegant probabilistic theory of individual choice behaviour is that of Luce; his paper in this book is a sketch of that theory and of its applications to risky choices and to psychophysics. The heart of the theory is a simple, subtle assumption. It is helpful to think of it as a probabilistic version of the assertion that if you prefer steak to lamb chops, that preference should not be affected by whether or not salmon is on the menu. (You might prefer salmon to either, but you should still prefer steak to lamb chops.)

The probabilistic theories considered in this book can be divided into two classes: constant utility models and random utility models. The constant utility models, of which Luce's is an example, assume or imply that each stimulus (act or outcome) has a fixed location on a single underlying utility scale; this is exactly like the classical utility models. But if stimulus A is higher than stimulus B on that scale, it does not necessarily follow that A will always be preferred to B. All constant utility models agree that under such circumstances A will be preferred to B more than half the time, and that the probability that A will be preferred to B is an increasing function of the distance between A and B on the underlying utility scale.

The random utility models assume that the decision maker chooses, with certainty, the stimulus that is highest in utility among those available to him at the moment of choice. But in random utility models, the locations of the stimuli on the underlying utility scale fluctuate from moment to moment. Thurstone's law of comparative judgement is such a model. The paper by Becker, DeGroot, and Marschak illustrates this class of models, and explores the relationships between the constant and the random utility models. These two classes of models are not as distinct as this presentation makes them sound. Some constant utility models are also random utility models; others are not. The classes of models are sufficiently distinct so as to yield differential testable consequences. Unfortunately, very few data concerning these models are available.

A particular random utility model has been explored by Coombs as an extension of his unfolding theory. On some dimensions, more is always preferred to less (e.g., money) or less to more (e.g., hangovers). On such dimensions, preference is said to increase or decrease monotonically. On other dimensions, such as amount of sugar in a cup of coffee or the temperature of a room, satisfaction, or utility, is not monotonically related to the physical scale. Coombs assumes that you have an ideal value of sugar or degrees, and that your utility for these quantities decreases monotonically on both sides of this ideal point. His study shows that probabilities of choice depend not only on how large the differences in utility are but also on whether all stimuli or acts being compared lie on the same side of the ideal point, or whether some lie on one side of the ideal and some on the other. Thus he raises the issue of the relationship between preference and the comparability of the options among which you must choose. This is one of the most challenging and intriguing aspects of the psychology of choice.

A subject in an experiment on hearing must judge whether a very feeble tone has been presented during a trial or not. That is, he must decide to say either 'Yes, I heard a tone' or 'No, I heard nothing'. In some experiments, he may be paid if right and fined if wrong; in all, he is encouraged to think well of himself when right and less well when wrong. Of course this traditional psychophysical experiment is a decision-making task, not different in principle from choosing between two gambles. In 1954 Wilson P. Tanner, Jr, and John Swets were the first to introduce to psychologists the idea that the same concepts that had been used to analyse other kinds of decisions should be used to analyse decisions in psychophysical experiments also. A large and fruitful literature has resulted, and is reviewed in the paper by Swets reprinted here. The two fundamental ideas of signal detectability theory are both familiar from earlier papers in this book: Bayes's theorem as a normative model for information processing, and the maximization of expected value as a normative model for decision making. The major goal of this analysis of psychophysical data is to separate these two processes. By offering an explicit treatment of the decision-making part of the sequence of events leading from stimulus to response, signal detectability theory permits a relatively pure measure of the operation of the sensory part of that sequence unaffected by those variables (e.g., prior probabilities and payoffs) that are so important in translating sensory processing into decisions.

Regardless of whether or not the specific assumptions of signal detectability theory are correct, the basic model is not limited to psychophysics. Psychologists interested in learning and perception are beginning to recognize that the decision to indicate that, for example, a stimulus is or is not a member of a previously presented list is a decision, affected by costs, payoffs, and prior probabilities in exactly the same way as any other decision. The same kind of decision-theoretical separation of information-processing variables from decision-making variables that has been fruitful in psychophysics should in the next few years play a prominent role in research on short and long term memory, choice reaction times, and indeed all varieties of research on human information processing.

12   C. H. Coombs

Inconsistency of Preferences: a Test of Unfolding Theory

Excerpt from C. H. Coombs, *A theory of data*, Wiley, 1964, pp. 106–18.

The best test I have been able to devise, as yet, of the unfolding theory of preferential choice revolves around its implications for the stochastic properties of choice behavior. The usual, 'reasonable' assumption is that the more consistent the pairwise choice, the more different the two stimuli, that is, the further apart the stimulus points should be. This corresponds to saying that pairwise probabilities of choice should satisfy strong stochastic transitivity. The condition of strong stochastic transitivity is

$$p(AB) \geqslant 0.5, p(BC) \geqslant 0.5 \Rightarrow p(AC) \geqslant \text{maximum}[p(AB), p(BC)].$$

There are two other levels or degrees of stochastic transitivity known as moderate and weak stochastic transitivity. Moderate stochastic transitivity may be defined as

$$p(AB) \geqslant 0.5, p(BC) \geqslant 0.5 \Rightarrow p(AC) \geqslant \text{minimum}[p(AB), p(BC)]$$

and weak stochastic transitivity as

$$p(AB) \geqslant 0.5, p(BC) \geqslant 0.5 \Rightarrow p(AC) \geqslant 0.5.$$

To illustrate these, suppose an individual prefers A over B 80% of the time and B over C 70% of the time; then the three levels of

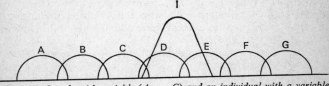

Figure 1   J scale with variable $(A, \ldots G)$ and an individual with a variable ideal (I).

stochastic transitivity would require that he prefer A over C strongly, at least 80% of the time, moderately at least 70%, and weakly at least 50%.

An implication of unfolding theory is that strong stochastic

319

transitivity will not hold in general but that moderate stochastic transitivity will. Indeed, the theory makes more detailed predictions.

The basic idea is that variability of an ideal point affects consistency of choice on certain pairs and not on others, depending on whether the pair of stimuli are on opposite sides of it on the J scale or on the same side. Consider an individual on a J scale, as in Figure 1, in which each stimulus is represented by a probability distribution as is the individual's ideal. When an individual evaluates any pair of stimuli, let us assume that he chooses an ideal point at random out of the distribution of ideals and also a pair of stimulus points from their respective distributions.

We now introduce a variable called *laterality*. Let the term *unilateral* pair signify a pair of stimuli whose distributions are both on the same side of the J scale relative to the distribution of the individual's ideals (for example, A and B or F and G) and

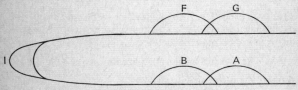

Figure 2   The J scale of Figure 1 partially folded.

let the term *bilateral* pair signify a pair of stimuli whose distributions are on opposite sides of the distribution of ideals (for example, B and F or A and G). The maximum range of the effect of laterality is found in the comparison between the unilateral and the bilateral conditions; stimuli whose distributions significantly overlap the distribution of ideals have an effect that falls between these two extremes.

It is evident from the unfolding theory of preferential choice[1] that the inconsistency of the individual's preference on a unilateral pair of stimuli will be unaffected by the variability of the ideal; only the overlap of the stimulus distributions will generate inconsistency. In the case of bilateral pairs, however, the varying ideal will contribute to the inconsistency of judgment. This may be visualized more clearly with the aid of Figure 2.

In each replication on a pair a folding point is chosen out of the

1. [Coombs develops this theory in chapter 23 of *A theory of data*.] See also Zinnes (1959) and Coombs, Greenberg and Zinnes (1961).

I distribution, and a pair of stimulus points out of their respective distributions. It is evident that if a pair of points is drawn at random, one from stimulus *A*'s distribution and one from *B*'s (a unilateral pair of stimuli), then the one that falls nearer an ideal point drawn from the *I* distribution is a matter independent of the variability of the ideal, and only dependent on the relation between the stimulus distributions. The same would be true for any other unilateral pair of stimuli such as *F* and *G*.

In contrast to unilateral pairs of stimuli, consider the case of a bilateral pair, such as *A* and *F*. Here the variability of the ideal is a very significant factor in the inconsistency of judgment. If from one replication to the next the ideal shifts toward the *A* distribution, it necessarily shifts away from the *F* distribution and of course vice versa. Using Figure 2 we may picture the two bilateral distributions rolling over each other in opposite directions as the ideal varies, whereas a pair of unilateral distributions slides back and forth locked tightly together. We would predict, therefore, that the variance of an ideal would enter into the inconsistency of judgment on a bilateral pair of stimuli and have no effect on the inconsistency of judgment on a unilateral pair.

An experimental study of this predicted effect of laterality (Coombs, 1958) was carried out at the University of Amsterdam using 12 shades of gray, presenting all sets of 4 stimuli and asking the subject to rank order them from the best representative of what he meant by the label 'gray' to the poorest ('order 3/4' from the searchingness structure). These instructions were used to try to make sure that the subject's ideals would be in the middle of the *J* scale in order to provide a reasonable number of both unilateral and bilateral pairs for each subject.

The 495 presentations of 4 stimuli at a time were sequentially arranged to insure reasonable control of any sequential or trend effect in the course of the experiment. The complete set of 495 presentations was run on each of 2 successive nights with the same 4 subjects. Each subject, of course, is a completely separate experiment, as the *J* scales and the distributions of ideals may be expected to be different for each of them.

Each pair of stimuli occurs in $\left(\dfrac{n-2}{2}\right)$ presentations, in this case $\left(\dfrac{10}{2}\right) = 45$; so the 2 evenings yield a total of 90 replications on a pair. These are obtained by decomposing the rank order on each presentation according to the decomposition model [shown at the end of this reading]. These 90 replications, however, do not have the channel capacity of 90 experimentally independent pairwise replications. An estimate of their channel capacity compared with pairwise presentations may be obtained as follows.

A presentation of 4 stimuli may be rank ordered in 4! = 24 different ways. The number of bits of channel capacity, assuming equal probabilities of the alternative orderings, is log 24 = 4·58 bits per presentation. Decomposing the rank order into 6 pair comparisons and allotting these 4·58 bits over them equally, on the average yields 0·763 bits of channel capacity on each pair. Experimentally independent replications accumulate the 0·763 bits on each pair, and so for 90 replications we have 68·67 bits on each pair.

We do not know whether channel capacity has any bearing on our interest here, that is, reliability of the estimates of the probabilities, but it is the best guess we can make at present. Undoubtedly some probabilities are estimated with better reliability than others but we do not know enough to provide more than a reasonable estimate of the number of degrees of freedom on which each estimate is based. For each individual we arrive at a pairwise probability for each pair of stimuli based on the 90 replications which is estimated to have a reliability equivalent to about 69 experimentally independent replications.

A pairwise probability is based on the number of times each member of a pair was ranked higher, in accordance with the decomposition model. The data for each individual may be placed in a square data matrix with each stimulus identifying a corresponding row and column and each cell indicating the percentage of times the row stimulus was preferred to the column stimulus. Table 1 contains the data of the four subjects in the original report. The identification of the rows and columns of this matrix is different for each subject and corresponds to the rank order of the stimuli on each subject's *I* scale given below the table. The labels of the stimuli are in alphabetical order from the lightest gray to the darkest.

The decomposition model used to arrive at the pairwise percentages does not impose even weak stochastic transitivity, as pointed out in the discussion of the model, so it is interesting to observe whether the data for each of the 4 subjects indicate that his preferences are essentially transitive underneath the fluctuations.

A necessary and sufficient condition for weak stochastic transitivity is that a permutation of the data matrix exists such that all the entries on one side of the diagonal are at least 50%.

Table 1

Inconsistency of Preferences for Each of the Four Subjects

	1	2	3	4	5	6	7	8	9	10	11	12
1		52 51 / 70 53	67 59 / 91 63	72 61 / 87 66	64 68 / 74 86	76 84 / 80 79	91 88 / 94 97	89 94 / 93 92	99 90 / 100 94	100 94 / 100 97	100 100 / 100 99	100 100 / 100 99
2			83 52 / 68 62	83 77 / 78 62	74 96 / 52 87	80 97 / 73 87	98 96 / 94 90	99 82 / 99 96	100 100 / 97 99	100 100 / 100 93	100 100 / 100 99	100 100 / 100 100
3				50 86 / 53 54	67 93 / 51 63	64 99 / 60 68	92 100 / 89 94	97 87 / 87 80	97 100 / 100 89	100 93 / 93 97	100 98 / 100 100	100 100 / 100 97
4					61 93 / 53 64	63 98 / 57 61	90 99 / 93 98	100 83 / 72 97	91 100 / 100 82	100 100 / 97 100	100 100 / 100 100	100 100 / 100 99
5						68 96 / 63 51	50 99 / 76 60	66 50 / 92 94	97 88 / 94 90	99 87 / 99 84	100 96 / 50 96	100 100 / 100 99
6							54 59 / 54 80	66 50 / 92 94	94 93 / 90 63	100 99 / 82 94	100 96 / 89 100	100 100 / 100 99
7								92 56 / 54 57	94 90 / 93 63	100 82 / 99 94	100 89 / 96 100	100 100 / 100 91
8									83 64 / 53 93	100 68 / 100 58	94 99 / 99 84	100 99 / 100 100
9										83 92 / 52 58	99 93 / 76 84	100 100 / 100 100
10											62 97 / 97 100	100 100 / 97 73
11												100 80 / 99 53

Note: The upper left-hand corner of each cell is subject 1; the upper right, subject 2; the lower left, subject 3; and the lower right, subject 4. The labels of the rows and columns from 1 to 12 are as follows for each of the four subjects: Subject 1: *GFEDHICBJAKL.* Subject 2: *JIHGFEDKCBLA.* Subject 3: *FGEDHICJBKLA.* Subject 4: *GFHIDEJCBKLA.*

The order of the rows (or columns) then corresponds to the stochastically dominant I scale.[2] It is an interesting observation that such a permutation of the data matrix existed for each of the four data matrices. In the case of subject 1 the I scale was found in this way to be $G F E D H I C B J A K L$, which is the J scale folded in the neighborhood of stimulus G.

The effect of laterality on the inconsistency of preferences should be revealed in the testing of strong stochastic transitivity *versus* moderate stochastic transitivity, which may be done by examining all the ordered triples of stimuli embedded in the I scale ordering. The unfolding theory leads to a distinction between different kinds of triples of stimuli and correspondingly different predictions as to whether strong stochastic transitivity or moderate stochastic transitivity can be expected to be satisfied.

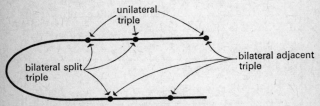

Figure 3   Illustrating the three kinds of stimulus triples.

Ordered triples from the I scale of subject 1 are used here to illustrate the three different kinds of triples. The three kinds of triples are defined as (1) *unilateral triples*, in which all three stimuli are unilateral to the distribution of the ideal, for example, D, C, and B; I, J, and K; (2) *bilateral adjacent triples*, in which two stimuli are from one side of the J scale and are adjacent in the ordered triple, as embedded in the I scale order, and the third is from the other side of the J scale and is either first or last in the ordered triple, for example, H, I, and B; C, J, and K; (3) *bilateral split triples*, in which two stimuli are from one side of the J scale and are separated in their I scale rank order by the stimulus from the other side, for example, C, J, and A; H, B, and K.

These three kinds of triples are illustrated in Figure 3.

2. If the distributions of the stimuli and of the ideals are all symmetric distributions, and the stimulus distributions have constant variance, then the stochastically dominant I scale gives the rank order of the means of the stimulus distributions in order of increasing distance from the mean of the distribution of ideals.

Since the laterality effect does not enter into unilateral triples, the variance of the ideal being irrelevant, we would expect strong stochastic transitivity to be satisfied by such triples to a statistically significant degree.

For bilateral adjacent triples (for example, H, I, and B in the I scale of subject 1) the first and last members of the triple always constitute a bilateral pair (for example, H and B), and there is always a unilateral pair embedded between them (for example, H and I). The inconsistency on the bilateral pair tends to be of a higher degree (that is, closer to 50%), than the inconsistency on the unilateral pair, because the latter inconsistency is not affected by the varying ideal. Hence the laterality effect would tend to counteract the effect of distance and should lead to a significant degree of violation of strong stochastic transitivity. Moderate stochastic transitivity, however, should be satisfied to a statistically significant degree.

Finally, for bilateral split triples (for example, C, J, and A in subject 1's I scale) the effect is just the opposite. The unilateral

Table 2

Effect of Laterality on Strong Stochastic Transitivity*

	Subject 1		Subject 2		Subject 3		Subject 4	
	SST Sat.	SST Not Sat.	SST Sat.	SST Not Sat.	SST Sat.	SST Not Sat.	SST Sat.	SST Not Sat.
Bilateral pairs bounding bilateral adjacent triples	9	11	2	10	6	13	1	19
Unilateral pairs bounding unilateral triples	11	1	19	2	10	2	7	5
p	<0·01		<0·001		<0·01		<0·001	

* The figures reported in this table are different from those reported in Coombs (1958). David Cross, working on a replication study for me, reanalysed the previous data and found some egregious errors due entirely to me. Fortunately, the corrected figures even more strongly supported the conclusions drawn from the original analysis.

325

pair (C and A) consists of the first and third elements of the ordered triple and there are two bilateral pairs embedded between them (C and J, and J and A) so the effect of laterality is added to the effect of psychological distance, and violation of strong stochastic transitivity for such triples should almost never occur.

For each of the four subjects, the number of bilateral pairs bounding bilateral adjacent triples and the number of unilateral pairs bounding unilateral triples which satisfied and which failed

Table 3

Number of the Various Kinds of Triples Satisfying the Three Different Levels of Stochastic Transitivity

| | | *Highest Level of Stochastic Transitivity Satisfied* | | | |
		SST	MST	WST	*Total Number of Triples*
S1	bilateral adjacent	48	16	2	66
Triples	unilateral	19	0	1	20
	bilateral split	34	0	0	34
S2	bilateral adjacent	16	19	5	40
Triples	unilateral	54	2	0	56
	bilateral split	24	0	0	24
S3	bilateral adjacent	32	28	2	62
Triples	unilateral	18	2	0	20
	bilateral split	38	0	0	38
S4	bilateral adjacent	14	48	0	62
Triples	unilateral	12	8	0	20
	bilateral split	38	0	0	38

to satisfy strong stochastic transitivity were counted, leaving out the first two stimuli on the I scale. These two stimuli are omitted because the location of the ideal point with respect to them is uncertain and hence the determination of laterality is uncertain too. The results are presented in Table 2 with χ^2 tests of significance.

It is clear that a very substantial proportion of bilateral adjacent triples fails to satisfy the condition of strong stochastic transitivity in contrast to the case for unilateral triples.

A more detailed analysis of some interest is the number of

triples of each kind satisfying the different levels of stochastic transitivity. The results for each subject are reported separately in Table 3.

Triples of stimuli embedded in an I scale are not independent, so a suitable statistical test does not seem to be available. The qualitative results, however, are clearly very close to those predicted by unfolding theory: that bilateral adjacent triples would violate strong stochastic transitivity to a substantial degree but not violate moderate stochastic transitivity; that unilateral triples would not substantially violate strong stochastic transitivity; that bilateral split triples would rarely, if ever, violate strong stochastic transitivity.

One further layer of analysis remains to be pursued. Unfolding theory not only predicts that a substantial number of bilateral adjacent triples will violate strong stochastic transitivity, but that when it occurs the violation will be of a particular kind, as follows. Each bilateral adjacent triple is bounded by a bilateral pair and so has another bilateral pair and a unilateral pair in between.

Consider, for example, the triple HIB, embedded in that order in subject 1's I scale. The pair HB is a bilateral pair with the pair HI, a unilateral pair, and the pair IB, a bilateral pair, in between. If such a triple violates strong stochastic transitivity, this should occur, according to unfolding theory, because the probability on the bounding bilateral pair, HB, is less than the probability on the embedded unilateral pair, HI.

We may examine, then, those bilateral adjacent triples in each subject's I scale which violate strong stochastic transitivity and see if the violation is of the particular kind predicted by the theory. The results are as follows:

(1) For subject 1 there is one triple, DCJ, which violates strong stochastic transitivity in a manner contrary to the theory: D is preferred over C 90% of the time, C over J 94%, D over J 91%. The situation may be portrayed as follows:

$$D_{0.90}C_{0.94}J$$

Clearly strong stochastic transitivity is violated, but the theory says that this violation should occur because the probability on the bounding bilateral pair, DJ, is less than that on the embedded unilateral pair, DC, that is, 0·91 is greater than 0·90, contrary to unfolding theory.

The corresponding analyses for the other three subjects may be summarized briefly.

(2) For subject 2 there are two such triples:

$$\overset{0.98}{\overgroup{G_{0.93}F_{1.00}L}} \text{ and } 0.98 \text{ is greater than } 0.93$$

$$\overset{0.93}{\overgroup{C_{0.92}B_{0.97}L}} \text{ and } 0.93 \text{ is greater than } 0.92$$

(3) For subject 3 there are three such triples:

$$\overset{0.93}{\overgroup{E_{0.53}D_{0.97}K}} \text{ and } 0.93 \text{ is greater than } 0.53$$

$$\overset{0.76}{\overgroup{H_{0.63}I_{0.80}C}} \text{ and } 0.76 \text{ is greater than } 0.63$$

$$\overset{0.99}{\overgroup{E_{0.53}D_{1.00}L}} \text{ and } 0.99 \text{ is greater than } 0.53$$

(4) For subject 4 there are two such triples:

$$\overset{0.61}{\overgroup{I_{0.64}D_{0.51}E}} \text{ and } 0.61 \text{ is greater than } 0.51$$

$$\overset{0.60}{\overgroup{D_{0.51}E_{0.71}J}} \text{ and } 0.60 \text{ is greater than } 0.51.$$

Taken all together we have 8 instances of triples that do not conform to prediction plus an *additional* 9 which only satisfy weak stochastic transitivity, making a total of 17 triples out of the total of 480, about 3·5%; and this is a penetration into the rather fine structure of the data. The evidence for the laterality effect predicted by unfolding theory is quite strong.

Luce (1959) has criticized this experiment on the grounds that the determination of the pairwise probabilities is based on the intermediate step involving my decomposition model and alternative decomposition models are conceivable. This legitimate criticism motivated me to conduct a replication study[3] in which

3. This study was carried out by Sally Sperling, with the assistance at various times of David Cross, Percival Tomlinson, Clint Fink, and John Dwyer. [For a description of the study and a report of additional results see Chapter 2, section 1 of *A Theory of data*.]

pairwise probabilities were determined by replication of pairs directly. The results of the previous study were confirmed for each of the two subjects run (see Table 4). Subject *B* was highly inconsistent, as was subject 4 in the original experiment.

A study involving pairwise presentations of gambles is reported by Coombs and Pruitt (1961) in which the effect of laterality is again evident. This was a study of the psychophysics of gambling in which gambles differing only in variance or only in skewness

Table 4

Replication Study of Effect of Laterality on Strong Stochastic Transitivity

	Subject A		Subject B	
	SST Sat.	SST Not Sat.	SST Sat.	SST Not Sat.
Bilateral pairs bounding bilateral adjacent triples	5	12	6	18
Unilateral pairs bounding unilateral triples	22	6	10	8
p	<0.005		<0.05	

(odds) were presented. On the average, about 25% of all triples of bets failed to satisfy strong stochastic transitivity.

In the theoretical analysis of the effect of laterality at the beginning of this section the assumption was made that an individual chose *one and only one* ideal point from his distribution of ideals when he evaluated a *pair* of stimulus points. Such an assumption appears gratuitous and *ad hoc* and demands supporting evidence. There is certainly no *a priori* ground for such an assumption as opposed to assuming that an individual chooses a new ideal point with each stimulus point. Two lines of evidence support the former assumption. The first lies in the fact that if the latter assumption were true, the laterality effect would not exist; and it apparently does, as predicted by the assumption of a single ideal point for a pair of stimuli.

The second line of evidence lies in a further analysis of this experimental data, which has not previously been reported. It will be recalled that in this experiment the stimuli were presented in sets of four at a time, not pairwise, and there is evidence for the stability of an ideal point during the interval the individual responded to the entire presentation. The relevant data are the individual's responses to those sets of four stimuli in which two of the stimuli are from distributions on one side of the individual's distribution of ideal points and the other two stimuli are from the other side, schematically illustrated in Figure 4, in which stimuli 1 and 2 are from one side and stimuli 3 and 4 are from the other side and the individual's distribution of ideal points is on the 'bend' of the *J* scale.

Of interest in such sets of four is the individual's ordering on the pair of stimuli 1 and 4 in the figure in relation to his ordering on the stimuli 2 and 3. If the individual's ideal point is relatively stable when responding to such sets of four stimuli, then if he is nearer stimulus 2 and stimulus 3 according to his preference

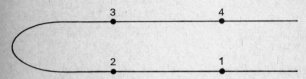

Figure 4   Presentations used to test stability of an ideal point.

ordering, he should, in general, tend to be nearer stimulus 1 than stimulus 4. Similarly, if he prefers stimulus 3 over stimulus 2, there should be a significant tendency to prefer stimulus 4 over stimulus 1. Such an effect, of course, is moderated by the other factors involved in making his choice but should be evident statistically over a large sample of such sets of four.

Table 5

Test of the Stability of the Ideal Point Within a Presentation

	Subject 1		Subject 2		Subject 3		Subject 4	
	2>3	3>2	2>3	3>2	2>3	3>2	2>3	3>2
1>4	237	31	69	26	122	107	116	37
4>1	146	83	62	53	79	141	116	158
p	<0·001		<0·01		<0·001		<0·001	

The results for each of the four subjects separately are presented in Table 5 in which the numbers in the cells are the number of presentations in which the preference orderings are as specified for that row and column. The ps reported are for χ^2 tests of significance.

There is evidence here, then, that the individual's i deal point was stable during the interval in which he responded to an entire presentation of four stimuli. This is the second line of evidence that supports the assumption that his ideal point is stable in pairwise presentations.

The significance of the effect of laterality on preferential choice lies in the application of such models as Thurstone's model for comparative judgment to convert the pairwise probabilities into measures of psychological distance in order to scale the stimuli. Pairwise probabilities of preferential choice should not be put in a common data matrix and transformed into psychological distance. Instead two separate data matrices are called for, one for probabilities for unilateral pairs and one for probabilities for bilateral pairs. The transformation of the probabilities into psychological distance must then take account of the effect of laterality on the inconsistency on bilateral pairs. These implications for Thurstone's model for comparative judgment are developed in Chapter 23 [of *A theory of data*].

Another implication in the effect of laterality should be pointed out. There is a certain *a priori*, intuitive reasonableness to the idea that individuals nearer the center of a *J* scale may hold their position less firmly, feel less intense about their position, and perhaps be more readily influenced or induced to change. These conclusions may be correct in themselves but they do not follow merely from greater inconsistency in judgment on the part of the more centrally located subjects. According to the laterality effect, subjects with the same variability of their ideal point will *behave* more inconsistently (whatever their susceptibility to influence and so forth) the nearer the distribution (of their ideal) is to the middle of the *J* scale. This is simply a consequence of their having to make a larger number of bilateral comparisons than do individuals more extreme than they are on the *J* scale.

A Decomposition Model [Reproduced from Coombs, C. H., *A theory of data*, Wiley, 1964, p. 53]

A problem with the more powerful methods of collecting data is that of translating the observations into the presumed equivalent observations that would have been obtained if the pair comparisons had been replicated. That is, having collected data by a complete 'order 2/3', how do we process them to determine the pairwise probabilities? Those who have used these methods of collecting data have customarily counted the number of times one stimulus is chosen over another in all presentations in which that pair is embedded. For example, the pair of stimuli A and B is embedded in $n - 2$ triads if the complete 'order 2/3' method is used. To estimate the probability that A will be chosen over B, the customary practice has been to determine the proportion of times A has been chosen over B in those $n - 2$ presentations in which both A and B appeared.

There is a model implicit in this procedure which for the method of triads may be constructed as follows:

Consider two fixed stimuli A and B and a third stimulus X, which may be any of a number of other stimuli. The joint probability that an individual will make the three judgments $A > B$, $B > X$, $A > X$, corresponds to the probability that he will rank the stimuli in the order $A\ B\ X$. We use $p(ABX)$, then, as a shorthand notation for the joint probability of the implicit pair comparison judgments. The notation for a conditional probability is a vertical bar; that is, $p(AB \mid AX)$ is the probability the individual chooses A over B having already chosen A over X. The following identities may be written:

$$p(ABX) = p(AB)\, p(AX \mid AB)\, p(BX \mid AB, AX)$$
$$p(AXB) = p(AB)\, p(AX \mid AB)\, p(XB \mid AB, AX) \qquad \textbf{(2.7)}$$
$$p(XAB) = p(AB)\, p(XA \mid AB)\, p(XB \mid AB, XA)$$

Summing these three equations gives

$$p(ABX) + p(AXB) + p(XAB) = p(AB)\{p(AX \mid AB)[p(BX \mid AB, AX) + p(XB \mid AB, AX)] + p(XA \mid AB)\, p(XB \mid AB, XA)\}$$

But $p(BX \mid AB, AX) + p(XB \mid AB, AX) = 1$. Also $p(XB \mid XA, AB) = 1$ by virtue of the imposition of transitivity within each triple by the method of collecting the data. Assuming that $p(AB)$ is independent of X, we have

$$p(AB) = p(ABX) + p(AXB) + p(XAB) \qquad \textbf{(2.8)}$$

The assumption that $p(AB)$ is independent of X is a strong form of the 'independence from other alternatives' axiom that continually crops up in choice theory and decision making.

References

COOMBS, C. H., *A theory of data*, Wiley, 1964, chapters 2 and 23.

COOMBS, C. H., 'On the use of inconsistency of preferences in psychological measurement', *J. exper. Psychol.*, vol. 55 (1958), pp. 1–7.

COOMBS, C. H., GREENBERG, M., and ZINNES, J. L., 'A double law of comparative judgement for the analysis of preferential choice and similarities data', *Psychometrika*, vol. 26 (1961), pp. 165–71.

COOMBS, C. H., and PRUITT, D. G., 'Some characteristics of choice behavior in risky situations', *Ann. New York Acad. Sci.*, vol. 89 (1961), pp. 784–94.

LUCE, R. D., *Individual choice behavior*, Wiley, 1959.

ZINNES, J. L., 'A probabilistic theory of preferential choice', Ph.D. dissertation, University of Michigan, 1959.

13 R. D. Luce

Psychological Studies of Risky Decision Making

R. D. Luce, 'Psychological studies of risky decision making', in
Strother, G. B. (ed.), *Social science approaches to business behavior*,
R. D. Irwin, Inc., 1962, pp. 141–61, Tavistock Publications Ltd, 1962.

Introduction

At the outset, let me acknowledge my ignorance of the world
of business. Professionally, I have had little to do with business
or with its study, and so I write with no more than an educated
layman's understanding of which intellectual endeavors are
relevant to business problems. Because of this, it would be foolish
and presumptuous to claim that the studies we shall examine here
are directly applicable to them. I suspect that my general problem – the choices that people make among alternatives whose
consequences are risky – is of quite general interest; however,
specific theories and experiments may very well be another
matter. But even if what I describe is not of direct relevance to
business, hopefully it will be at least intriguing. I plan simply to
sketch some of the ideas and findings that theoretical and experimental psychologists have made in this stimulating, confusing,
and conflictful area of research.

The problem is, let me repeat, to describe the formal structure
of a person's choices when the consequences following from a
choice are risky. That is, we are searching for a satisfactory
abstract – mathematical – description of a person choosing
among two or more alternatives, each of which is, in more
familiar terms, a lottery or gamble. Although the specific outcome to him depends to some extent on his choice, it also depends
on chance events that are quite beyond his control.

Some early mathematicians were interested in choices among
money gambles. It was Daniel Bernoulli, for example, who so
neatly established that people do not choose on the basis of
expected money returns alone. Out of these early studies grew,
on the one hand, the mathematical notions of probability and,
on the other hand, the economic notions of cardinal utility for
nonnumerical commodities. Although separately evolved, these
two groups of ideas have always had a close affinity, and less than
15 years ago they were reunited in the work of von Neumann and

Morgenstern, Savage, and Wald, to name only the most prominent contributors.

Even though history seems to suggest that our problem lies in the province of economics and statistics, it is evident that in part it also belongs to psychology. Indeed, I think the claim can be defended that the study of the choices which individuals and institutions should make to attain certain ends forms a part of – and quite possibly is equivalent to – statistics; that the study of the choices which individuals do in fact make forms a part of – but definitely is not equivalent to – psychology; and that the study of the choices which aggregates of people and institutions make forms a part of economics and sociology. That much theoretical work about the choices that individuals make when the alternatives are risky appears in the economic literature is, it seems to me, no more than a historical accident. Some approaches to economics seem to demand psychological underpinnings, and economists have never been loath to create their own psychologies when none could be borrowed.

Accepting that the descriptive half of the problem of individuals making choices belongs to psychology, what then have we done to solve it? Speaking broadly, there have been two mathematical tacks. One group of psychologists has developed models which, although different in detail, are similar in spirit to those proposed by the economists. These theories have been designed to account for the results of preference studies. For the most part, they have been applied only to choices among what we may call 'sure' alternatives, i.e., to those for which the outcome depends only on the subject's choice and not on any other events. Usually, there is no reason why preference theories cannot be applied to risky alternatives, but, until recently, such theories have failed to include in their structure the added richness provided by dealing with risky alternatives.

A second group of psychologists concerned with the processes of human learning have, almost inadvertently, studied choices among risky alternatives. Their end was not to understand the interrelations among the choices that subjects make in different situations of risk but rather to use these situations as devices to generate particular temporal patterns of responses. The subjects in these experiments initially know little or nothing about the events controlling the outcomes that result from their choices. But the same choices are offered over and over, and, in the course of time, the subjects acquire considerable statistical information about the events. Ultimately, their responses settle down to some stable pattern of behavior, much like that discussed by the utility and preference theorists. During the past decade, a sizable mathematical literature has evolved in the attempt to describe this and related sorts of learning.

So, in total, we have three general classes of theories which attempt to describe an individual's choices among risky alternatives – the economists' and statisticians' utility theories and the psychologists' preference and learning theories. The distinction between utility and preference theory is often somewhat fuzzy, for to a considerable extent it rests upon who did the work. I shall sharpen it for present purposes by restricting attention to those utility theories centered around the expected utility hypothesis and to those preference theories explicitly assuming stochastic behavior.

Subjective Expected Utility Theories

A characteristic of all utility theories, expected or otherwise, is that one can assign numerical quantities – utilities – to alternatives in such a way that alternative a is chosen from a set T of alternatives if and only if the utility of a is larger than that of any other alternative in T. When such an assignment is possible, we say that the person behaves optimally relative to his utility scale, that he maximizes utility.

When we study risky alternatives, we have a second guiding idea which is called the 'subjective expected utility hypothesis'. It holds that, in addition to utility assignments to all alternatives – risky as well as sure – one can also assign numbers to events. The numbers are interpreted as the subject's evaluation of the likelihood of the event's occurring; they are called 'subjective probabilities'. Like ordinary objective ones, they lie between 0 and 1. These two numerical scales are interlocked in the following way: the utility of a risky alternative is the sum of the utilities of its component outcomes, each weighted according to the subjective probability of its occurring. For example, if $a\alpha b$ denotes the risky alternative in which a is the outcome when the event α occurs and b when it fails to occur, then the subjective expected utility hypothesis asserts in this simple case that

$$u(a\alpha b) = u(a)\,\psi(\alpha) + u(b)[1 - \psi(\alpha)],$$

where u denotes the utility scale and ψ the subjective probability scale.

The primary theoretical problem has been to justify this representation. Typically, a series of empirically testable assumptions is stated which relate choices one to another, and from these it is shown by mathematical argument that the expected utility representation follows. The assumptions made are always plausible as canons of rational behavior. For example, they usually include one something like this: when a is preferred to b and when event α is more likely than event β, then $a\alpha b$ is preferred to $a\beta b$. Usually it is easy to persuade oneself and one's more rational friends that one should abide by these axioms, but rather fewer of us are willing to claim that they actually describe our behavior.

There are three major theories of this type. In 1947 von Neumann and Morgenstern (35) stated the first such system of axioms, which served as a normative underpinning for their theory of games. As a normative theory it may well be satisfactory, but as description it was badly marred by the supposition that objective probability can substitute for subjective probability. In 1954, Savage (31) rectified this weakness by incorporating into a single, elegant axiom system both their utility ideas and de Finetti's (19, 20) subjective probability notions. Although this is probably the definitive axiomatization, other more special ones are often useful. For example, Davidson and Suppes (9), working out an idea suggested in 1931 by the philosopher Ramsey (30), developed a utility theory that required only data from choices among gambles generated by but one event – one having a subjective probability of $\frac{1}{2}$. This considerably simplifies certain experimental problems.

Only two major empirical studies have been carried out, one to test the von Neumann–Morgenstern theory and the other the Davidson–Suppes theory. Without directly examining the correctness of the von Neumann–Morgenstern axiom system, Mosteller and Nogee (29) applied the expected utility equation, using objective probabilities, to certain observed choices and attempted to construct individual utility functions for money. They found that such functions could, in fact, be calculated and that they were reasonably smooth, increasing functions of money. With these functions in hand and again assuming the expected utility hypothesis, they then predicted the subject's choices between risky alternatives different from those used to construct the functions. These predictions, although somewhat more accurate than those calculated from expected money returns, were far from perfectly accurate. By strict standards, the model failed, but the failure was ambiguous. Did it stem from the expected utility hypothesis itself or from the equating of subjective to objective probability? No one could be sure.

The second study, performed by Davidson, Suppes, and Siegel (10), required only an event having a subjective probability of $\frac{1}{2}$. With that in hand, the utility function was generated by carrying out an extremely careful exploration of the choices made when the money outcomes were changed by 1-cent amounts. Although a 1-cent change is small in absolute value, it was actually a sizable percentage change of the sums involved: from 3 to 25 per cent. The most important consequence of this procedure was that it prevented an exact determination of the utility function; only upper and lower bounds could be found. Once the bounds were determined, the experimenters tested the theory in much the same way as Mosteller and Nogee by predicting choices in situations different from those used to generate the utility functions. Because of the indeterminacy of the utility functions, however, a number of the more sensitive predictions could not be made. Of those that were unambiguous, an extremely high proportion were correct.

It is generally agreed that this experiment provides the strongest support for the subjective expected utility hypothesis as a description of behavior, but, even so, its success is equivocal. One doubts that the hypothesis has been adequately taxed both because of the indeterminacy of the utility function and because the theory is restricted to only one chance event.

Several other experimental studies have been interpreted as unfavorable to the expected utility hypothesis (Coombs [6]; Coombs and Pruitt [7]; and Edwards [11–14, 16]). Some of these have been concerned with preferences among gambles having different money variances but the same expected values, and others with preferences among the probabilities of the events themselves. For example, Edwards' subjects chose between bets having the same expected money values. When that expectation was positive, they consistently preferred those bets with a 50:50 chance of winning and avoided those with a 75:25 chance; when the expected value was negative, these preferences were reversed.

It is not easy to know what to make of such studies. For one thing, the gambles all involve only two outcomes, and so when one variable, such as variance, is changed, others, such as range, must also automatically change. Thus it is impossible to know which of several variables is actually relevant to the behavior. For another, most, if not all, of the results are explicable in terms of the subjective expected utility hypothesis, provided that we are willing to accept utility and subjective probability functions with enough twists and bends.

Where do we stand? It is impossible at present to cite a study either clearly supporting or clearly rejecting the subjective expected utility hypothesis. Because of the freedom to select both the utility and the subjective probability functions, I do not find it surprising that we have been unable clearly to reject it. What would be truly surprising would be for the experimental evidence to fail to give strong support, were the hypothesis in fact correct. This, coupled with the peculiar results that Edwards and others have obtained, has made some psychologists suspicious that, at least in detail, the subjective expected utility hypothesis is wrong. A number of us suspect that the structure of choices is somewhat more subtle than can be satisfactorily encompassed by this very simple and appealing model. Of course, it may well turn out that under some conditions this model is a good approximation to a more nearly correct one, but we probably will not know what the conditions are until we have discovered the more correct one. Consequently, many of us have turned to other approaches.

Preference Theories

An incidental result of the Mosteller–Nogee experiment which has since been seen in a number of other studies is that subjects are not always consistent in their choices. If a pair of alternatives is presented many times, successive presentations being well separated by other choices, a given subject does not necessarily choose the same alternative each time. At first, one is tempted to attribute such inconsistency to changes of state in the subject or to other errors of measurement, much as one would in testing a physical theory. There are, however, two features of the data which lead one to suspect that the phenomenon may in fact be basic to the choice process. The pattern of inconsistency is very regular when it occurs. For example, suppose the two alternatives are the gamble $x\alpha - 5\cent$ and the pure outcome nothing. When x is small, say $1\cent$, the gamble is never chosen: when it is larger, say \$1, it is always chosen. And as x varies from $1\cent$ to \$1, the probability of choosing the gamble increases in a smooth S-shaped curve, such as that shown in Figure 1. In contrast, there are other pairs, such as x versus nothing, where the behavior is perfectly discontinuous: when $x < 0$, x is never chosen, and when $x > 0$, it is always chosen. It appears that a wonderfully complex error theory will be needed to account for such different results.

As an alternative to treating these results as errors, we can try to construct inherently probabilistic choice models. The postulates so far suggested are numerous and their interrelations complex; much of this net of implications was worked out by Block and Marschak (2) and by Marschak (28). Of the various postulates, the two that have received most empirical attention are weak and strong stochastic transitivity. In both it is assumed that we have three alternatives – a, b, and c – such that when a and b are presented, the subject selects a at least half the time and that when b and c are presented, he chooses b at least half

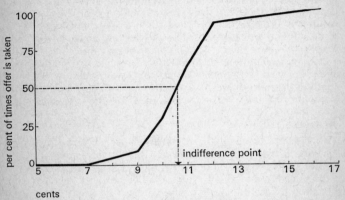

Figure 1   Percentage of times a gamble of the form xα – 5¢, where event α has a probability 0·332 of occurring, was chosen over nothing as reported by Mosteller and Nogee (29, Figure 2). [See page 122.]

the time. The question is what happens when a and c are presented. Weak stochastic transitivity says that a will be chosen at least half the time. Strong stochastic transitivity says that the proportion of times a is selected over c will be at least as large as the proportion of times a is selected over b and at least as large as the proportion of times b is selected over c. In symbols, if $P(a, b) \geqslant \frac{1}{2}$ and $P(b, c) \geqslant \frac{1}{2}$, then weak transitivity says simply that $P(a, c) \geqslant \frac{1}{2}$, and strong says that $P(a, c) \geqslant P(a, b)$ and $P(b, c)$. Strong clearly implies weak transitivity, and it reduces to ordinary algebraic transitivity when the probabilities are 0 or 1.

Neither assumption is strong enough to stand alone as a theory of behavior – certainly not as a theory about choices among risky alternatives, because nothing is assumed about the nature of the alternatives. Aside from a certain *a priori* reasonableness, they are of interest mainly because weak transitivity is a consequence of practically every more elaborate stochastic theory that has been proposed and strong transitivity, of many. Thus, should we collect data that rejected either, with it would be swept away many other proposed theories.

Almost any preference study that one might perform affords an opportunity to test these hypotheses, but few, if any, studies that have been performed provide, in my view, adequate tests. Davidson and Marschak (8) obtained single observations from each subject for each pair of alternatives in several triplets. Because single observations do not permit very subtle estimates of probabilities, they were forced to a subtle statistical analysis to test the two hypotheses. Although they interpret their results as supporting both, it would have required such extreme data to reject either that I do not find their evidence very convincing. Chipman (5) and Coombs and Pruitt (7) made several observations for each pair of alternatives, estimated the choice probabilities from these, and tested the two hypotheses. The authors in both cases concluded that strong transitivity may well be wrong. For example, Coombs and Pruitt found that strong transitivity was violated in 25 per cent of the triples where it could be tested. However, as they point out, one is bound to have some apparent rejections as a result of sampling variability, and when each probability is estimated from only 6 or 8 observations, as was the case in these two studies, one suspects that this may be quite a serious problem. No one has yet worked out the necessary statistical analysis to know whether their results should be accepted at face value. Griswold and Luce (22) employed 30 to 50 observations per pair to estimate the choice probabilities, and among 103 triples of money gambles they found a total of 13 violations of strong transitivity. Moreover, most of these violations were within one standard deviation of the quantities estimated and so may very well not really indicate violations. In their opinion, there was no substantial reason to doubt strong transitivity.

As I have said, neither transitivity assumption is a complete theory of behavior, and neither has anything in particular to do with risky alternatives; so let me consider next a theory which is restricted to that case. It is described in detail in *Individual Choice Behavior* (Luce [24]). The basic assumptions are three forms of statistical independence. The first, called the 'choice axiom', is a probabilistic version of the ubiquitous independence of irrelevant alternatives notion in decision theory (Luce and

Raiffa [26]). It says that the probability of choosing alternative a from a set S of alternatives is identical with the conditional probability of choosing a from a larger set T, provided that we consider only those choices which, in fact, lie in S, i.e.,

$$P_S(a) = P_T(a \mid S),$$

assuming that the conditional probability exists. For example, suppose that two thirds of the time a person selects steak over lamb chops when they are the only two alternatives. Suppose we now confront him with chicken and liver as well as steak and lamb chops, and let us look only at those occasions when he selects either steak or chops. The axiom asserts that the relative frequency of steak choices will be exactly the same as when the chicken and liver were not present, namely, two thirds.

Our second major assumption limits the theory to risky alternatives. Suppose one must choose between $a \alpha b$ and $a \beta b$. There are two conditions when one should prefer the former, namely, when one prefers a to b and judges α as more likely than β and also when one prefers b to a and judges β more likely than α. If we suppose that a person's preference decisions are statistically independent of his judgments of likelihood, then

$$P(a \alpha b, a \beta b) = P(a, b)Q(\alpha, \beta) + P(b, a)Q(\beta, \alpha),$$

where P denotes the preference probability and Q the judgment probability. This has been called the 'decomposition axiom'.

The third assumption is the choice axiom applied to likelihood selections among events; it is the same equation as before with Q replacing P and events replacing alternatives.

Of the two results I shall cite, the second leads to an experimental test of the theory. Recall that there are data which suggest that the probability paint is spread somewhat unevenly over the pairs of risky alternatives. The decomposition theory not only allows this to happen but in a sense requires it. Specifically, it can be shown either that the choice probabilities for pairs of sure alternatives are 0, $\frac{1}{2}$, or 1, as happens with money, or that the probabilities of judging one event as more likely than another can assume only three possible values. The probabilities of choice among gambles are not so severely restricted. This somewhat surprising and strong result has, on the whole, made psychologists skeptical of the theory. There is a common view that weaker theories are better than strong ones, for the strong ones are bound to be wrong. My view is just the opposite: the stronger, the better, for, on the one hand, a correct theory will be strong and, on the other hand, an incorrect one is much more quickly discovered to be incorrect if it is strong than if it is weak.

Our testable conclusion concerns choices in the following situation:

$$\begin{array}{cc} & \text{I} \quad\quad \text{II} \\ \alpha & \begin{bmatrix} a & b \\ d & c \end{bmatrix} \\ \alpha & \end{array}$$

The subject selects a column, the event α selects the row, and the payoff is the corresponding sum of money. On the assumption that $a > b > c > d$, it is evident that if α is an event which never occurs, the subject should never choose column I; whereas if α is certain to occur, then he should always choose column I. Thus,

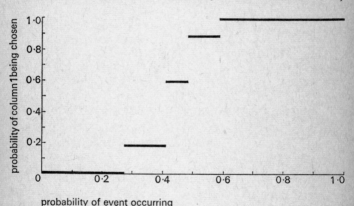

Figure 2   A typical example of the prediction of the decomposition theory that the choice probability is a step function of the event probability. This figure is reproduced from Luce (24) by permission of John Wiley & Sons.

as the probability of α occurring changes from 0 to 1, the probability of choosing column I should also go from 0 to 1. Judging by the data shown in Figure 1 and from related results in other parts of psychology, one might expect this to be a continuous change. Not so, if the decomposition theory is correct. It must be a step function of the sort shown in Figure 2. Just how many steps to expect or where to find them is not specified by the theory, but it says that the function is not continuous.

Obviously, it will be possible to confirm this prediction only if the steps are large and conspicuous. Taking the risk that they might not be, Elizabeth Shipley and I (27) ran the experiment. We used six different payoff matrices for each subject and 15 closely spaced events whose probabilities were known to the subjects. The events were located in the region where the choice probability changed from 0 to 1. We made 50 observations for each event-payoff condition. Of our five subjects, two exhibited

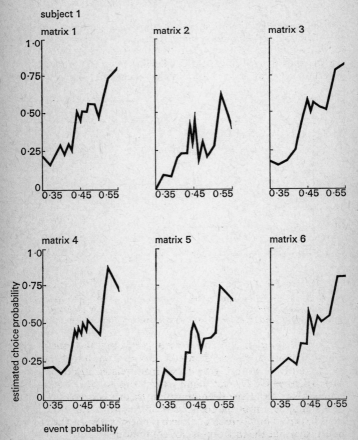

Figure 3 Estimated choice probabilities as a function of event probability for six payoff matrices and three subjects (Luce and Shipley [27]).

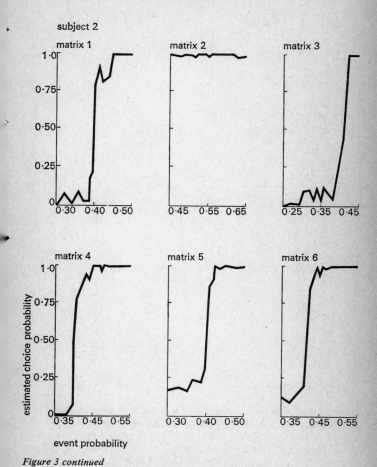

Figure 3 continued

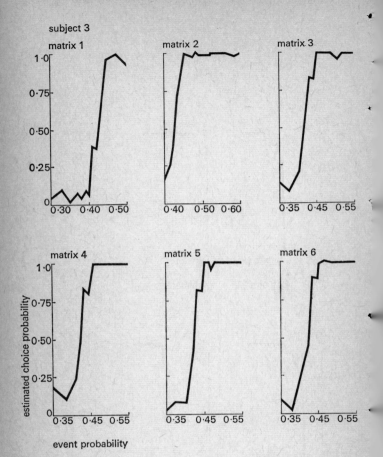

Figure 3 continued

almost perfectly discontinuous functions, and so were consistent with the prediction, but not in a very interesting way. The other three subjects yielded the data shown in Figure 3. You will note that there are curious plateaus of a sort not found in, say, psychophysical data. To see whether these results might have arisen from sampling fluctuations, we fit the data as best we could with smooth *S*-shaped curves (logistic functions). Assuming that these continuous functions described the probabilities involved, we carried out Monte Carlo computer runs which mimicked the experimental runs. The question was how often in a set of 200 Monte Carlo runs did a pattern of reversals occur that was at least as marked as that exhibited by the data. It turned out that such patterns were very rare indeed. As a result, we concluded that the data could not have arisen from such smooth probability functions. Whether this means that the decomposition theory is approximately correct is another matter; I am not prepared to argue that it is until we have more studies which confirm it.

Learning Theories

Our third group of theorists who study human choice behavior when the alternatives are risky have, like the preference theorists, assumed that responses are stochastically controlled. But rather than seek out relations among the response probabilities in related choice situations, learning theorists have focused upon the mechanisms whereby these choice probabilities change with repeated experience in one situation. Without entering into the mathematical details of the learning models,[1] two of their most important features can be mentioned. First, they all describe an organism with an extremely limited memory. This means that they are totally incapable of accounting for human learning of, for example, periodic binary sequences. Second, the learning models assume that when a subject makes a response and it is rewarded, his probability for making that response again is increased a little bit and that when he makes one and it is unrewarded or punished, the probability is decreased a little.

Naïve as these postulates may seem, some data suggest that they are not always grievously incorrect. Suppose, for example, that on each trial a subject must predict which of two lights will appear, the one being correct a random 75 per cent of the time and the other only 25 per cent. Depending on just what specific model one assumes, the subject's asymptotic response probability is predicted to be the same or nearly the same as the event probability of 0·75. A rational analysis says that, to maximize the number of correct predictions, he should always select the 0·75 light. The data, even after hundreds of trials, indicate that human subjects overshoot the event probability but that, in general, they fail to adopt the rational solution.

1. The details can be found in Bush and Mosteller (4) and Bush and Estes (3).

Or consider another kind of experiment. On each trial, a faint light increment may or may not be presented in a background patch of light, and the subject reports whether or not he thinks it is there. Following his response, he is told whether or not he was correct, and he wins or loses money according to a given payoff schedule. Suppose that there are sensory discrimination thresholds such that internal fluctuations cause the patch to exceed the threshold with one probability, whereas the increment in the patch exceeds it with another, somewhat larger probability. Moreover, suppose not only that the subject bases his responses

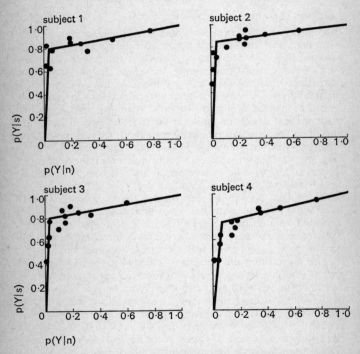

Figure 4   Plots of the estimated conditional probability of detection response when a signal is presented versus conditional probability of detection when no signal is presented. The data points were generated by using the same visual signal and background but different payoff matrices (Swets, Tanner, and Birdsall [33]), and the theoretical curves are those of a threshold theory (Luce [25]).

on what he thinks he sees but that he biases what he says in terms of the payoff matrix used. Then it can be shown that a maximization of expected utility leads to just one of three possible modes of behavior (Luce [25]). Either on all trials he says no increment is present, or he always says it is present, or he simply reports what he detects. Which he does depends on the proportion of trials having increments present and on the exact payoffs used. In contrast, if we suppose that the subject learns to bias his responses as a result of the information feedback, then all the intermediate points on the straight lines connecting the above three points are possible. This prediction is shown as the theoretical lines in Figure 4. The actual value of the response probabilities depends on the payoffs and frequency of stimulus presentations. Of these two models, the learning one is favored, judging by the data shown in Figure 4.

I should add, however, that if we assume a different psycho-physical model, such as the signal detection model in which there are no thresholds, then the maximization of expected value may yield sensible results. For expositions of this approach, see Green (21), Licklider (23), and Tanner and Swets (34).

Both the guessing and the threshold analyses suggest that a simple adaptive learning process is not, in general, consistent with an optimizing model. This seems, indeed, to be a general proposition. So far as I know, no one has yet stated a learning process which, when the behavior stabilizes at its asymptotic values, results in optimal choices. If, instead of trying to find mechanisms that lead to optimizing behavior, we look for ones leading to the stochastic preference models, the relations are more complex, Suppes (32) has shown that an existing linear learning model, due originally to Estes (18), predicts that the choice axiom holds asymptotically, although it may not hold during the learning phase itself. On the other hand, there do not seem to be any indications that the learning models lead asymptotically to the decomposition axiom. Probably this is related to their failure to lead to a maximization of expected utility, for the decomposition axiom and the expected utility decomposition are certainly very similar in spirit.

Concluding Remarks

These, then, are some of the main outlines of experimental and theoretical psychological research on the question of choices among risky alternatives. Much the most dominant theoretical ideas have been the subjective expected utility hypothesis and the notion that a person chooses optimally relative to his utility function. Although I cannot cite an unambiguous experimental refutation of these utility notions, their *a priori* flexibility, coupled with the failure to achieve really smashing experimental successes by using them, leads me to feel that other formulations must be seriously considered.

Of these, we examined two. Both postulate stochastic choice mechanisms. Preference theory is concerned with static constraints existing among the choice probabilities in different, but related, choice situations. Learning theory is concerned with the dynamic constraints relating the choice probabilities on successive exposures to the same choice situation. Ultimately, we must find a way to fuse these two approaches into a single model, specializations of which lead to the restricted theories we are now trying to develop. At present, however, we are far from that ideal state. Our learning models, which have received some experimental support, are not able to account for all our static assumptions, which also have received some experimental support. Moreover, there are some simple learning situations, e.g., prediction of simple periodic sequences, for which the learning models are completely inadequate.

It is not difficult to indicate where some of the trouble lies, but it is quite another matter to recast the models in such a way as to overcome it. Human beings appear to be both 'adaptive' and 'cognitive'; they sometimes adjust their behavior gradually to experience, and they sometimes 'understand' and analyze choice situations. Furthermore, both processes often seem to go on at the same time. The current learning theories are exclusively adaptive, whereas, almost by definition, the static assumptions of the preference theories are cognitive. By appropriately designing our experiments so as to draw upon just one of these two aspects of behavior, we are able to find support for each class of models. But other experiments in which both processes occur can also be designed, and these are bound to reject both classes of models. Such studies are interesting beyond being mere demonstrations, for it is from them that we shall begin to understand which features of a choice situation control the degree to which the behavior is adaptive or cognitive. Only when we develop such insights, will we be able to construct models that effectively take both into account.

If I am not mistaken, students of business have been much more deeply influenced by those theories that are primarily cognitive, especially those in which the decision maker is supposed to behave optimally. At best, this is only a part of what goes on, and certainly in some situations adaptive models are much more to the point. Regrettably, we cannot yet begin even to indicate what differentiates the two classes of situations or to suggest how to synthesize the two classes of models. It is certain, however, that these problems will receive a good deal of attention in the near future, and, judging by the rapid developments during the past decade, we may have a much clearer idea about the relations between these two aspects of behavior in another ten years.

References

1. ADAMS, E. W., 'Survey of Bernoullian Utility Theory', in H. Solomon (ed.), *Mathematical Thinking in the Measurement of Behavior*, pp. 151–268. Glencoe, Ill.: Free Press, 1960.

2. BLOCK, H. D., and MARSCHAK, J., 'Random Orderings and Stochastic Theories of Responses', in I. Olkin *et al.* (eds.), *Contributions to Probability and Statistics*, pp. 97–132. Stanford: Stanford University Press, 1960.

3. BUSH, R. R., and ESTES, W. K. (eds.), *Studies in Mathematical Learning Theory*. Stanford: Stanford University Press, 1959.

4. BUSH, R. R., and MOSTELLER, F., *Stochastic Models for Learning*. New York: John Wiley & Sons, 1955.

5. CHIPMAN, J. S., 'Stochastic Choice and Subjective Probability', in D. Willner (ed.), *Decisions, Values, and Groups*, Vol. I, pp. 70–95. New York: Pergamon Press, 1960.

6. COOMBS, C. H., 'On the Use of Inconsistency of Preferences in Psychological Measurement', *Journal of Experimental Psychology*, Vol. LV (1958), pp. 1–7.

7. COOMBS, C. H., and PRUITT, D. G., 'Components of Risk in Decision Making: Probability and Variance Preferences', *Journal of Experimental Psychology*, Vol. LX (1960), pp. 265–77.

8. DAVIDSON, D., and MARSCHAK, J., 'Experimental Tests of a Stochastic Decision Theory', in C. W. Churchman and P. Ratoosh (eds.), *Measurement: Definitions and Theory*, pp. 238–69. New York: John Wiley & Sons, 1959.

9. DAVIDSON, D., and SUPPES, P., 'A Finitistic Axiomatization of Subjective Probability and Utility', *Econometrica*, Vol. XXIV (1956), pp. 264–75.

10. DAVIDSON, D., SUPPES, P., and SIEGEL, S., *Decision Making*. Stanford: Stanford University Press, 1957.

11. EDWARDS, W., 'Probability-Preferences in Gambling', *American Journal of Psychology*, Vol. LXVI (1953), pp. 349–64.

12. ——. 'Probability Preferences among Bets with Differing Expected Values', *ibid.*, Vol. LXVII (1954), pp. 56–67.

13. ——. 'The Reliability of Probability Preferences', *ibid.*, pp. 68–95.

14. ——. 'Variance Preferences in Gambling', *ibid.*, pp. 441–52.

15. ——. 'The Theory of Decision Making', *Psychological Bulletin*, Vol. LI (1954), pp. 380–417.

16. ——. 'The Prediction of Decisions among Bets', *Journal o Experimental Psychology*, Vol. LI (1955), pp. 201–14.

17. ——. 'Behavioral Decision Theory', in *Annual Review of Psychology*, pp. 473–98. Palo Alto, Calif.: Annual Reviews, Inc., 1961.

18. ESTES, W. K., 'Toward a Statistical Theory of Learning', *Psychological Review*, Vol. LVII (1950), pp. 94–107.

19. FINETTI, B. DE., 'La prévision: ses lois logiques, ses sources subjectives', *Annales de l'Institut Henri Poincaré*, Vol. VII (1937), pp. 1–68.

20. ——. 'Recent Suggestions for the Reconciliation of Theories of Probability', in *Proceedings of the Second Berkeley Symposium on Mathematical Statistics and Probability*. Berkeley, Calif.: University of California Press, 1951.

21. GREEN, D., 'Psychoacoustics and Detection Theory', *Journal of the Acoustical Society of America*, Vol. XXXII (1960), pp. 1189–1203.

22. GRISWOLD, B., and LUCE, R. D., 'Choices among Uncertain Outcomes: A Test of the Decomposition, Transitivity, and Strong Stochastic Transitivity Assumptions', *American Journal of Psychology*, in press, 1961.

23. LICKLIDER, J. C. R., 'Three Auditory Theories', in S. Koch (ed.), *Psychology: A Study of a Science*, Vol. I, pp. 41–144. New York: McGraw-Hill Book Co., 1959.

24. LUCE, R. D., *Individual Choice Behavior*. New York: John Wiley & Sons, 1959.

25. ——. 'A Threshold Theory for Simple Detection and Recognition Experiments'. Department of Psychology Memorandum MP-12. University of Pennsylvania, 1961. Mimeographed.

26. LUCE, R. D., and RAIFFA, H., *Games and Decisions*. New York: John Wiley & Sons, 1957.

27. LUCE, R. D., and SHIPLEY, E., 'Preference Probability between Gambles as a Step Function of Event Probability', *Journal of Experimental Psychology*, in press, 1961.

28. MARSCHAK, J., 'Binary-Choice Constraints and Random Utility Indicators', in K. Arrow, S. Karlin, and P. Suppes (eds.), *Mathematical Methods in the Social Sciences*, 1959, pp. 312–29. Stanford: Stanford University Press, 1960.

29. MOSTELLER, F., and NOGEE, P., 'An Experimental Measurement of Utility', *Journal of Political Economy*, Vol. LIX (1951), pp. 371–404.

30. RAMSEY, F. P., *The Foundations of Mathematics and Other Logical Essays*. New York: Harcourt, Brace & Co., 1931.

31. SAVAGE, L. J., *The Foundations of Statistics*. New York: John Wiley & Sons, 1954.

32. SUPPES, P., *Behavioristic Foundations of Utility*. Technical Rept. No. 23, Institute for Mathematical Studies in Social Sciences, Stanford University, 1959.

33. SWETS, J. A., TANNER, W. P., JR., and BIRDSALL, T. G., *The Evidence for a Decision-Making Theory of Visual Detection*. Technical Rept. No. 40, Engineering Research Institute, University of Michigan, 1955.

34. TANNER, W. P., JR., and SWETS, J. A., 'A Decision-Making Theory of Visual Detection', *Psychological Review*, Vol. LXI (1954), pp. 401–9.

35. VON NEUMANN, J., and MORGENSTERN, O., *Theory of Games and Economic Behavior*. Princeton: Princeton University Press, 1947.

14 G. M. Becker, M. H. DeGroot and J. Marschak

Stochastic Models of Choice Behavior

G. M. Becker, M. H. DeGroot and J. Marschak, 'Stochastic models of choice behavior', *Behav. Sci.*, vol. 8 (1963), pp. 41–55.

The notion of 'utility' is fundamental in most current theories of human decision. The problem of determining the utility function of a given decision maker, however, presents grave difficulties. It is not sufficient to determine the decision maker's rank-order preference of choices, because such a rank-order preference would determine his utility only on an ordinal scale, not the interval scale required in many decision problems. The problem is further complicated by the fact that even the preference choices of the chooser are often inconsistent with each other. To circumvent the latter difficulty, stochastic definitions of utilities have been proposed in which probabilities (frequencies) of preference choices become the basic data. Here the implications of some of these models are derived which enable the experimenter to decide whether a given model is consistent with a set of data. Appropriate statistical sampling tests are worked out.

Introduction

Let S denote a finite set of n objects, or rewards, which can be thought of as being numbered serially, $1, 2, \ldots, n$. An *offered set* is a nonempty subset of S. We will be concerned with experiments in which a subject chooses a reward from each of several offered sets. The word 'rewards' is used here to describe the objects in S in order to convey the notion that the subject will choose the reward that he prefers from any offered set. Thus, if the subject knows he will receive the reward that he chooses, presumably he will choose the reward that he would most like to possess.

From these considerations it would seem plausible to postulate the existence of an ordering (by preference) of the n objects in S such that from any offered set the subject will choose that object which ranks highest in the ordering. The existence of an ordering of this type implies that the subject's choices from various offered sets will be consistent in a very strong sense. For example, if a subject chooses object x from the offered set $\{x, y\}$ containing the two objects x and y, and if he chooses y from $\{y, z\}$, then he must choose x from $\{x, z\}$. Furthermore, if he is presented with

353

the offered set $\{x, y\}$ at two different times under similar conditions, then his choice should be the same at both times.

It is not difficult to envisage situations in which the subject's choices would be consistent in the sense just described. If, for example, the objects in S were different amounts of money, presumably the subject would always choose the largest amount present in any offered set. On the other hand, simple experiments reveal that if S comprises different commodity bundles, or different lottery tickets whereby the subject receives a random amount of money according to some probability distribution, or indeed any objects for which there is no 'natural' simple ordering, then the subject's choices will very often not be consistent.[1] In order to account for these inconsistencies, it is convenient to introduce what is called a stochastic model.

A *stochastic model* is a specification, for each offered set M and each object $x \epsilon M$, of the probability that the subject will choose x from M. This probability is denoted by $x(M)$. Clearly, under any stochastic model it must be true, that $0 \leqslant x(M) \leqslant 1$ and $\sum_{x \epsilon M} x(M) = 1$ for all x and all M.

Random Utility Models

A large class of stochastic models, called the random utility models, can be derived from the following considerations.

Each object $x \epsilon S$, no matter how simple it might appear, has many attributes. For each $x \epsilon S$, let Ω_x denote the set of all attributes of x. To simplify the following discussion it is assumed that each set Ω_x is finite. When making a choice from among the objects in S a subject does not necessarily consider all of the attributes of all of the objects. Rather, he may consider for each $x \epsilon S$ some subset A_x of its attributes that happens to come to mind and seems to be particularly relevant at the time that he must make a choice. Thus, for each object, we can think of the subset of attributes that the subject considers at a given time as being randomly chosen according to some probabilistic law. Let $Pr\{A_x; x \epsilon S\}$ denote the probability that the subject considers

1. If the objects in S are commodity bundles, lottery tickets, or other objects that can be represented as vectors, then there is a natural partial ordering of the objects, and a subject's choices from among the objects in a simply ordered subset of S would typically be consistent. Thus, if every component of commodity bundle a is larger than the corresponding component of commodity bundle b, then a subject would typically always choose a rather than b. Situations of this type are discussed in the section on Wagers.

the subsets A_x, $x \epsilon S$. Finally, for each $x \epsilon S$, there is a number $U_x(A_x)$ associated with each subset A_x of attributes. This number can be thought of as the utility of x with respect to the given subset A_x. The subject, when choosing from S, considers a subset A_x of attributes for each $x \epsilon S$ that is determined by the probability distribution $Pr\{A_x; x \epsilon S\}$ and chooses that object x from S for which $U_x(A_x)$ is largest.

When choosing from an offered set M, other than S, the subject chooses that object $x \epsilon M$ for which $U_x(A_x)$ is largest among all objects in M. In making this statement we are, in effect, assuming that the subsets of attributes that the subject considers are always determined by the probability distribution $Pr\{A_x; x \epsilon S\}$ regardless of the offered set from which the subject is choosing. A more elaborate theory in which the probability distribution of subsets of attributes depends on the offered set could be given, but it does not seem worthwhile to do so at this stage of development. Since the subsets of attributes that the subject considers are randomly chosen, it follows that the utilities U_x, $x \epsilon S$, constitute a random vector. Furthermore, if the subject considers a certain subset of attributes of one of the objects in S, then it is likely that he will consider subsets of similar attributes of the other objects. In other words, it is not necessarily true that $Pr\{A_x; x \epsilon M\}$ and $\prod_{x \epsilon M} Pr\{A_x\}$ are always equal. Thus, the random utilities U_x, $x \epsilon S$,

need not be independent random variables.

To clarify these notions consider the following simple example (see also Quandt, 1956). A person is trying to decide which of three suits of clothes, x, y, and z, to wear on a certain occasion. When making this decision he might: (1) consider the style of a suit of primary importance and the material secondary; (2) consider the material of primary importance and the style secondary; or (3) consider style and material of equal importance. Let us say that the occurrence of (1) means that the person considers the subsets of A_x, A_y, and A_z of attributes of x, y, and z; the occurrence of (2) means that he considers the subsets B_x, B_y, and B_z; and the occurrence of (3) means that he considers C_x, C_y, and C_z.

Suppose that $Pr\{A_x, A_y, A_z\} = \frac{3}{8}$, $Pr\{B_x, B_y, B_z\} = \frac{1}{8}$, and $Pr\{C_x, C_y, C_z\} = \frac{4}{8}$. These are the probabilities of occurrence of (1), (2), and (3).

Suppose also that $U_x(A_x) > U_y(A_y) > U_z(A_z)$, $U_z(B_z) > U_y(B_y) > U_x(B_x)$, and $U_y(C_y) > U_x(C_x) > U_z(C_z)$. Then, x is preferred when (1) occurs; z is preferred when (2) occurs; and y is preferred when (3) occurs.

It follows that when the subject chooses from the set S containing all three suits, the probabilities of choice are $x(S) = \frac{3}{8}$, $y(S) = \frac{4}{8}$, and $z(S) = \frac{1}{8}$. If suit z is being cleaned at the time of decision so that the choice is restricted to the set M containing only x and y, then $x(M) = \frac{3}{8}$ and $y(M) = \frac{5}{8}$.

The following formal definition was given by Block and Marschak (1960). (The term 'random utility indicator' is used in Marschak [1960].) A stochastic model is said to be a *random utility model* if there exists a random vector $(U_1, \ldots, U_n)$ such that, for all offered sets M and all $x \epsilon M$,

$$x(M) = Pr\{U_x \geqslant U_y \text{ for all } y \epsilon M\}. \tag{1}$$

It is an easy consequence of this definition and is proved in Block and Marschak (1960) that under any random utility model

$$Pr\{U_x = U_y\} = 0 \text{ for all } x \neq y. \tag{2}$$

In effect, this means that every time the subject makes a choice from an offered set it is possible for him to strictly order the objects by their utilities, although this ordering is random and may change for the next choice the subject makes. The possibility that two objects have equal utility could be admitted at the expense of a more complicated definition instead of Equation (1). This will not be done here.

Luce or Strict Utility Models

We now define a special class of stochastic models originally introduced by Luce (1959). A stochastic model will be called a *Luce or strict utility model*[2] if there exist positive constants $u_1, \ldots, u_n$ such that

$$x(M) = \frac{u_x}{\sum\limits_{y \epsilon M} u_y}, \tag{3}$$

for all offered sets M and all $x \epsilon M$. It is easily seen that this is equivalent to the requirement that $x(S) > 0$ for all $x \epsilon S$ and

$$x(M) = \frac{x(S)}{\sum\limits_{y \epsilon M} y(S)}, \tag{4}$$

for all M and all $x \epsilon M$. The following theorem is stated and proved in Block and Marschak (1960).

2. Luce admitted the further possibility that $x(M)$ might be 0 or 1, in which case Equation (3) need not hold. The general question that this raises is discussed in the section on Wagers.

Theorem I. – Every Luce model is a random utility model.

The meaning of this theorem is that if the probabilities $x(M)$ are given by Equation (3) for some set of positive numbers $u_1, \ldots, u_n$, then there exists a random vector $(U_1, \ldots, U_n)$ with an appropriate multivariate distribution such that the probabilities $x(M)$ are also given by Equation (1). Thus, the Luce models form a subclass of the random utility models.

We will now give two characterizations of this subclass, but before doing so it is convenient to introduce some notation. For a given random utility model and any two offered sets $L \subset M$, let $E(L, M)$ denote the event that there exists an object $x \epsilon L$ such that $U_x \geqslant U_y$ for all $y \epsilon M$. Thus, $E(L, M)$ is the event that the object with largest utility among all the objects in M belongs to the subset L. When $x \epsilon M$, and L contains only the object x, we write $E(x, M)$ instead of $E(L, M)$. If $x \epsilon L \subset M$ then $E(x, M) \subset E(L, M)$, $E(x, M) \subset E(x, L)$ and $Pr\{E(L, M)\} = \sum_{y \epsilon M} y(M)$.

Theorem II. – A random utility model is a Luce model if and only if $x(S) > 0$ for all $x \epsilon S$ and

$$x(M) = Pr\{E(x, S) \mid E(M, S)\} \tag{5}$$

for all M and all $x \epsilon M$.

Proof. If $x(S) > 0$ for all $x \epsilon S$ then

$Pr\{E(x, S) \mid E(M, S)\}$

$$= \frac{Pr\{E(x, S) \cap E(M, S)\}}{Pr\{E(M, S)\}}$$

$$= \frac{Pr\{E(x, S)\}}{Pr\{E(M, S)\}} = \frac{x(S)}{\sum_{y \epsilon M} y(S)}. \tag{6}$$

Hence, if $x(S) > 0$ for all $x \epsilon S$ and Equation (5) holds, then

$$x(M) = x(S) / \sum_{y \epsilon M} y(S), \tag{7}$$

and these are the defining properties of a Luce model.

Conversely, if the random utility model is a Luce model, then by definition, $x(S) > 0$ for all $x \epsilon S$ and Equation (7) holds. Consequently, so do Equations (6) and (5).

Theorem III. – A random utility model is a Luce model if and only if $x(S) > 0$ for all $x \epsilon S$ and, for every offered set M,

$$Pr\{E(x, S) \mid E(x, M)\} = k_M, \text{ a constant, for all } x \epsilon M. \qquad (8)$$

Proof. If $x(S) > 0$ for all $x \epsilon S$ then

$$\begin{aligned} x(S) = Pr\{E(x, S)\} &= Pr\{E(x, S) \cap E(x, M)\} \\ &= P\{E(x, S) \mid E(x, M)\} Pr\{E(x, M)\} \\ &= P\{E(x, S) \mid E(x, M)\} x(M), \end{aligned} \qquad (9)$$

for all M and all $x \epsilon M$.

Hence, if $x(S) > 0$ for all $x \epsilon S$ and Equation (8) holds, then

$$x(S) = k_M x(M) \qquad (10)$$

and

$$\sum_{x \epsilon M} x(S) = k_M \sum_{x \epsilon M} x(M) = k_M. \qquad (11)$$

Thus,

$$x(M) = \frac{x(S)}{k_M} = \frac{x(S)}{\sum_{y \epsilon M} y(S)} \qquad (12)$$

and the model is a Luce model.

Conversely, if the random utility model is a Luce model, then by definition, $x(S) > 0$ for all $x \epsilon S$ and Equation (7) holds. Hence, from Equation (9),

$$Pr\{E(x, S) \mid E(x, M)\} = \frac{x(S)}{x(M)} = \sum_{y \epsilon M} y(S), \qquad (13)$$

which is constant for all $x \epsilon M$. This concludes the proof.

Fechner or Strong Utility Models

In many experiments each of the offered sets from which a subject must choose contains exactly two of the objects in S. An experiment of this type is called a *binary experiment* and an offered set containing exactly two objects is called a *binary offered set*. Binary experiments have been discussed in detail by Marschak (1960). In such experiments the specification of the probabilities $x(M)$ for offered sets M containing more than two objects is irrelevant, since no pertinent experimental data can be obtained. A specification of the probabilities $x(M)$ for all binary offered sets M is called a *binary model*.

Clearly every stochastic model can be thought of as a binary stochastic model simply by considering only those probabilities $x(M)$ that refer to binary M. Thus, all random utility models and, in particular, all Luce models are binary stochastic models when the defining Equations (1) and (3) are restricted to binary M. These restricted models will be called *binary random utility models* and *binary Luce models*. A binary model is called a *strong utility or Fechner model* if there exist constants $v_1, \ldots, v_n$ and a nondecreasing real-valued function $\Phi(r)$ defined for all real numbers r, such that for every binary offered set $M = \{x, y\}$,

$$x(M) = \Phi(v_x - v_y). \qquad (14)$$

Since (14) restricts the values of $\Phi(r)$ at only a finite number of values of r and since $x(M) + y(M) = 1$, it is easily seen that $\Phi(r)$ can be chosen to be a continuous, nondecreasing function such that

$$\lim_{r \to -\infty} \Phi(r) = 0, \lim_{r \to \infty} \Phi(r) = 1, \quad \text{and}$$

$$\Phi(r) + \Phi(-r) = 1 \text{ for all } r. \qquad (15)$$

The following derivation of the Fechner models, in the same spirit as the derivation given for the random utility models, is sometimes helpful. The function $\Phi(r)$ can be thought of as the distribution function of a continuous random variable ϵ, with a symmetric distribution around the value 0. For each object $x \epsilon S$, the number v_x represents, in some appropriate sense, the utility, or value, of x to the subject. Thus, when presented with a choice from $\{x, y\}$, the subject would ideally want to choose x if $v_x - v_y > 0$ and y if $v_x - v_y < 0$. However, because of some inherent limitations in the choice-making process (e.g., not being able to consider all attributes of both x and y) the subject cannot calculate $v_x - v_y$ exactly, but rather can calculate only $v_x - v_y + \epsilon$, where ϵ is the random variable just defined. He then chooses x if $v_x - v_y + \epsilon > 0$ and y otherwise. This leads to Equation (14).

We now mention some relations between the Fechner, binary Luce, and binary random utility models.

Theorem IV. – Every binary Luce model is a binary random utility model, but not conversely.

Theorem V. – Every binary Luce model is a Fechner model, but not conversely.

Calling a Luce model strict and a Fechner model strong is

justified by Theorem V, the word 'strict' conveying the greater restriction. Correspondingly, the constants $u_1, \ldots, u_n$ are called strict utilities, and the constants $v_1, \ldots, v_n$ are called strong utilities, both distinct from the random utilities, $U_1, \ldots, U_n$ which are random variables, not constants.

Proofs are given in Block and Marschak (1960). (Indeed, Theorem V is proved by choosing $\Phi(r)$ as in Equation (17) below.) It is also shown there that not every binary random utility model is a Fechner model, but it is not known whether every Fechner model is a binary random utility model. However, the following theorem shows that at least a large class of Fechner models are also binary random utility models.

Theorem VI. – Every Fechner model such that $\Phi(r)$ is the distribution function of the difference of two independent and identically distributed random variables is a binary random utility model.

Proof. Define the random vector $(U_1, \ldots, U_n)$ by

$$U_i = v_i + \epsilon_i, i = 1, \ldots, n$$

where $\epsilon_1, \ldots, \epsilon_n$ are independent and identically distributed random variables such that $\Phi(r)$ is the distribution function of $\epsilon_i - \epsilon_j$ for all $i \neq j$, and $v_1, \ldots, v_n$ are the constants appearing in the Fechner model. Then, for any $M = \{x, y\}$,

$$x(M) = Pr\{U_x \geqslant U_y\} = Pr\{v_x + \epsilon_x \geqslant v_y + \epsilon_y\} = \\ Pr\{\epsilon_y - \epsilon_x \leqslant v_x - v_y\} = \Phi(v_x - v_y). \quad (16)$$

It follows from this theorem that, for example, any Fechner model in which $\Phi(r)$ is a normal distribution function is also a binary random utility model.

Statistical Analysis of Experimental Data

Consider an experiment in which a subject makes choices from several offered sets. It is assumed throughout this paper that the subject's choices in such an experiment are independent. That is, it is assumed that for any finite collection $M_1, \ldots M_k$ of the offered sets presented in the experiment, the probability that the subject will choose object x_i from $M_i, i = 1, \ldots, k$, is $\prod_{i=1}^{k} x_i (M_i)$.

This assumption excludes the possibility that the subject undergoes some learning process in the course of the experiment whereby his choice from an offered set depends on the previously offered sets from which he has already chosen and on his choices from those offered sets. The reason for making the assumption of independence of choices is that it yields an explicit, simple, probabilistic model for a wide variety of situations. However, in order that the assumption be satisfied in an experiment, it is very often essential that the subject does not make a choice from any particular offered set more than a few times. Indeed, if some offered set is to be presented to the subject more than once during the experiment it is important that sufficient precautions are taken to insure that when the subject is presented with the offered set for the second time he has forgotten his earlier choice.

In general, the purpose of performing an experiment and observing the subject's choices is to gain information about the probabilities $x(M)$, which are typically not completely known to the experimenter (or to the subject). The questions about the probabilities $x(M)$ that the experimenter wants to answer can very often be classified either as questions of testing some hypotheses about the stochastic model or as questions of estimating some parameters appearing in the stochastic model. To the authors' knowledge, the only relevant statistical methods that have thus far appeared in the literature are concerned with Fechner models for binary experiments.

Consider a Fechner model in which the function $\Phi(r)$ is the logistic function

$$\Phi(r) = \frac{1}{1 + e^{-r}}. \tag{17}$$

(Fechner models in which $\Phi(r)$ is of the form of Equation (17) are also binary Luce models. We will return to this relationship below.) Berkson (1955, 1957) has used this function in problems of bioassay. His approach can be slightly generalized as follows. Suppose that on each of a sequence of trials one observes either a success or a failure. Suppose that the probability p of observing a success on a given trial is

$$p = \frac{1}{1 + exp\left\{-\sum_{i=1}^{n} c_i v_i\right\}}, \tag{18}$$

where $v_1, \ldots, v_n$ are unknown parameters and $c_1, \ldots, c_n$ are known constants whose values are fixed by the experimenter on each trial. The problem is to estimate the parameters $v_1, \ldots,$

v_n from observations made at several sets of constants $c_1, \ldots, c_n$. Berkson has derived the maximum likelihood and other estimates of $v_1, \ldots, v_n$ and Cox (1958) has suggested some further techniques. Their methods obviously apply to experiments on binary choices by regarding the presentation of the offered set $\{x, y\}$ as the assignment of the values $c_x = 1$, $c_y = -1$, $c_i = 0$ for $i \neq x$, $i \neq y$, and regarding the choice of x from $\{x, y\}$ as the observation of a success. However, the known properties of their estimates are large sample properties, and no evaluation has been made when none of the sets of constants $c_1, \ldots, c_n$ are repeated in the experiment.

If, in a Fechner model, $\Phi(r)$ is given by Equation (17), then it is readily verified that the model is also a binary Luce model, with the relation between the constants $u_1, \ldots, u_n$ of the Luce model and the constants $v_1, \ldots, v_n$ of the Fechner model given by

$$u_i, = e^{v_i}, i = 1, \ldots, n. \tag{19}$$

Maximum likelihood estimation of the parameters $u_1, \ldots, u_n$ has been discussed by Abelson and Bradley (1954), Bradley (1954a, 1955), Bradley and Terry (1952), and Ford (1957) in the context of paired comparisons, but again this is a large sample technique. The maximum likelihood estimates of $u_1, \ldots, u_n$ and of $v_1, \ldots, v_n$ are related by Equation (19), just as the parameters are, but the work dealing with the logistic function and that dealing with paired comparisons seem to have developed independently of each other.

Brunk (1960) has presented a technique for computing the maximum likelihood estimates of the parameters $v_1, \ldots, v_n$ in a Fechner model when the function $\Phi(r)$ belongs to an exponential family of distribution functions.

Bradley (1954b) has derived a test of goodness-of-fit for testing whether a binary stochastic model is a binary Luce model, but the distribution of his test statistic is known only when each binary offered set is presented many times.

To summarize, no statistical techniques have as yet been given for other than binary experiments, and for binary experiments the existing techniques depend on repetitions of the offered sets. Such repetitions should not be essential since if S contains n objects there are $2^n - n - 1$ distinct offered sets containing at least two objects, and $\binom{n}{2}$ distinct binary offered sets. Hence, if the stochastic model is known except for the values of n parameters, then even though no offered set is presented to the subject more than once during the experiment, the number of choices that the subject makes will still be much larger than the number of unknown parameters when n is not too small. In this situation one would still expect to be able to find good estimates of the parameters, but as yet no general techniques are known.

Wagers

In many situations, each of the objects in an offered set from which a subject must choose contains some degree of uncertainty, in the sense that even after having chosen one of the objects from the offered set, the actual reward that the subject will receive is a random variable. In such situations, by choosing an object from an offered set, the subject is in fact choosing a probability distribution for the reward that he will receive. The offered set is simply some set of possible (or available) probability distributions. We now make this notation precise.

As before, let S denote a finite set of n rewards numbered 1, 2, ..., n. Let $E_1, \ldots, E_t$ denote a finite class of mutually exclusive and exhaustive events. (For example, in simple experiments the events $E_1, \ldots, E_t$ might be the various possible outcomes when a card is drawn from a deck of some specified composition.) For convenience we assume that each of the events $E_1, \ldots, E_t$ has positive probability. A *wager* $\mathbf{w} = (w_1, \ldots, w_t)$ is a vector such that each component w_i, $i = 1, \ldots, t$, is one of the integers 1, 2, ..., n. In other words, a wager associates with each of the events E_i a reward w_i in S. An *offered set* is a nonempty, finite subset of the set of all wagers.

The interpretation is as follows. A subject must choose one of the wagers from a given offered set. If he chooses the wager $\mathbf{w} = (w_1, \ldots, w_t)$ then he receives one of the rewards $w_1, \ldots, w_t$ depending on which of the events $E_1, \ldots, E_t$ occurs. Thus, the subject's preferences among the rewards in S will lead to preferences among the wagers in the offered set.

For any wager $\mathbf{w}$, let $p_i(\mathbf{w})$ be the probability that reward i is received, $i = 1, \ldots, n$. Thus, $p_i(\mathbf{w})$ is the total probability of those events E_j for which $w_j = i$. Let $\mathbf{p}(\mathbf{w})$ denote the vector $(p_1(\mathbf{w}), \ldots, p_n(\mathbf{w}))$, and consider two wagers $\mathbf{w}$ and $\mathbf{w}'$ such that $\mathbf{p}(\mathbf{w}) = \mathbf{p}(\mathbf{w}')$. Since the probabilities of receiving the various rewards are identical for both of the wagers $\mathbf{w}$ and $\mathbf{w}'$, it seems reasonable to assume that a subject would be indifferent when making a choice between them. In order for this assumption to be reasonable it is essential that the occurrence of any of the

363

events $E_1, \ldots, E_t$ does not affect the worth of any of the rewards to the subject. In other words, it is essential that the only features of the events $E_1, \ldots, E_t$ that are relevant to the subject's choice are the probabilities of the events. For this reason it is convenient to think of the events $E_1, \ldots, E_t$ as outcomes of some gambling device such as a deck of cards or a pair of dice.

We make full use of this argument by assuming that if $\mathbf{p}(\mathbf{w}) = \mathbf{p}(\mathbf{w}')$ then the wagers $\mathbf{w}$ and $\mathbf{w}'$ are interchangeable in the sense that we can replace one of them by the other in any offered set without changing the chances of any of the wagers in the offered set being chosen. Indeed, the stochastic models for wagers to be presented in the next section depend on the wagers in an offered set only through the vectors $\mathbf{p}(\mathbf{w})$.

Consider now the situation in which the n rewards in the set S are n different amounts of money. Suppose that reward i is the amount a_i, $i = 1, \ldots, n$, and suppose that the rewards have been numbered so that $a_1 < a_2 < \ldots < a_n$. It seems reasonable to assume that any subject, when asked to choose from among different amounts of money, will always choose the largest amount.

Let $\mathbf{w} = (w_1, \ldots, w_t)$ and $\mathbf{w}' = (w_1', \ldots, w_t')$ be two wagers such that $w_i \geq w_i'$, $i = 1, \ldots, t$, and $w_i > w_i'$ for at least one value of i. We then say that $\mathbf{w}$ *dominates* $\mathbf{w}'$. It follows that a subject will never choose the wager $\mathbf{w}'$ if the wager $\mathbf{w}$ is also available in the offered set. This is so because no matter which event E_i occurs, the subject will receive at least as much money from $\mathbf{w}$ as from $\mathbf{w}'$, and might receive more from $\mathbf{w}$.

It is convenient to make the following definition. The wager $\mathbf{w}$ is said to be *absolutely preferred* to the wager $\mathbf{w}'$ if, for every offered set M containing both $\mathbf{w}$ and $\mathbf{w}'$, $w'(M) = 0$. Thus, if $\mathbf{w}$ dominates $\mathbf{w}'$ then w is *absolutely* preferred to w'.

Suppose then that

$$w_i \geq w_i', i = 1, \ldots, t. \qquad (20)$$

Since, regardless of which event occurs, the reward received from $\mathbf{w}$ is at least as large as the reward received from $\mathbf{w}'$, it follows that for any amount of money a, the probability of receiving at least a is at least as large for $\mathbf{w}$ as it is for $\mathbf{w}'$. Thus,

$$\sum_{=x}^{n} p_j(\mathbf{w}) \geq \sum_{j=x}^{n} p_j(\mathbf{w}'), x = 1, \ldots, n, \qquad (21)$$

and if inequality holds in (20) for at least one value of i, then inequality holds in (21) for at least one value of x.

Furthermore, it can be shown that if (21) holds for some pairs of wagers **w** and **w**′ with inequality for some value of x then there exist wagers **w**″ and **w**‴ such that $p(w'') = p(w)$, $p(w''') = p(w')$, and $w_i'' \geqslant w_i'''$, $i = 1, \ldots, t$, with inequality for some value of i. Thus, **w**″ dominates **w**‴ and, hence, **w**″ is absolutely preferred to **w**‴. Since **w** and **w**″ are interchangeable and **w**′ and **w**‴ are also interchangeable, it follows that **w** is absolutely preferred to **w**′. Hence, we conclude that if **w** and **w**′ satisfy (21) with inequality for some value of x, then **w** is absolutely preferred to **w**′.

All of this can be illustrated with an example. Suppose that the ten events, $E_1, \ldots, E_{10}$, are equally probable, and consider the wagers w^1, w^2, and w^3 associating rewards (integers representing amounts of money) with outcomes as follows:

	E_1	E_2	E_3	E_4	E_5	E_6	E_7	E_8	E_9	E_{10}
w^1:	3	1	4	2	2	5	3	4	4	2
w^2:	4	2	4	3	2	5	3	4	5	2
w^3:	2	4	2	4	5	1	4	3	2	3

It is immediately seen that for every event the reward from w^2 is at least as large as the reward from w^1. Hence, w^2 dominates w^1 and is absolutely preferred to w^1. Since the rewards from w^3 are simply a permutation of the rewards from w^1 (and all E_i are equally probable), w^3 and w^1 are interchangeable, and hence w^2 is also absolutely preferred to w^3. In an actual experiment a subject might easily note that w^2 dominates w^1 and would never choose w^1. However, since w^3 yields larger rewards than w^2 for some events, a subject might at times choose w^3 in preference to w^2. If, as is done in the stochastic models that will now be presented, a wager **w** is characterized simply by the vector $p(w)$, it must be reasonable to assume that such violations of interchangeability do not occur. This assumption is very often reasonable when dealing, for example, with fewer than ten events, or when the subject has ample time to consider his choice.

Stochastic Models for Wagers

As discussed in the preceding section, we now represent a wager as an n-dimensional vector $\mathbf{p} = (p_1, \ldots, p_n)$ such that $p_i \geq 0$, $i = 1, \ldots, n$, and $\sum_{i=1}^{n} p_i = 1$. The interpretation is that if a subject chooses the wager $\mathbf{p} = (p_1, \ldots, p_n)$ from some offered set then he receives reward i with probability p_i, $i = 1, \ldots, n$.

365

(An offered set is accordingly to be thought of as a finite set of vectors of the above form.)

For reasons similar to those given in the Introduction (and which are no doubt even more compelling when dealing with wagers), it is again convenient to introduce a stochastic model for subjects' choices.

A *stochastic model for wagers* is a specification, for every offered set M and every wager $\mathbf{p} \epsilon M$, of the probability that $\mathbf{p}$ will be chosen from M. This probability is denoted by $\mathbf{p}(M)$. Clearly, under any stochastic model for wagers it must be true that $0 \leqslant \mathbf{p}(M) \leqslant 1$ and $\sum_{\mathbf{p} \epsilon M} \mathbf{p}(M) = 1$.

The celebrated von Neumann–Morgenstern (1947) concept of utility provides a very special type of model for a subject's choices. A model for wagers is said to be a *von Neumann–Morgenstern* model if there exist constants $t_1, \ldots, t_n$ with the property that, for any offered set M and any wager $\mathbf{p} \epsilon M$, $\mathbf{p}(M) = 0$ whenever there exists $\mathbf{q} \epsilon M$ with

$$\sum_{i=1}^{n} q_i t_i > \sum_{i=1}^{n} p_i t_i.$$

The constant t_i is called the *utility of reward i*, $i = 1, \ldots, n$, and $\sum_{i=1}^{n} p_i t_i$ is called the *utility of the wager*, $\mathbf{p}$. Thus, the von Neumann–Morgenstern model says that the utility of a wager is the expected utility of the reward received from the wager, and the subject always chooses, from any offered set, a wager of maximum utility.

Except for those offered sets in which more than one wager has maximum utility (in this case nothing has been said about the subject's choice from among them), the above model is nonstochastic in the sense that it exactly specifies the subject's choices. Consequently, it is desirable to develop models that admit more randomness in these choices. The stochastic models for wagers that will now be presented attempt to combine the stochastic models given in the earlier sections of this paper with the von Neumann–Morgenstern concept of the utility of a wager.

A stochastic model for wagers is said to be a *random utility model for wagers* if there exists a random vector $(U_1, \ldots, U_n)$ such that, for any offered set M and every $\mathbf{p} \epsilon M$,

$$\mathbf{p}(M) = Pr \left\{ \sum_{i=1}^{n} p_i U_i \geqslant \sum_{i=1}^{n} q_i U_i \text{ for all } \mathbf{q} \epsilon M \right\}. \qquad (22)$$

A wager **p** such that $p_i = 1$ for some value of i is said to be a *sure thing*: in this case the subject is certain of the reward that he will receive from this wager. Clearly, if the only wagers that appear in the offered sets presented to the subject are sure things, then these models[3] reduce to the random utility models presented in the section on Random Utility Models. Analogous to (2), it follows from Equation (22) that

$$Pr\left\{\sum_{i=1}^{n} p_i U_i = \sum_{i=1}^{n} q_i U_i\right\} = 0 \text{ for all } \mathbf{p} \neq \mathbf{q}. \tag{23}$$

A stochastic model for wagers is said to be a *Luce model for wagers* if there exist constants $u_1, \ldots, u_n$ and a positive, strictly increasing function $h(r)$ defined for all real numbers r, such that

$$\mathbf{p}(M) = \frac{h\left(\sum_{i=1}^{n} p_i u_i\right)}{\sum_{q \in M} h\left(\sum_{i=1}^{n} q_i u_i\right)} \tag{24}$$

for all M and every $\mathbf{p} \in M$. Again, if the only wagers appearing in an experiment are sure things, then these models reduce to the Luce models presented earlier, with u_i as defined there equal to $h(u_i)$ as defined here, $i = 1, \ldots, n$.

An offered set containing exactly two wagers is a *binary offered set*. An experiment in which the only offered sets presented to the subject are binary is a *binary experiment*. A stochastic model for wagers that specifies the probabilities $\mathbf{p}(M)$ only for binary M is a *binary stochastic model for wagers*. The *binary random utility models for wagers* and *binary Luce models for wagers* are obtained by restricting the definitions of Equations (22) and (24) to binary M.

A binary stochastic model for wagers is said to be a *Fechner model for wagers* if there exist constants $v_1, \ldots, v_n$, a strictly increasing function $k(r)$, and a nondecreasing function $\Phi(r)$,

3. It should be noted that in Equation (22) only a single realization of the random vector $(U_1, \ldots, U_n)$ is needed. Under an alternative class of models one might assume that independent realizations of $(U_1, \ldots, U_n)$ are made for each wager in M. When choosing from offered sets containing sure things, these models would not reduce to the ones presented in the section on Random Utility Models unless the components of $(U_1, \ldots, U_n)$ were independent.

defined for all real numbers r, such that for every binary $M = \{\mathbf{p}, \mathbf{q}\}$,

$$\mathbf{p}(M) = \Phi\left(k\left(\sum_{i=1}^{n} p_i v_i\right) - k\left(\sum_{i=1}^{n} q_i v_i\right)\right). \qquad (25)$$

Clearly, $\Phi(r)$ can be chosen so that

$$\Phi(r) + \Phi(-r) = 1 \qquad (26)$$

for all r. Again, if the only wagers considered are sure things, then the Fechner models for wagers reduce to the Fechner models defined earlier, with v_i as defined there equal to $k(v_i)$ as defined here, $i = 1, \ldots, n$.

Relationships among the Models

In the section on Fechner Models we discussed various inclusion relations between the stochastic models. Not surprisingly, some of these relations no longer hold between the corresponding stochastic models for wagers. Indeed, the class of Luce models for wagers is not contained in the class of random utility models for wagers. This is seen by considering four wagers

$$\mathbf{p}^j = (p_1{}^j, \ldots, p_n{}^j), \ j = 1, 2, 3, 4, \qquad (27)$$

such that

$$p_i{}^1 - p_i{}^2 = p_i{}^3 - p_i{}^4, \ i = 1, \ldots, n. \qquad (28)$$

It follows from (22) that under any random utility model for wagers,

$$\begin{aligned}
\mathbf{p}^1(\{\mathbf{p}^1, \mathbf{p}^2\}) &= Pr\left\{\sum_{i=1}^{n} p_i{}^1 U_i \geqslant \sum_{i=1}^{n} p_i{}^2 U_i\right\} \\
&= Pr\left\{\sum_{i=1}^{n} (p_i{}^1 - p_i{}^2)\, U_i \geqslant 0\right\} \\
&= Pr\left\{\sum_{i=1}^{n} (p_i{}^3 - p_i{}^4)\, U_i \geqslant 0\right\} \\
&= \mathbf{p}^3(\{\mathbf{p}^3, \mathbf{p}^4\}). \qquad (29)
\end{aligned}$$

Clearly, this equality need not hold under a Luce model for wagers. Furthermore, since the only offered sets used in this demonstration were binary, we can conclude that the class of binary Luce models for wagers is not contained in the class of binary random utility models for wagers.

Theorem VII. – Every binary Luce model for wagers is a Fechner model for wagers.

Proof. – Consider a binary Luce model for wagers defined by constants $u_i, \ldots, u_n$ and the function $h(r)$. A Fechner model for wagers is characterized by the constants $v_i, \ldots, v_n$ and the functions $k(r)$ and $\Phi(r)$. It is readily checked that if these are defined by

$$v_i = u_i, \, i = 1, \ldots, n,$$
$$k(r) = \log h(r),$$
$$\Phi(r) = \frac{1}{1 + e^{-r}}, \tag{30}$$

then the two models yield the same values for all $\mathbf{p}(M)$.

It follows from Theorem VII and the comments preceding it that the class of Fechner models for wagers is not contained in the class of binary random utility models for wagers. Finally, it can be easily checked that no inclusion relationships in the reverse direction hold.

Absolute Preferences and Stochastic Models

Let us now return to the situation discussed under Wagers, where the set S of rewards comprise different amounts of money. Reward i is the amount $a_i, \, i = 1, \ldots, n$; and

$$a_1 < a_2 < \ldots < a_n.$$

It was argued there that if the wagers $\mathbf{p} = (p_1, \ldots, p_n)$ and $\mathbf{q} = (q_1, \ldots, q_n)$ satisfy the relations

$$\sum_{j=x}^{n} p_j \geqslant \sum_{j=x}^{n} q_j, \, x = 1, \ldots, n, \tag{31}$$

with inequality for at least one value of x, then $\mathbf{p}$ is absolutely preferred to $\mathbf{q}$. That is, the probability that $\mathbf{q}$ will be chosen from an offered set that also contains $\mathbf{p}$ is 0.

However, it is important to recognize that no provision has been made for this property in the Luce and Fechner models for wagers as presented above. Indeed, in the Luce model for wagers as given by Equation (24) it is readily seen that, since $h(r) > 0$ for all values of r, every wager in any offered set has positive probability of being chosen. In the Fechner model for wagers as given by Equation (25), it is quite possible for two wagers

369

p and **q** to satisfy Equation (31) and still have a very small difference,

$$k \left(\sum_{i=1}^{n} p_i v_i \right) - k \left(\sum_{i=1}^{n} q_i v_i \right).$$

Thus, in conducting an experiment relating to these models, special treatment is required for offered sets containing a pair of wagers satisfying (31).

Finally, we point out that the concept of absolute preference between wagers can be naturally injected into the random utility models for wagers. In fact, the statement that a subject always prefers a larger amount of money to a smaller amount is precisely the statement that the distribution of the random vector $(U_1, \ldots, U_n)$ satisfies the condition.

$$Pr\{U_1 < U_2 < \ldots < U_n\} = 1. \tag{32}$$

It then follows easily that if **p** and **q** are two wagers such that (31) holds, then

$$Pr \left\{ \sum_{i=1}^{n} p_i U_i \geqslant \sum_{i=1}^{n} q_i U_i \right\} = 1, \tag{33}$$

and, hence, **p** is absolutely preferred to **q**.

Some Properties of the Models

In this section we will derive a few special properties of the stochastic models for wagers that were presented earlier. These properties make it possible to test certain hypotheses about the models on the basis of observations of the subject's choices from a limited number of offered sets.

Consider a Luce model for wagers, defined by the constants $u_1, \ldots, u_n$ and the function $h(r)$, and suppose that $h(r) = r$ for all real numbers r. Then, for any offered set M and any wager $\mathbf{p}\epsilon M$,

$$\mathbf{p}(M) = \frac{\sum_{i=1}^{n} p_i u_i}{\sum_{q \epsilon M} \sum_{i=1}^{n} q_i u_i}, \tag{34}$$

where the constants $u_i, \ldots, u_n$ are necessarily positive.

Let M^* be an offered set containing the $m + 1$ wagers

$$\mathbf{p}^j = (p_1{}^j, \ldots, p_n{}^j), j = 1, \ldots, m + 1, \tag{35}$$

and suppose that

$$p_i{}^{m+1} = \frac{1}{m} \sum_{j=1}^{m} p_i{}^j, \ i = 1, \ldots, n; \tag{36}$$

that is, the wager $\mathbf{p}^{m+1}$ is the average of the other m wagers in M^*. It then follows from (34) and (36) that

$$\mathbf{p}^{m+1}(M^*) = \frac{\sum_{i=1}^{n} p_i{}^{m+1}u_i}{\sum_{j=1}^{m}\sum_{i=1}^{n} p_i{}^j u_i + \sum_{i=1}^{n} p_i{}^{m+1}u_i}$$

$$= \frac{\frac{1}{m}\sum_{i=1}^{n}\sum_{j=1}^{m} p_i{}^j u_i}{\sum_{j=1}^{m}\sum_{i=1}^{n} p_i{}^j u_i + \frac{1}{m}\sum_{i=1}^{n}\sum_{j=1}^{m} p_i{}^j u_i} = \frac{1}{m+1}. \quad (37)$$

Thus, $\mathbf{p}^{m+1}(M^*) = \dfrac{1}{m+1}$ regardless of the values of $u_i, \ldots,$ u_n. This provides an obvious test of the model (34) as follows. If a subject is presented with several distinct offered sets, each having the form of M^* (i.e., each containing an 'average wager'), then under this model the distribution of the number of times the subject chooses the average wager is binomial with parameter $\dfrac{1}{m+1}$.

Furthermore, if in a Luce model for wagers the function $h(r)$ is convex, then it can be shown that $\mathbf{p}^{m+1}(M^*) \leqslant \dfrac{1}{m+1}$ for all values of $u_i, \ldots, u_n$. If $h(r)$ is concave then $\mathbf{p}^{m+1}(M^*) \geqslant \dfrac{1}{m+1}$ for all values of $u_1, \ldots, u_n$. These remarks indicate that the usual 1-tailed or 2-tailed test of the hypothesis that $\mathbf{p}^{m+1}(M^*) = \dfrac{1}{m+1}$ would be appropriate for testing the linearity of h.

We now consider the same probability $\mathbf{p}^{m+1}(M^*)$ under a random utility model for wagers. From Equation (22),

$$\mathbf{p}^{m+1}(M^*) = Pr\left\{ \sum_{i=1}^{n} p_i{}^{m+1}U_i \right. $$

$$\left. \geqslant \sum_{i=1}^{n} p_i{}^j U_i \text{ for } j = 1, \ldots, m \right\}. \quad (38)$$

But

$$\sum_{i=1}^{n} p_i{}^{m+1}U_i = \frac{1}{m}\sum_{i=1}^{n}\sum_{j=1}^{n} p_i{}^j U_i = \frac{1}{m}\sum_{j=1}^{m}\left(\sum_{i=1}^{n} p_i{}^j U_i\right); \quad (39)$$

that is, $\sum_{i=1}^{n} p_i{}^{m+1}U_i$ is the average of the m quantities $\sum_{i=1}^{n} p_i{}^{j}U_i$, $= 1, \ldots, m$. Hence,

$$\sum_{i=1}^{n} p_i{}^{m+1}U_i \leqslant \max_{j=1,\ldots,m} \sum_{i=1}^{n} p_i{}^{j}U_i, \tag{40}$$

and equality holds if and only if the quantities $\sum_{i=1}^{n} p_i{}^{j}U_i$, $j = 1, \ldots, m$, are all equal. But it follows from (23) that

$$Pr\left\{ \sum_{i=1}^{n} p_i{}^{1}U_i = \ldots = \sum_{i=1}^{n} p_i{}^{m}U_i \right\} = 0. \tag{41}$$

Hence,

$$Pr\left\{ \sum_{i=1}^{n} p_i{}^{m+1}U_i < \max_{=1,\ldots,m} \sum_{i=1}^{n} p_i{}^{j}U_i \right\} = 1. \tag{42}$$

and, from (38),

$$p^{m+1}(M^*) = 0. \tag{43}$$

Equation (43) provides a test of the random utility models[4] for wagers; if the 'average wager' is ever chosen from an offered set of the form M^* the stochastic model cannot belong to this class.

The results of an experiment testing both the Luce and the random utility model for wagers will be published in a separate paper.

Consider now a Fechner model for wagers defined by the constants $v_1, \ldots, v_n$ and the functions $k(r)$ and $\Phi(r)$. Then for every binary offered set $M = \{\mathbf{p}, \mathbf{q}\}$,

$$\mathbf{p}(M) = \Phi\left[k\left(\sum_{i=1}^{n} p_i v_i \right) - k\left(\sum_{i=1}^{n} q_i v_i \right) \right]. \tag{44}$$

Suppose that the n rewards in S are different amounts of money, numbered in order of increasing amount. It is then reasonable to assume that in the Fechner model for wagers, $v_1 < v_2 < \ldots < v_n$. Consider c binary offered sets $M^j = \{\mathbf{p}^j, \mathbf{q}^j\}$, $j = 1, \ldots, c$, where the wagers $\mathbf{p}^j = (p_1{}^j, \ldots, p_n{}^j)$ and $\mathbf{q}^j = (q_1{}^j, \ldots, q_n{}^j)$, $j = 1, \ldots, c$ have been chosen so that

$$p_i{}^j - q_i{}^j \, d_i, j = = 1, \ldots, c; i = 1, \ldots, n, \tag{45}$$

4. Under the alternative models mentioned in Footnote 3, $p^{m+1}(M^*)$ need not be 0.

and

$$\sum_{l=x}^{n} q_l{}^j \geqslant \sum_{l=x}^{n} q_l{}^{j'}, \quad x = 1, \ldots, n, \quad (46)$$

whenever $j > j'$.

As examples of such wagers, suppose that $n = 3$ and define

$$\mathbf{p}^1 = (0.8, 0, 0.2), \quad \mathbf{p}^2 = (0.7, 0, 0.3),$$
$$\mathbf{p}^3 = (0.6, 0.1, 0.3), \quad \mathbf{p}^4 = (0.4, 0.2, 0.4),$$
$$\mathbf{q}^1 = (0.7, 0.3, 0), \quad \mathbf{q}^2 = (0.6, 0.3, 0.1),$$
$$\mathbf{q}^3 = (0.5, 0.4, 0.1), \quad \mathbf{q}^4 = (0.3, 0.5, 0.2). \quad (47)$$

The binary offered sets $M^j = \{\mathbf{p}^j, \mathbf{q}^j\}$, $j = 1, 2, 3, 4$, satisfy (45) and (46), and it should be clear from (47) how this list could be made arbitrarily long.

It follows from (44) and (45) that

$$\mathbf{p}^j(M^j) = \Phi\left[k\left(\sum_{i=1}^{n} q_i{}^j v_i + \sum_{i=1}^{n} d_i v_i \right) - k\left(\sum_{i=1}^{n} q_i{}^j v_i \right) \right], \quad (48)$$

and from (46) that

$$\sum_{i=1}^{n} q_i{}^1 v_i < \sum_{i=1}^{n} q_i{}^2 v_i < \ldots < \sum_{i=1}^{n} q_i{}^c v_i. \quad (49)$$

Hence, if $k(r)$ is a convex function of r, then either $\mathbf{p}^1(M^1) \leqslant \ldots \leqslant \mathbf{p}^c(M^c)$ or $\mathbf{p}^1(M^1) \geqslant \ldots \geqslant \mathbf{p}^c(M^c)$, depending on whether $\sum_{i=1}^{n} d_i v_i \geqslant 0$ or $\sum_{i=1}^{n} d_i v_i \leqslant 0$. A similar statement can be made if $k(r)$ is concave. In particular, if $k(r)$ is linear, then $\mathbf{p}^1(M^1) = \ldots = \mathbf{p}^c(M^c)$. These equalities would also hold if $\sum_{i=1}^{n} d_i v_i = 0$, but since the experimenter typically has at least a rough idea of the magnitudes of $v_1, \ldots, v_n$, he can choose $d_1, \ldots, d_n$ so that the chance that $\sum_{i=1}^{n} d_i v_i = 0$ is negligible.

We can then test the hypothesis that $k(r)$ is linear against the alternative that it is strictly convex or concave as follows. Record the subject's choices from the offered sets $M^1, \ldots, M^c$ as a sequence of ps and qs. Then conditionally on the observed number of ps and qs in the sequence, all sequences with these numbers are equally likely if $k(r)$ is linear, whereas there is a greater chance that the ps will be grouped at one end and the qs at the other if $k(r)$ is strictly convex or concave. Thus, the usual runs test would be appropriate. If $k(r)$ is linear, the number of runs of ps and qs in the sequence has the distribution that results when all sequences are equally likely; if $k(r)$ is strictly convex or concave, we would expect to observe fewer runs.

Finally, it is easily seen from Equations (22) and (45) that under any binary random utility model for wagers,

$$\mathbf{p}^j(M^j) = \mathbf{p}r\left\{ \sum_{i=1}^{n} d_i U_i \geqslant 0 \right\}, j = 1, \ldots, c. \tag{50}$$

Hence, $\mathbf{p}^1(M^1) = \ldots = \mathbf{p}^c(M^c)$, and rejection of this hypothesis implies rejection of the binary random utility models for wagers.

The Sign Test

The following situation arises quite often in analyzing experiments of the type we are considering in this paper. Let $(R_1, T_1), \ldots, (R_m, T_m)$ be m independent pairs of random variables. (This does not assume that R_j and T_j are independent.) Suppose that each of the random variables $R_j, T_j, j = 1, \ldots, m$, takes only the values 0 and 1, and let

$$Pr\{R_j = 1, T_j = 1\} = \pi_{11}{}^j,$$
$$Pr\{R_j = 1, T_j = 0\} = \pi_{10}{}^j,$$
$$Pr\{R_j = 0, T_j = 1\} = \pi_{01}{}^j,$$
$$Pr\{R_j = 0, T_j = 0\} = \pi_{00}{}^j, j = 1, \ldots, m. \tag{51}$$

Define $D_j = R_j - T_j, j = 1, \ldots, m$. Then

$$Pr\{D_j = 1\} = \pi_{10}{}^j,$$
$$Pr\{D_j = 0\} = \pi_{11}{}^j + \pi_{00}{}^j,$$
$$Pr\{D_j = -1\} = \pi_{01}{}^j, j = 1, \ldots, m. \tag{52}$$

Suppose that we are interested in testing the hypothesis

$$H_0 : \pi_{10}{}^j = \pi_{01}{}^j, j = 1, \ldots, m, \tag{53}$$

against one of the hypotheses

$$H_1 : \pi_{10}{}^j > \pi_{01}{}^j, j = 1, \ldots, m,$$
$$H_2 : \pi_{10}{}^j < \pi_{01}{}^j, j = 1, \ldots, m,$$
$$H_3 : \text{Either } H_1 \text{ or } H_2. \tag{54}$$

It follows from (52) that

$$Pr\{D_j = 1 \mid D_j \neq 0\} = \frac{\pi_{10}{}^j}{\pi_{10}{}^j + \pi_{01}{}^j} \begin{array}{c} \geq \\ = \\ < \end{array} \frac{1}{2}$$

$$\text{according as } \pi_{10}{}^j \begin{array}{c} > \\ = \\ < \end{array} \pi_{01}{}^j. \tag{55}$$

Let

$$m^* = \sum_{j=1}^{m} |D_j|,$$

$$D^* = \tfrac{1}{2} \sum_{j=1}^{m} D_j(1 + D_j); \tag{56}$$

that is, m^* is the number of nonzero observations D_j, and D^* is the number of D_j such that $D_j = 1$. It follows from (53) and (55) that if H_0 is true, the conditional distribution of D^*, given the value of m^*, is a binomial distribution with parameter $\tfrac{1}{2}$, and a 1-tailed or 2-tailed test is appropriate depending on which of the alternative hypotheses H_1, H_2, or H_3 is of interest. Furthermore, if for each conditional value of m^* a test of size α is used, then the over-all test of H_0 has size α.

We now give two examples of the use of this test. The first example is based on a comment of Debreu (1960); the second deals with the problems of predicting subjects' choices. The examples do not deal with wagers explicitly, and so we revert to the term 'objects' to denote the alternatives in an offered set.

Consider m pairs of offered sets, $M_j = \{x_j, y_j\}$ and $M_j' = \{x_j, y_j, y_j'\}$, $j = 1, \ldots, m$, where the objects y_j and y_j' are essentially identical (or indistinguishable) in each pair, $j = 1, \ldots, m$. There are (at least) two points of view regarding the probabilities $x_j(M_j)$ and $x_j(M_j')$. One point of view is that since y_j and y_j' are essentially identical objects, adding y_j' to the offered set M_j should not affect the probability that x_j is chosen; that is, $x_j(M_j) = x_j(M_j')$, $j = 1, \ldots, m$. The second point of view – as would be true, for example, under the Luce model – is that adding another object to the offered set M_j should reduce the probability that x_j is chosen; that is, $x_j(M_j) > x_j(M_j')$, $j = 1, \ldots, m$.

Let $R_j = 1$ if x_j is chosen from M_j and let $R_j = 0$ otherwise; let $T_j = 1$ if x_j is chosen from M_j' and let $T_j = 0$ otherwise. Then assuming all choices are independent,

$$Pr\{D_j = 1\} = \pi_{10}{}^j$$
$$= (x_j(M_j))(1 - x_j(M_j')),$$
$$Pr\{D_j = -1\} = \pi_{01}{}^j$$
$$= (1 - x_j(M_j))(x_j(M_j')). \tag{57}$$

It is readily checked that the hypothesis that $x_j(M_j) = x_j(M_j')$, $j = 1, \ldots, m$, is the hypothesis H_0 of Equation (53), and the hypothesis that $x_j(M_j) > x_j(M_j')$, $j = 1, \ldots, m$, is the hypothesis H_1 of (54).

An experiment testing these two hypotheses will be reported in a separate paper.

As a second example, consider two techniques, A and B, for predicting a subject's choices from offered sets. Suppose that each technique is used to predict the choices from offered sets M_j, $j = 1, \ldots, m$. Let $R_j = 1$ if A predicts the correct choice from M_j and let $R_j = 0$ otherwise; let $T_j = 1$ if B predicts the correct choice from M_j and let $T_j = 0$ otherwise. Suppose that one person claims that $Pr\{R_j = 1\} = Pr\{T_j = 1\}$, $j = 1, \ldots, m$, and another claims that $Pr\{R_j = 1\} > Pr\{T_j = 1\}$, $j = 1, \ldots, m$. That is, one person claims that both techniques have the same chance of being correct on each offered set and another claims that A has a better chance than B of being correct. Note that R_j and T_j are not necessarily independent, since A and B are predicting the choice from the same offered set. Since

$$Pr\{R_j = 1\} = \pi_{10}{}^j + \pi_{11}{}^j,$$
$$Pr\{T_j = 1\} = \pi_{01}{}^j + \pi_{11}{}^j, \tag{58}$$

it is easily seen that the two claims correspond to the hypotheses H_0 and H_1 of (53) and (54).

Heterogeneous Populations

Very often an experiment on choice behavior is performed not just with one subject but with a random sample of subjects from some population. In this situation the experimenter is typically interested not only in deciding whether the choice behavior of each subject satisfies a certain condition but also in making some inference about the proportion of individuals in the population whose choice behavior satisfies the condition. It is this problem that will now be considered.

Suppose that a random sample of s subjects is selected from some population and the choices of each subject from several offered sets are observed. Denote the probability distribution of the choices of the jth subject by f_j, $j = 1, \ldots, s$. Suppose that we want to decide for each subject in the sample whether his probability distribution f_j satisfies a certain condition C (written $f_j \epsilon C$) or not ($f_j \epsilon' C$). Assume that for each subject in the sample we perform a test of the hypotheses

$$H_0 : f_j \epsilon C$$
$$H_1 : f_j \epsilon' C, \tag{59}$$

of size α. That is, for each subject the probability of rejecting H_0 when it is true is at most α.

Let π represent the proportion of individuals in the entire population whose probability distribution f of choices satisfies the hypothesis $f \epsilon C$. Suppose we are also interested in testing the hypotheses

$$H_0':\pi \geqslant 1 - \delta$$
$$H_1':\pi < 1 - \delta, \tag{60}$$

where δ is a fixed (typically small) positive number. Intuitively, if we reject H_0 too many times when testing each individual in the sample, then we will want to reject H_0'. More precisely, let β denote the probability that H_0 will be rejected for a subject drawn at random from the population. Then

$$\beta = Pr\{\text{Rej. } H_0 \mid f \epsilon C\} \, Pr\{f \epsilon C\} + Pr\{\text{Rej. } H_0 \mid f \epsilon' C\}$$
$$Pr\{f \epsilon' C\} \leqslant \alpha \pi + (1 - \pi) = 1 - (1 - \alpha) \pi. \tag{61}$$

If H_0' is true, then $\pi \geqslant 1 - \delta$ and

$$\beta \leqslant 1 - (1 - \alpha)(1 - \delta) = \alpha + \delta - \alpha \delta. \tag{62}$$

Thus, under H_0' the number of subjects in the sample for whom H_0 is rejected has a binomial distribution with parameter $\beta \leqslant \alpha + \delta - \alpha \delta$. Thus, we can test the hypotheses (60) with the usual 1-tailed test of a binomial parameter.

References

ABELSON, R. M., and BRADLEY, R. A., A 2×2 factorial with paired comparisons. *Biometrics*, 1954, **10**, 487–502.

BERKSON, J., Maximum likelihood and minimum χ^2 estimates of the logistic function. *J. Amer. statist. Assoc.*, 1955, **50**, 130–162.

BERKSON, J., Tables for the maximum likelihood estimate of the logistic function. *Biometrics*, 1957, **13**, 28–34.

BLOCK, H. D., and MARSCHAK, J., Random orderings and stochastic theories of response. In I. Olkin *et al.* (Eds.), *Contributions to probability and statistics*. Stanford: Stanford Univ. Press, 1960, pp. 97–132.

BRADLEY, R. A., Rank analysis of incomplete block designs. II. Additional tables for the method of paired comparisons. *Biometrika*, 1954, **41**, 502–537. (a)

BRADLEY, R. A., Incomplete block rank analysis: on the appropriateness of the model for a method of paired comparisons. *Biometrics*, 1954, **10**, 375–390. (b)

BRADLEY, R. A., Rank analysis of incomplete block designs. III. Some large sample results on estimation and power for a method of paired comparisons. *Biometrika*, 1955, **42**, 450–470.

BRADLEY, R. A., and TERRY, M. E., Rank analysis of incomplete block designs. I. The method of paired comparisons. *Biometrika*, 1952, **39**, 324–345.

BRUNK, H. D., Mathematical models for ranking from paired comparisons, *J. Amer. statist. Assoc.*, 1960, **55**, 503–520.

COX, D. R., The regression analysis of binary sequences. *J. Royal Statist. Soc., Series B*, 1958, **20**, 215–242.

DEBREU, G., Review of R. D. Luce, *Individual choice behavior. Amer. Econ. Rev.*, 1960, **50**, 186–188.

FORD, L. R., Jr, Solution of a ranking problem from binary comparisons. *Amer. Math. Monthly*, 1957, **64**, 8 (suppl.), 28–33.

LUCE, R. D., *Individual choice behavior*. New York: Wiley, 1959.

MARSCHAK, J., Binary-choice constraints and random utility indicators. In K. J. Arrow *et al.* (Eds.), *Mathematical methods in the social sciences, 1959.* Stanford: Stanford Univ. Press, 1960, pp. 312–329.

VON NEUMANN, J., and MORGENSTERN, O., *Theory of games and economic behavior*. Princeton, N.J.: Princeton Univ. Press, 1947.

QUANDT, R. E., A probabilistic theory of consumer behavior. *Quart. J. Econ.*, 1956, **70**, 507–536.

15 J. A. Swets

Detection Theory and Psychophysics: a Review

J. A. Swets, 'Detection theory and psychophysics: a review', *Psychometrika*, vol. 26 (1961), pp. 49–63.

I am particularly pleased to discuss the application in psychophysics of the general theory of signal detection at a symposium commemorating Fechner's founding work. Although this effort is in part a theoretical and experimental critique of Fechner's principal concepts and methods, which indicates that they should be replaced, I suspect that he would have welcomed it warmly – in fact, that he would have been among the first to recognize the value of these new tools had they become available in his time. I suspect this on the basis of his interest in Bernoulli's early ideas about statistical decision ([3], p. 284), and in the notion of subthreshold, or 'negative', sensations ([3], p. 293) – two central concepts in the psychophysical application of the theory of signal detectability.

The theory of signal detectability (henceforth called TSD) was developed most fully in the years 1952–1954 by Peterson, Birdsall, and Fox (35) at the University of Michigan, and by Van Meter and Middleton (55) at the Massachusetts Institute of Technology. At the same time, although working apart from TSD, Smith and Wilson (39) at the Massachusetts Institute of Technology and Munson and Karlin (33) at the Bell Telephone Laboratories were conducting psychoacoustic experiments that demonstrated the relevance of the theory to human observers; their experimental results led them to suggest a similar theory of the human detection process. Meanwhile, Tanner, and Swets (52, 53) were making a formal application of TSD in the field of vision.

Since then, other general discussions and reviews similar to this one have appeared; I should mention the 1955 paper by Swets, Tanner, and Birdsall (47) that includes a complete review of the data collected in vision; the 1956 paper by Tanner, Swets, and Green (54) that includes several studies in audition; Green's (22) exposition in the current series of tutorial articles in the *Journal of the Acoustical Society*; and Licklider's chapter (30) in the series edited by Koch for the American Psychological Association. The present discussion is distinguished from the first three of these in that it is not tutorial, detailed, nor documentary. The statistical and psychophysical bases of the work are not considered here, and no data are presented. In this sense, the present discussion is most like Licklider's. Its only advantage is that of time – it comes three years later and is based on three times as many papers.

It will be helpful to emphasize at the outset (as Green [22] has suggested) that TSD is a combination of two distinct theoretical structures: (i) statistical decision theory, or the theory of statistical inference, as developed principally by Wald (59) who built upon the earlier work of Neyman and Pearson (34), and (ii) the theory of ideal observers, initiated by Siegert (see 29). In TSD, statistical decision theory is used to treat the detection task as a decision process, specifically, as an instance of testing statistical hypotheses. This enables TSD to deal effectively with the long-standing problem in psychophysics of the control and measurement of the *criterion for signal existence* that is employed by the observer. The theory of ideal observers makes it possible to relate the level of the detection performance attained by a real observer to the mathematically ideal detection performance. The mathematical ideal is the upper limit on the detection performance that is imposed by the environment. This limit is stated in terms of measurable parameters of the signal and of the masking noise for a variety of types of signal and noise. It is often instructive, as we shall see, to consider the nature of the discrepancy between observed and ideal performance.

We have used TSD as a framework for the experimental study of sensory systems. The framework role suggests itself for the theory, because the theory specifies the nature of the detection process, and it defines the experimental methods that are appropriate, given its conception of the detection process. TSD is also, to a limited extent, but to a far larger extent than is generally recognized, a 'substantive' theory of vision and audition. We have examined the correspondence between the human observer's detection process and the process described by the theory. The methods that the theory prescribes have been compared with others available. We have examined some substantive implications of the theory and have applied the theory and methods to other substantive problems.

I shall discuss, in turn, how the decision-theory aspects and the ideal-observer concepts of TSD have been applied to human behavior, with an emphasis on theory and experimental method.

Unfortunately, the time available will permit only a slight ad-mixture of substantive results. I shall concentrate on the simplest detection task, mentioning only briefly extensions of the theory and experimental procedures to more complex perceptual tasks.

Decision Aspects of Signal Detection

As I have noted, the decision-theory part of TSD impressed us strongly at our first acquaintance because it gave promise of dealing with a difficult problem in psychophysics – namely, the determination of the dichotomy between the observer's positive and negative reports, between stimuli he reports he does and does not see or hear, etc. To state the problem otherwise, it is the definition of the observer's criterion for making a positive res-ponse. Let us review briefly just how TSD deals with this prob-lem.

The fundamental detection problem and the concept of the likeli-hood ratio

I shall first define a particular detection problem, a very simple one – in terms of TSD, the fundamental detection problem. The observer is instructed to attend to a certain class of physical events (perhaps visual or auditory) that the experimenter gener-ates during a specified interval of time, and to make a report following the interval about these events. Coincident with the specified observation interval, presumably, is some (neural) activity of the relevant sensory system. This activity forms the sensory basis, a part of the total basis, for the observer's report. This *sensory response*, as we shall call it for the moment (mean-while noting that the sensory activity coincident with the specified temporal interval need not be entirely a response to the physical events produced by the experimenter), may be *in fact* either simple or complex, it may have many dimensions or few, it may be qualitative or quantitative, it may be anything – the exact, or even the general, nature of the actual sensory response is of no concern to the application of the theory.

Only two assumptions are made about the sensory response. One is that the sensory response that occurs in the presence of a given signal is *variable*. In particular, the response is perturbed by random interference or 'noise' – noise produced inadvertently by the experimenter's equipment for generating stimuli, or deliberately introduced by the experimenter, or inherent in the sensory system. It is assumed that some noise, whatever its origin, is always present. Thus the sensory response will vary over time in the absence of any signal, as well as vary from one presentation to the next of what is ostensibly the same signal. In the fundamental detection problem, the observation interval contains either the noise alone, or a specified signal and the noise. The observer's report is limited to these two classes of stimulus events – he says 'Yes' (the interval contained the specified signal) or 'No' (the interval did not contain the specified signal, i.e., it contained noise alone). Note that he does not say whether or not he *heard* (or *saw*) the signal – but whether or not, under the circumstances, he prefers the decision that it was present to the decision that it was absent.

The second assumption made about the sensory response is that, whatever it may be in fact, it may be represented (insofar as it affects the observer's report) as a *unidimensional* variable. In particular, the observer is assumed to be aware of the probability that each possible sensory response will occur during an observation interval containing noise alone, and also during an observation interval containing a signal in addition to the noise. He is assumed to base his report on the ratio of these two quantities, the *likelihood ratio*. The likelihood ratio derived from any observation interval is a real, nonzero number and may thus be represented along a single dimension.

The likelihood ratio criterion

According to TSD, following statistical decision theory, the observer's report following an observation interval will depend upon whether or not the likelihood ratio measured in that interval exceeds some critical value of the likelihood ratio, some *criterion*. The criterion (or decision rule) is presumed to be established by the observer in accordance with his detection goal and the relevant situational parameters. For example, if his goal is to maximize the expected value of his decisions, i.e., to maximize his total payoff over several trials in which each of the four possible decision outcomes has a value associated with it, then his criterion will depend on these values and on the *a priori* probability that a signal will occur on a given trial. Statistical decision theory prescribes the optimal criterion for any values assumed by this set of parameters. (We shall discuss shortly the relationship between the optimal criterion and the criterion used by the human observer.) The observer may try to achieve any of a number of other detection goals, and there will be, in general, a different optimal criterion corresponding to each goal. The criterion under each of these goals, i.e., under each definition of optimum, can be expressed in terms of the likelihood ratio (35, 59). (It can be shown that the optimal criterion is defined equally as well on any monotonic function of the likelihood ratio – the number corresponding to the criterion will differ, but the decisions will be the same.)

We next consider a probability defined on the variable likelihood ratio, in particular, the probability that each value of the likelihood ratio will occur with each of the classes of possible stimulus events, noise alone, and signal plus noise. We have, therefore, two probability distributions. The one associated with signal plus noise will have a greater mean – indeed, its mean is assumed to increase monotonically with increases in the signal strength. If the observer follows the procedure described (i.e., if he reports that the signal that was specified is present whenever the likelihood ratio exceeds a certain criterion, and that noise alone is present whenever it is less than this criterion) then, from the four-fold stimulus-response matrix that results, we can extract two independent, quantitative measures – a measure of the observer's criterion and a measure of his sensitivity.

The operating characteristic

The important concept here is the *operating characteristic* (OC). Suppose we induce the observer to change his criterion from one set of trials to another. Suppose for each criterion we plot the proportion of *Yes* reports made when the signal was present (the proportion of correct detections, or hits) versus the proportion of *Yes* reports made when noise alone was present (the proportion of false alarms). Then as the criterion varies, we trace a single curve (running from 0 to 1·0 on both coordinates) showing the proportion of hits to be a nondecreasing function of the proportion of false alarms. This curve describes completely the successive stimulus-response matrices that are obtained, since the complements of these two proportions are the proportions that belong in the other two cells of the matrix. The particular curve generated in this fashion depends upon the signal and noise parameters and upon the observer's sensitivity. The point on this curve that corresponds to any given stimulus-response matrix represents the criterion employed by the observer in generating that matrix.

We have found that, to a good approximation, the OC curves produced by human observers correspond to theoretical OC curves based on normal probability distributions (47, 54). (This is an empirical fact; it is not necessary to make in advance any

DETECTION THEORY AND PSYCHOPHYSICS: A REVIEW

particular assumptions about the form of the probability distributions in order to use the OC analysis.) These OC curves have the convenient property of being characterized by a single parameter: the difference between the means of the signal-plus-noise and noise-alone distributions divided by the standard deviation of the noise distribution. This parameter has been called d'. Further, the slope of the curve at any point is equal to the value of the likelihood ratio criterion that produces that point. Thus, to repeat, from any stimulus-response matrix, one can obtain two independent measures: one an index of the sensitivity of the observer to the particular signal and noise used, the other an index of his criterion.

The experimental invariance of d'

It has been shown experimentally, in both vision (47) and audition (54), that the measure d' remains relatively constant with changes in the criterion. Thus, TSD provides a measure of sensitivity that is practically uncontaminated by attitudinal or motivational variables, i.e., by variables that might be expected to affect the observer's criterion.

It has also been shown that the measure d' remains relatively invariant over different experimental procedures. Specifically, we have compared estimates of d' obtained from the Yes–No procedure (i.e., the fundamental detection problem) with estimates of d' obtained from a forced-choice procedure. Under forced-choice, n temporal intervals were defined on each trial, exactly one of which contained the signal; the observer selected one of the n intervals. The probability of a correct response as a function of d' can be calculated by using the empirical OC curve or by making some assumptions about the form of the probability distributions. We have calculated this probability as a function of d', under the assumptions that the probability distributions are normal and of equal variance. The relations between the probability of a correct response and d', for several different numbers of alternatives in a forced-choice trial, have been tabulated (15).

For both vision (52) and audition (41) the estimates of d' from the Yes–No procedure and from the four-interval forced-choice procedure are very nearly the same. We have further found remarkably consistent estimates of d' from forced-choice procedures with 2, 3, 4, 6, and 8 intervals (41). Also, the rating procedure in which the observer chooses one of *several* categories of certainty about the presence of a signal in a *single* interval yields

OC curves (or estimates of d') in both vision (42) and audition (14), that are indistinguishable from those obtained with the Yes–No procedure. These results are particularly fortunate since, as Licklider has pointed out, they represent 'a break in the trend . . . to regard the results of a psychophysical test as meaningless except in relation to the procedure of the test' ([30], p. 73). It is evidently possible to have one rather than many psychophysical sciences.

The observer's criterion and the optimal criterion

I have mentioned earlier that we would return to a brief discussion of the relationship of the observer's criterion to the criterion specified as optimal by statistical decision theory. Let us note, first, that TSD can be a useful tool in analyzing psychophysical data if it is merely the case that the observer controls a criterion (in terms of the likelihood ratio or some monotonic function of the likelihood ratio), whether or not his criterion bears any relationship to the optimal one. We have worked with the expected-value definition of the optimal criterion (in which the optimal criterion is a function of the *a priori* probability of signal occurrence and the values associated with the decision outcomes) simply because the manipulation of these parameters is a convenient and effective way of inducing the observer to change his criterion in a psychophysical experiment. This manipulation enables us to trace an empirical OC curve. Strictly speaking, whether or not the observer adjusts his criterion in terms of these variables in everyday life is of no concern in the laboratory. Neither are we concerned with subjective probabilities or the linearity of the utility of money. We are, of course, interested in the result we observed: the observer's successive criteria in our experiments were highly correlated with the optimal expected-value criteria, that is, the human observer is capable of approximating the optimal criterion. Even though our experimental situation is artificial in this respect, the result teaches us something about the observer's capabilities.

I should quickly add that it is difficult to compare the observer's criterion and the optimal criterion in more than a correlational sense. The reason for this is that the function relating the expected value to the criterion is very flat: any criterion within a very wide range (a range of as much as 0·40 in false-alarm rate) will result in a payoff that is at least 90 per cent of the maximum payoff possible. Nonetheless, the fact that our observers respond to a change in *a priori* probabilities or decision values by setting a new criterion – the fact that they can adopt successively and repeatedly as many as five criteria showing a perfect rank-order correlation with the optimal criteria – has made it possible to achieve in our experiments what Graham has called 'a quantification of the instruction stimuli' ([18], p. 868). Egan (who has been successful in controlling the criterion with such verbal instructions as 'lax', 'moderate', and 'strict' [see 14]) is now preparing to examine, in more detail than was done previously, the relationship between the observer's criterion and various definitions of the optimal criterion, i.e., the relationship between quantitative instruction stimuli and quantitative estimates of the resulting criterion (10).

Implications for Psychophysical Methods

I would now like to return to the proposition that TSD provides a framework for the study of sensory systems, in particular, that it specifies the experimental procedures that may be properly used given its conception of the nature of the detection process.

Perhaps the most salient procedural implications of TSD are those concerned with the use of catch trials (trials containing noise alone) and the treatment of positive (Yes) responses made on those trials. As I have remarked, when we first became acquainted with TSD, it was apparent that the theory would be valuable in psychophysics because it spoke forth eloquently on exactly those conceptual and procedural problems that many of us believed to be handled inadequately in classical psychophysics. Licklider has expressed our discomfiture very aptly: 'More and more, workers in the field are growing dissatisfied with the classical psychophysical techniques, particularly with the method of 'adjustment' or 'production' that lets the listener attend to the stimulus for an unspecified length of time before deciding that he can 'just hear it' and with the methods of 'limits' and 'constants' (in their usual forms) that ask the listener to report 'present' or 'absent' when he already knows 'present'. It is widely felt that the 'thresholds' yielded by these procedures are on such an insecure semantic basis that they cannot serve as good building blocks for a quantitative science' ([30], p. 75).

It is simply not adequate to employ a few catch trials, enough to monitor the observer, and then to remind him to avoid false-positive responses each time one is made. This procedure merely serves to drive the criterion up to a point where it cannot be measured, and it can be shown that the calculated threshold varies by as much as 6 db as the criterion varies in this unmeasurable range. Precision is also sacrificed when highly trained observers are employed along with the untestable assumption that they do maintain a constant high criterion. Even if all laboratories should be fortunate enough to have such observers, the figure of 6 db is a reasonable estimate of the range of variation among 'constant criterion' observers in different laboratories. To be sure, for some problems, this amount of variability is not bothersome; for others, however, it is.

Experiments have also shown that the use of enough catch trials to provide a good estimate of the probability of a false-positive response will again leave one far short of the precision attainable – if this estimate is used to correct the data on signal trials for spurious positive responses on the grounds that these responses are independent of sensory-determined positive responses. Suffice it to say here that several experimenters, in a number of different experiments in different laboratories, have failed to find any evidence for the independent existence of a sensory threshold, a threshold that is independent of the probability of a false-positive report. We find *response* thresholds aplenty – any criterion used by the observer is such – but no measurable *sensory* thresholds. Of course, the validity of the various classical procedures depends directly on the validity of the concept of a sensory threshold.

In view of a large collection of data, it seems to me to be only reasonable (1) to add enough noise in psychophysical experiments (a background of some kind) to bring the noise to a level where it can be measured, (2) to manipulate the response criterion so that it lies in a range where it can be measured, (3) to include enough catch trials to obtain a good estimate of this response criterion, and (4) to use a method of analysis that yields a measure of sensitivity that is independent of the response criterion. This prescription will stand, I believe, until such time that it becomes possible to demonstrate that all traces of noise can be eliminated from a sensory experiment. The only other qualifying remark I would make is a positive one: we can forgo estimating the response criterion in a forced-choice experiment. Experience has shown that we can reasonably view the observer as choosing the interval having the greatest 'sensory response' associated with it, without regard to any criterion. For this reason, the forced-choice procedure is a highly desirable procedure for use in purely sensory studies.

The theory of Ideal Observers

The portion of TSD that pertains to the optimal or ideal performance in the sense of detectability, or sensitivity, rather than the decision criterion, is known as the theory of ideal observers. This theory gives, for several types of signal and noise, the maximum possible detectability as a function of the parameters of the signal and noise (35). Under certain assumptions, this relationship can be stated precisely. We have regarded the case of the 'signal specified exactly' (in which everything about the signal is known, including its frequency, phase, starting time, duration, and amplitude) as a useful standard in psychoacoustic experiments. In this case, the maximum d' is equal to $\sqrt{2E/N_0}$ in which E is the signal energy, or time integral of power and N_0 is the noise power in a one-cycle band. Recently, an ideal observer applicable to visual signals has also been developed (51).

We believe that a theory of ideal performance is a good starting point in working toward a descriptive theory. Ideal theories involve few variables, and these are simply described. Experiments can be used to uncover whatever additional variables may be needed to describe the performance of real observers. Alternatively, experiments can be used to indicate how the ideal theory can be degraded, i.e., to identify those functions of which the ideal detection device must be deprived, in order to describe accurately real behavior. Measures can be defined to describe the real observer's efficiency; Tanner and Birdsall (50) have, for example, described the efficiency measure η as used in the expression

$$d'_{\text{obs}} = \eta \sqrt{2E/N_0}$$

in which the value of d' is that observed experimentally. They have suggested that substantive problems may be illuminated by the computation of η for different types of signals and for different parameters of a given type of signal. The observed variation of this measure should be helpful in determining the range over which the human observer can adjust the parameters of his sensory system to match different signal parameters. (He is, after all, quite proficient in detecting a surprisingly large number of different signals.) This variation should also be helpful in determining which parameters of a signal the observer is not using, or not using precisely, in his detection process.

The human observer, of course, performs less well than does

the ideal observer in the great majority of, if not in all, detection tasks. The interesting question, one that usually turns out to be a heuristic question, concerns not the amount but the nature of the discrepancy that is observed. The next few paragraphs illustrate how asking this question led to information about certain substantive issues in audition and vision.

We find that the human observer performs less well than the ideal observer defined for the case of the 'signal specified exactly'. That is, the human observer's 'psychometric function' (the proportion of correct positive responses as a function of the signal energy) is shifted to the right. Further, the slope of the human observer's function is greater than that of the ideal function for this particular case – a result sometimes referred to as low-signal suppression. Let us consider three possible reasons for these discrepancies.

First, the human observer may well have a *noisy decision process*, whereas the ideal decision process is noiseless. For example, the human observer's criterion may be unstable. If he vacillates between two criteria, the resulting point of his OC curve will be on a straight line connecting the points corresponding to the two criteria; this average point falls below the OC curve (a curve with smoothly decreasing slope) on which the two criteria are located. Again, the observer's decision axis may not be continuous – as far as we know, it may be divided into a relatively small number of categories. This possibility has not been studied intensively.

A second likely reason for the deviation from ideal is the *noise inherent in the human sensory systems*. We have attempted to estimate the amount of internal noise (including noise in the decision process and in the sensory system) in two ways: by examining the decisions of an observer over several presentations of the same signal and noise (on tape) (46), and by examining the correlation among the responses of several observers to a single presentation (2, 23). Both Egan and Green (10, 24) are continuing this line of work with taped presentations.

A third, and favored, possibility is *faulty memory*. This explanation is favored, *a priori*, because it easily accounts not only for the shift of the human's psychometric function but also for the greater slope of his function. The reasoning proceeds as follows: if the detection process involves some sort of tuning of the receptive apparatus, and if the observer's memory of the characteristics of the incoming signal is faulty (these characteristics being amplitude, frequency, starting time, duration, phase in audition, and location in vision), then the observer is essentially confronted with a signal not specified exactly, but specified only statistically. He has some uncertainty about the incoming signal. When we introduce some uncertainty into our calculations of the psychometric function of the ideal detector (35), we find that performance falls off as uncertainty increases, and that this decline in performance is greater for weak signals than strong ones. That is, a family of theoretical uncertainty curves shows progressively steeper slopes coinciding with progressive shifts to the right. This is intuitively proper – the accuracy of knowledge about signal characteristics is less critical for strong signals, since strong signals carry more information about these characteristics with themselves. For visual (51) and auditory data (22) the slopes are fitted well by the theoretical curve that corresponds to uncertainty among approximately 100 orthogonal signal alternatives. It is not difficult to imagine that the product of the uncertainties about the time, location, and frequency of the signals used in these experiments could be as high as 100.

It is possible to obtain empirical corroboration of this theoretical analysis of uncertainty due to faulty memory. This is achieved by providing various aids to memory within the experimental procedure. (Tanner [48] has used this technique in auditory studies; Green [22] has replicated his results in audition, and Green and Swets [28] have obtained similar results in visual studies.) In these experiments, the memory for frequency is made unnecessary by introducing a continuous tone or light (a carrier) of the same frequency as the signal, so that the signal to be detected is an increment in the carrier. This procedure also eliminates the need for phase memory in audition and location memory in vision. In further experiments, instead of a continuous carrier, a pulsed carrier (one that starts and stops along with the signal) is used in order to make memory for starting time and duration unnecessary. In all of these experiments a forced-choice procedure is used, so that the memory for amplitude beyond a single trial can also be considered irrelevant. In this way, all of the information thought to be relevant may be contained in the immediate situation. Experimentally, our observers' psychometric functions show progressively flatter slopes as we introduce more and more memory aids in this way. In fact, when all of the aids mentioned above are used, the observer's slope parallels that for the ideal observer without uncertainty, and it is as little as 3 db from the ideal curve in absolute value.

Examples of Substantive Problems Studied in this Framework

I shall simply list some other examples of substantive problems in vision and audition that have been studied within the framework of TSD. A way of treating one set of related problems follows directly from statistical theory. These are problems in which the observation is expanded in one way or another: (i) the observation interval is lengthened, (ii) the number of observations preceding a decision is increased, (iii) the number of signals presented in a given interval is increased, or (iv) the number of observers concentrating on the same signal is increased. From statistical theory, the distribution of the sum of n random variables with the same mean and variance has a mean equal to n times the mean and a variance equal to n times the variance. Since the measure of detectability d' is equal to the mean of the hypothetical probability distribution that is due to the signal (we can consider the mean of the noise distribution to be zero) divided by the standard deviation (the square root of the variance), we would predict that, as the number of signals or observations is increased, the measure d' will increase as the square root of the number. Or we might think in terms of the result in statistics that the standard deviation of the estimate of a population mean decreases as the square root of the number of samples, and be led to the same prediction. Experiments in audition have shown d' to increase, within certain limits, as $\sqrt{t}$, where t is the duration of a tone-burst signal in white noise (26), and to increase as $\sqrt{n}$, where n is the number of tonal components of a complex signal (up to 16) (27), or the number of observation intervals preceding a decision (up to five) (46), or the number of observers (up to three) (2).

A persistent favorite among the substantive problems in audition that have been studied experimentally in this setting is the problem of frequency analysis, or the problem of the critical band. Fletcher's (17) original experiment, in which the width of the band of noise that masked a tonal signal was varied systematically, has been repeated with signals of a specified duration and with a different type of analysis (54). A variety of other procedures has been used in the attack on this problem, including signals of uncertain frequency (7, 20, 46, 54, 56, 57), complex signals compounded of several frequencies (21, 27, 31), and signals consisting of a band of noise (19). Other studies of substantive problems that were guided by TSD include studies of reaction time (45), physiological recording (16), and some aspects of color vision (40).

Extended Applications to More Complex Problems

I have spoken, so far, primarily about simple detection procedures (Yes–No and forced-choice procedures involving a single, specified observation interval) employing single, simple signals (a tone burst in white noise, or a spot of light on a larger uniform background). I should at least mention some of the areas in which extensions of the basic theory have been applied to somewhat more complex problems.

The theory has been applied to the recognition or identification process as well as to the detection process: to the recognition of one of two frequencies (49), and to problems requiring both detection and recognition (43). Very recently, following Anderson's (1) work in statistics, some preliminary attempts have been made to deal with the recognition of one of a large number of signals and thus to move closer to some significant problems in perception (25, 32).

Following Wald's (58) developments in sequential analysis, we have studied the problem of deferred decision (44). In this problem, the observer decides after each observation interval whether to make a terminal decision (Yes or No) or to request another observation before making a terminal decision. Values and costs are assigned to the possible outcomes of a terminal decision, and a fixed cost is assessed for each additional observation that is requested. This deferred decision paradigm, it will be recognized, represents another way of striking out in the direction of realism. We have examined in this way the trading relationship that commonly exists in perceptual tasks between time and error. In a similar vein, the theory has recently been extended to handle the case of detection in which the observation interval is not specified for the observer – the so-called vigilance, or low-probability watch, problem (13).

Still another more complex area of research that has received extensive study is that of speech communication. Many of the techniques employed in studies with simple signals have been used with success here, including operating characteristics, confidence ratings, repetition of items, deferred decisions, and analyses in terms of the degree of uncertainty that exists (4, 5, 6, 8, 9, 11, 12, 36, 37, 38).[1]

1. A scheme for organizing the rather extensive bibliography of this paper (and other related publications) may be helpful. As it happens, an organization is most effectively accomplished in terms of personalities. After the original applications of TSD, Tanner, Green, and I have gone some-

References

1. ANDERSON, T. W., *An introduction to multivariate statistical analysis.* New York: Wiley, 1958.
2. BIRDSALL, T. G., and SWETS, J. A., Unpublished work.
3. BORING, E. G., *A history of experimental psychology.* (2nd ed.). New York: Appleton Century-Crofts, 1950.
4. CARTERETTE, E. C., Message repetition and receiver confirmation of messages in noise. *J. acoust. Soc. Amer.*, 1958, **30**, 846–855.
5. CLARKE, F. R., Confidence ratings, second-choice responses, and confusion matrices in intelligibility tests. *J. acoust. Soc. Amer.*, 1960, **32**, 35–46.
6. CLARKE, F. R., Constant-ratio rule in speech communication. *J. acoust. Soc. Amer.*, 1957, **29**, 715–720.
7. CREELMAN, C. D., Detection of signals of uncertain frequency. *J. acoust. Soc. Amer.*, 1960, **32**, 805–809.
8. DECKER, L., and POLLACK, I., Confidence ratings and message reception for filtered speech. *J. acoust. Soc. Amer.*, 1958, **30**, 432–434.
9. EGAN, J. P., Monitoring task in speech communication. *J. acoust. Soc. Amer.*, 1957, **29**, 482–489.
10. EGAN, J. P., Personal communication.
11. EGAN, J. P., and CLARKE, F. R., Source and receiver behavior in the use of a criterion. *J. acoust. Soc. Amer.*, 1956, **28**, 1267–1269.
12. EGAN, J. P., CLARKE, F. R., and CARTERETTE, E. C., On the transmission and confirmation of messages in noise. *J. acoust. Soc. Amer.*, 1956, **28**, 536–550.
13. EGAN, J. P., GREENBERG, G. Z., and SCHULMAN, A. I., Detection of signals presented at random time. *J. acoust. Soc. Amer.*, 1959, **31**, 1579. (Abstract).
14. EGAN, J. P., SCHULMAN, A. I., and GREENBERG, G. Z., Operating characteristics determined by binary decisions and by ratings. *J. acoust. Soc. Amer.*, 1959, **31**, 768–773.
15. ELLIOTT, P. B., Tables of d'. Tech. Rep. No. 97, Electronic Defense Group, Univ. Michigan, 1959.
16. FITZHUGH, R., The statistical detection of threshold signals in the retina. *J. gen. Physiol.*, 1957, **40**, 925–948.
17. FLETCHER, H., Auditory patterns. *Rev. mod. Phys.*, 1940, **12**, 47–65.
18. GRAHAM, C. H., Visual perception. In S. S. Stevens (Ed.), *Handbook of experimental psychology.* New York: Wiley, 1951.
19. GREEN, D. M., Auditory detection of a noise signal. *J. acoust. Soc. Amer.*, 1960, **32**, 121–131.
20. GREEN, D. M., Detection of a pulsed sinusoid of uncertain frequency. Unpublished paper.

what separate ways. Tanner's efforts have been directed principally toward an examination of the role of models in experimental studies and toward applications of the concept of the ideal observer; Green has concentrated on substantive problems in audition, especially the problem of frequency analysis; I have been primarily concerned with the decision process and with applications of the theory to psychophysical tasks that are less idealized than those studied initially. Egan, Pollack, and Clarke have employed the theory in studying various problems in speech communication and have contributed a number of studies dealing with methodological problems.

21. GREEN, D. M., Detection of multiple component signals in noise. *J. acoust. Soc. Amer.*, 1958, **30**, 904–911.

22. GREEN, D. M., Psychoacoustics and detection theory. *J. acoust. Soc. Amer.*, 1960, **32**, 1198–1203.

23. GREEN, D. M., Unpublished work.

24. GREEN, D. M., Personal communication.

25. GREEN, D. M., and BIRDSALL, T. G., The effect of vocabulary size on articulation score. Tech. Rep. No. 81, Electronic Defense Group, Univ. Michigan, 1958.

26. GREEN, D. M., BIRDSALL, T. G., and TANNER, W. P., Jr, Signal detection as a function of signal intensity and duration. *J. acoust. Soc. Amer.*, 1957, **29**, 523–531.

27. GREEN, D. M., MCKEY, M. J., and LICKLIDER, J. C. R., Detection of a pulsed sinusoid in noise as a function of frequency. *J. acoust. Soc. Amer.*, 1959, **31**, 1446–1452.

28. GREEN, D. M., and SWETS, J. A., Unpublished work.

29. LAWSON, J. L., and UHLENBECK, G. E., *Threshold signals.* New York: McGraw-Hill, 1950. Ch. 7.

30. LICKLIDER, J. C. R., Three auditory theories. In S. Koch (Ed.), *Psychology: a study of a science.* Vol. 1. New York: McGraw-Hill, 1958.

31. MARILL, T., Detection theory and psychophysics. Tech. Rep. No. 319, Research Laboratory of Electronics, Mass. Inst. of Tech., 1956.

32. MARILL, T., and GREEN, D. M., Statistical recognition functions and the design of pattern recognizers. *IRE Trans. on Electronic Computers*, (in press).

33. MUNSON, W. A., and KARLIN, J. E., The measurement of the human channel transmission characteristics. *J. acoust. Soc. Amer.*, 1956, **26**, 542–553.

34. NEYMAN, J., and PEARSON, E., The testing of statistical hypotheses in relation to probabilities. *Proc. Cambridge Phil. Soc.*, 1933, **29**, 492–510.

35. PETERSON, W. W., BIRDSALL, T. G., and FOX, W. C., The theory of signal detectability. Inst. Radio Engrs. *Trans. Professional Group on Information Theory*, 1954, *PGIT-4*, 171–212.

36. POLLACK, I., Message repetition and message reception. *J. acoust. Soc. Amer.*, 1959, **31**, 1509–1515.

37. POLLACK, I., Message uncertainty and message reception. *J. acoust. Soc. Amer.*, 1959, **31**, 1500–1508.

38. POLLACK, I., and DECKER, L. R., Confidence ratings, message reception, and the receiver operating characteristic. *J. acoust. Soc. Amer.*, 1958, **30**, 286–292.

39. SMITH, M., and WILSON, EDNA A., A model for the auditory threshold and its application to the multiple observer. *Psychol. Monogr.*, 1953, **67**, No. 9 (Whole No. 359).

40. SWETS, J. A., Color vision. Quarterly Progress Rep., Research Laboratory of Electronics, Mass. Inst. of Tech., April 15, 1960.

41. SWETS, J. A., Indices of signal detectability obtained with various psychophysical procedures. *J. acoust. Soc. Amer.*, 1959, **31**, 511–513.

42. SWETS, J. A., Unpublished work.

43. SWETS, J. A., and BIRDSALL, T. G., The human use of information, III: decision-making in signal detection and recognition situations involving multiple alternatives. Inst. Radio Engrs. *Trans. Information Theory*, 1956, *IT-2*, 138–165.

44. SWETS, J. A., and GREEN, D. M., Sequential observations by human observers of signals in noise. In C. Cherry (Ed.) *Information theory*. London: Butterworths Scientific Publications, 1961.

45. SWETS, J. A., SCHOUTEN, J. F., and LOPES-CARDOZO, B., On the span of attention, in preparation.

46. SWETS, J. A., SHIPLEY, ELIZABETH F., McKEY, M. J., and GREEN, D. M., Multiple observations of signals in noise. *J. acoust. Soc. Amer.*, 1959, **31**, 514–521.

47. SWETS, J. A., TANNER, W. P., JR, and BIRDSALL, T. G., The evidence for a decision-making theory of visual detection. Tech. Rep. No. 40, Electronic Defense Group, Univ. Michigan, 1955. This material, slightly revised, will appear as: Decision processes in perception, *Psychol. Rev.*, in press.

48. TANNER, W. P., JR, Memory. (Mimeo.)

49. TANNER, W. P., JR, Theory of recognition. *J. acoust. Soc. Amer.*, 1956, **28**, 882–888.

50. TANNER, W. P., JR, and BIRDSALL, T. G., Definitions of d' and η as psychophysical measures. *J. acoust. Soc. Amer.*, 1958, **30**, 922–928.

51. TANNER, W. P., JR, and JONES, R. C., The ideal sensor system as approached through statistical decision theory and the theory of signal detectability. In Minutes and Proceedings of the Armed Forces-NRC Vision Committee meeting, held at Washington, D.C., November, 1959.

52. TANNER, W. P., JR, and SWETS, J. A., A decision-making theory of visual detection. *Psychol. Rev.*, 1954, **61**, 401–409.

53. TANNER, W. P., JR, and SWETS, J. A., The human use of information, I: signal detection for the case of the signal known exactly. Inst. Radio Engrs. *Trans. Professional Group on Information Theory*, 1954, *PGIT-4*, 213–221.

54. TANNER, W. P., JR, SWETS, J. A., and GREEN, D. M., Some general properties of the hearing mechanism. Tech. Rep. No. 30, Electronic Defense Group, Univ. Michigan, 1956.

55. VAN METER, D., and MIDDLETON, D., Modern statistical approaches to reception in communication theory. Inst. Radio Engrs. *Trans. Professional Group on Information Theory*, 1954, *PGIT-4*, 119–145.

56. VENIAR, F. A., Effect of auditory cue on discrimination of auditory stimuli. *J. acoust. Soc. Amer.*, 1958, **30**, 1079–1081.

57. VENIAR, F. A., Signal detection as a function of frequency ensemble, I. *J. acoust. Soc. Amer.*, 1958, **30**, 1020–1024; II. 1075–1078.

58. WALD, A., *Sequential analysis*. New York: Wiley, 1947.

59. WALD, A., *Statistical decision functions*. New York: Wiley, 1950.

Further Reading

The literature of decision theory is vast, and its boundaries are ill-defined. Even a very restrictive definition of the limits of that literature would produce several thousand titles, drawn primarily from the fields of psychology, economics, statistics, business, and operations research. Every scientifically significant country in the world would be represented. Anyone who sets out to read in decision theory will soon find it necessary to define his interests more precisely. And even so, he will be overwhelmed. Moreover, he will soon find that researchers in this field are especially likely to produce preprints, working papers, government reports, and similar unfindable documents; far too seldom are such documents the precursors of eventual journal or book publications.

The would-be browser in the field can profit exceedingly from reading all the books of which we have reprinted excerpts. His next step should be to mine the reference lists of the articles reprinted here, the reference lists in those references, and so on; that process, pursued thoroughly enough, will ultimately identify essentially all references in the field except the most recent. He might find Wasserman and Silander's not-very-recent annotated bibliography (cited below) useful, especially if he is interested in business decision making, leadership, and similar topics. Or he might obtain a copy of one of the numerous unpublished bibliographies in the field.

A short cut into parts of the literature is the brief reference list given below. In compiling it, we made a special effort to include books, articles by European scientists currently active in the field, articles pointing towards aspects of the field we have slighted in this book, reviews, and important very recent articles.

The three very recent reviews are by Becker and McClintock, Luce and Suppes, and Peterson and Beach. Becker and McClintock's is a general review, in much the same spirit as its 1961 predecessor by Edwards reprinted here. Luce and Suppes, while reviewing the field generally, are most interested in the stochastic models of choice and experiments related to them. Their article, technically quite difficult, is indispensable to the serious student. Peterson and Beach extend the boundaries of decision theory to include a relatively new topic, intuitive statistics; their paper is not difficult and its topic is exciting.

No book since Luce and Raiffa's (excerpts of which are included in this book) has attempted a coherent exposition of the field. Some are collections of articles; others are technical treatises on specialized topics. Particularly interesting are the books by Kyburg and Smokler reprinting the most fundamental articles on subjective probability, by Luce presenting stochastic models of choice behaviour, by Mosteller and Wallace performing a large-scale computational exercise in the development of practical Bayesian statistical techniques, and by Swets reprinting the classic papers of signal detectability theory.

The article by Rapoport and Orwant leads into the literature on experimental games. The Siegel–Fouraker book exhibits the scarcely-born topic of experimental economics. The Kogan–Wallach book is a recent contribution to the large, often shoddy literature on personality variables in decision making. The Edwards, Lindman, and Savage article has become the standard psychologist's introduction to the Bayesian point of view. The special issue of the I E E E journal edited by Edwards, the Edwards–Lindman–Phillips article, and the Yntema–Torgerson article point the way to applications of decision theory in the design of man-machine systems for information processing and decision making. The books by Restle and Luce and the Luce–Suppes review article point the way to much of contemporary stochastic choice theory. The impact of conjoint measurement on decision theory can be expected to be large; unfortunately, the ideas are so new that few of them have reached publication yet. Tversky's article reprinted here is one.

ATKINSON, J. W., 'Motivational determinants of risk-taking behavior', *Psychol. Rev.*, vol. 64 (1957), pp. 359–72.

AUDLEY, R. J., 'A stochastic model for individual choice behavior', *Psychol. Rev.*, vol. 67 (1960), pp. 1–15.

BECKER, G. M., and McCLINTOCK, C. G., 'Value: Behavioral decision theory', *Ann. Rev. Psychol.*, vol. 18 (1967), pp. 239–86.

BROADBENT, D. E., 'Common principles in perception, reaction and intellectual decision', in Geldard, F. (ed.), *Defense psychology*, Pergamon, 1962.

COHEN, J., *Chance, skill, and luck*, Penguin Books, 1960.

DEBREU, G., 'Topological methods in cardinal utility theory', in Arrow, K. T., Karlin, S., and Suppes, P. (eds.), *Mathematical methods in the social sciences*, 1959, Stanford Univ. Press, 1960.

EDWARDS, W., 'Subjective probabilities inferred from decisions', in Luce, R. D., Bush, R. R., and Galanter, E. (eds.), *Readings in mathematical psychology*, vol. II, Wiley, 1965. Reprinted from *Psychol. Rev.*, vol. 69 (1962), pp. 109–35.

EDWARDS, W., 'Optimal strategies for seeking information: Models for statistics, choice reaction time, and human information processing,' *J. math. Psychol.*, vol. 2 (1965), pp. 312–29.

EDWARDS, W. (ed.), 'Revisions of opinions by men and man-machine systems', *IEEE Trans. on hum. Fact. in Electronics*, vol. 7 (1966), no. 1, pp. 1–63. (Whole issue.)

EDWARDS, W., LINDMAN, H., and PHILLIPS, L. D., 'Emerging technologies for making decisions', in *New Directions in Psychology*, vol. II, Holt, Rinehart, & Winston, 1965, pp. 261–325.

EDWARDS, W., LINDMAN, H., and SAVAGE, L. J., 'Bayesian statistical inference for psychological research', in Luce, R. D., Bush, R. R., and Galanter, E. (eds.), *Readings in mathematical psychology*, vol. II., Wiley, 1965. Reprinted from *Psychol. Rev.*, vol. 70 (1963), pp. 193–242.

ESTES, W. K., 'Probability learning', in Melton, A. W. (ed.), *Categories of human learning*, Academic Press, 1964.

FAVERGE, J. M., 'Le principe du maximum de l'utilité attendue dans les décisions humaines', *Cahiers du Centre de Recherche Operationelle*, vol. 3 (1961), pp. 165–76.

FEATHER, N. T., 'Subjective probability and decision under uncertainty' *Psychol. Rev.*, vol. 66 (1959), pp. 150–64.

FLAMENT, C., 'Analyse pluridimensionelle des structures hiérarchiques intransitives', *Bull. Centre d'Études et Recherches Psychotechniques*, vol. 7 (1958), pp. 171–9.

GRAYSON, C. J., JR, *Decisions under uncertainty: Drilling decisions by oil and gas operators*, Graduate School of Business Administration, Harvard U., 1960.

FURTHER READING

IRWIN, F. W., and SMITH, W. A. S., 'Value, cost, and information as determiners of decision', *J. exp. Psychol.*, vol. 54 (1957), pp. 229–32.

KOGAN, N., and WALLACH, M. A., *'Risk taking: A study in cognition and personality'*, Holt, Rinehart, & Winston, 1964.

KYBURG, H. E., JR, and SMOKLER, H. E. (eds.), *Studies in subjective probability*, Wiley, 1964.

LUCE, R. D., *Individual choice behavior*, Wiley, 1959.

LUCE, R. D., and SUPPES, P., 'Preference, utility and subjective probability', in Luce, R. D., Bush, R. R., and Galanter, E. (eds.), *Handbook of mathematical psychology*, Wiley, 1965, vol. 3, pp. 249–410.

MESSICK, S., and BRAYFIELD, A. H. (eds.), *Decision and choice: Contributions of Sidney Siegel*, McGraw-Hill, 1964.

MOSTELLER, F., and WALLACE, D., *Inference and disputed authorship: The Federalist*, Addison Wesley, 1964.

MYERS, J. L., REILLY, R. E., and TAUB, H. A., 'Differential cost, gain, and relative frequency of reward in a sequential choice situation', *J. exp. Psychol.*, vol. 62 (1961), pp. 357–60.

PETERSON, C., and BEACH, L. R., 'Man as an intuitive statistician', *Psychol. Bull.*, vol. 67 (1967), in press.

RAPOPORT, A., and ORWANT, C., 'Experimental games: A review', *Behav. Sci.*, vol. 1 (1962), pp. 1–37.

RESTLE, F., *Psychology of judgment and choice*, Wiley, 1961.

SCHMIDT, HANS-DIETER, *Leistungschance, Erfolgserwartung und Entscheidung.* Veb Deutscher Verlag der Wissenschaften, 1966.

SHELLY, M. W., II, and BRYAN, G. L., *Human judgments and optimality*, Wiley, 1964.

SIEGEL, S., and FOURAKER, L. E., *Bargaining behavior*, McGraw-Hill, 1963.

SWETS, J. A. (ed.), *Signal detection and recognition by human observers*, Wiley, 1964.

TODA, M., 'The design of a fungus-eater', *Behav. Sci.*, vol. 7 (1962), pp. 164–83.

VAN NAERSSEN, R. F., 'A scale for the measurement of subjective probability', *Acta Psychologica*, vol. 20 (1962), pp. 156–66.

WASSERMAN, P. S., and SILANDER, F. S. *Decision making: An annotated bibliography*, Grad. School Business and Public Admin., Cornell Univ., Ithaca, New York, 1958.

WASSERMAN, P., and SILANDER, F. S., *Decision making: An annotated bibliography, Supplement*, 1958–1963, Grad. School Business and Public Admin., Cornell Univ., Ithaca, New York, 1964.

WILLIAMS, J., *The compleat strategyst*, McGraw-Hill, 1954.

Acknowledgements

Acknowledgements are due to the following for permission to publish extracts in this volume:

ACADEMIC PRESS

A. Tversky, 'Additivity, utility and subjective probability', *J. math. Psychol.*, vol. 4 (1967), pp. 175–202.

AMERICAN PSYCHOLOGICAL ASSOCIATION

W. Edwards, 'The theory of decision making', *Psychol. Bull.*, vol. 51 (1954), pp. 380–417.

L. Phillips and W. Edwards, 'Conservatism in a simple probability inference task', *J. exper. Psychol.*, vol. 72 (1966), pp. 346–54.

ANNUAL REVIEWS, INC.

W. Edwards, 'Behavioral decision theory', *Ann. Rev. Psychol.*, vol. 12 (1961), pp. 473–98.

BEHAVIORAL SCIENCE

E. W. Adams and R. F. Fagot, 'A model of riskless choice', *Behav. Sci.*, vol. 4 (1959), pp. 1–10.

G. M. Becker, M. H. DeGroot and J. Marschak, 'Stochastic models of choice behavior', *Behav. Sci.*, vol. 8 (1963), pp. 41–55.

INSTITUTE OF ELECTRICAL AND ELECTRONICS ENGINEERS, INC.

D. B. Yntema and W. S. Torgerson, 'Man-computer cooperation in decisions requiring common sense', *IRE Transactions on human factors in electronics*, HFE-2 (1961), pp. 20–26.

JOHN WILEY & SONS, INC.

C. H. Coombs, *A theory of data*, 1964, pp. 106–18.

R. D. Luce and H. Raiffa, *Games and decisions: introduction and critical survey*, 1957, pp. 23–31.

L. J. Savage, *The foundations of statistics*, 1954, pp. 91–104.

R. N. Shepard, 'On subjectively optimum selection among multi-attribute alternatives', in Shelley, M. W., and Bryan, G. L., *Human judgements and optimality*, 1964, pp. 257–81.

PSYCHOMETRIKA

J. A. Swets, 'Detection theory and psychophysics: a review', *Psychometrika*, vol. 26 (1961), pp. 49–63.

RICHARD D. IRWIN, INC.

R. D. Luce, 'Psychological studies of risky decision making', in Strother, G. B. (ed.), *Social science approaches to business behavior*, 1962, pp. 141–61.

399

ACKNOWLEDGEMENTS

STANFORD UNIVERSITY PRESS

D. Davidson, P. Suppes and S. Siegel, *Decision-making: an experimental approach*, 1957, pp. 19–30, 49–81.

UNIVERSITY OF CHICAGO PRESS

F. Mosteller and P. Nogee, 'An experimental measurement of utility', *J. polit. Econ.*, vol. 59 (1951), pp. 371–404.

Author Index

Subject Index

Penguin Modern Psychology Readings

Titles available in this series are:

MOTIVATION ed. Dalbir Binbra and Jane Stewart
A collection of papers which deal most directly with the three
central problems of motivation: *drive* (what instigates an organism
to action); *goal direction* (what directs behaviour towards certain
ends); *reinforcement* (what precisely makes certain events
rewarding and others punishing). UPS 1

EXPERIMENTS IN VISUAL PERCEPTION
ed. M. D. Vernon
The volume reviews four central topics – the perception of form,
space and distance, 'constancy' phenomena and movement – and then
explains the variations in perception which occur within the individual
and between individuals. Four excerpts from Piaget on perception in
infancy complete the volume. UPS 2

ATTITUDES ed. Marie Jahoda and Neil Warren
Three sections of readings which cover studies and problems in
concepts, research, and theory and measurement. UPS 3

PERSONALITY ASSESSMENT ed. Boris Semeonoff
Readings on variations in normal personality, which include
Galton and the early writings on typology, and the applications of
psychometric methods and of controlled observations in selection
procedures. UPS 4

INTELLIGENCE AND ABILITY ed. Stephen Wiseman
'The slow emergence of a coherent theory of the structure of
human abilities' is both the subject and the object of this volume.
Professor Wiseman has chosen readings from philosophers and
psychologists, covering a century of speculation, hypothesis and
research on man's intellectual powers. The earlier papers provide
the student with a historical perspective from which he can
appraise the present position. In the last section of the book
Professor Wiseman presents some of the results of research into
learning theory and into human ability. The integration of these
two sectors of psychological enquiry will, he believes,
revolutionize the work of the educational and vocational
psychologists of the future. UPS 5

ABNORMAL PSYCHOLOGY ed. Max Hamilton
The papers are grouped into four categories; first, clinical
descriptions, second, the application of psychological methods to
abnormal psychology, third, experimental work on animals, and
fourth, psychodynamic theory. The first two sections include work
by theorists such as Kraepelin and Pavlov, and Freud and
Masserman. UPS 6

ANIMAL PROBLEM SOLVING ed. A. J. Riopelle
Dr Riopelle's selection of papers raises questions about
human as well as animal functioning, and includes writings
from Romanes, K. R. L. Hall, P. H. Schiller, I. Kretchevsky,
Lloyd Morgan and Harlow. As the editor points out, this
material is not only interesting to the student, but can be
read by anyone for sheer enjoyment. UPS 7